INFANTRY WEAPONS OF THE WORLD

BRASSEY'S INFANTRY WEAPONS OF THE WORLD 1950–1975

Infantry weapons and combat aids in current use by the regular and reserve forces of all nations

Editor: Major General J. I. H. Owen, O.B.E., late Royal Marines

Compiled by: Gerald Wyndham, Stanley Parr, James Dowdall and John Marriott

Advisory Editors: Major S. R. Elliott, C.D., late Canadian Army
R. H. F. Cox, T.D.

BONANZA BOOKS • NEW YORK

Acknowledgements

Regrettably, it has proved impossible to acknowledge individually the source of all the many excellent drawings and photographs that appear in this book. A great many have been supplied by the manufacturers whom we thank gratefully. We also wish to thank the following:
Ministry of Defence, London
Central Office of Information, London
Royal Small Arms Factory, Enfield
Weapons Museum, School of Infantry, Warminster
Headquarters, United States Marine Corps, Washington
Tass News Agency
Blitz Publications Limited
John Weeks
Richard Cox

Library of Congress Catalog Card Number: 74-20627

This edition is published by Bonanza Books
a division of Crown Publishers, Inc.
by arrangement with Brassey's
e f g h

BONANZA 1979

Contents

The PRB 423 controlled fragmentation hand grenade

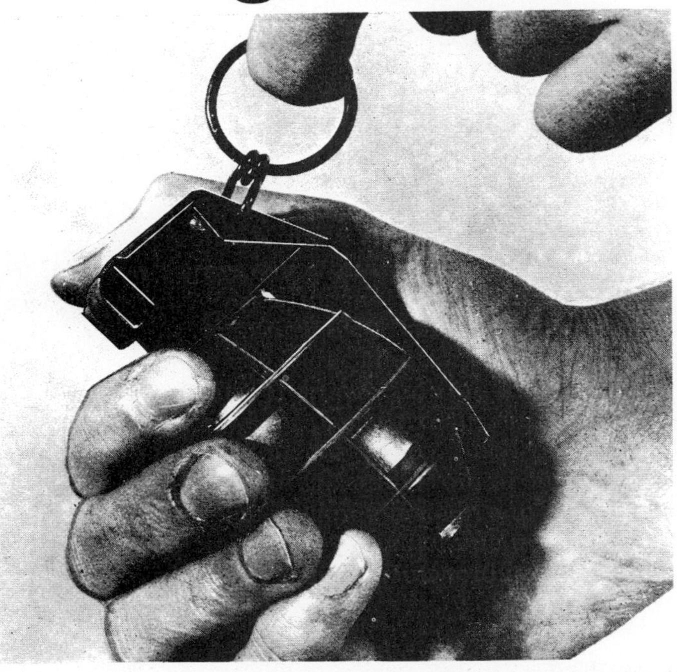

Characteristics

- highly effective at short range
  100% (2.5 splinters per m²) at 6 m from the point of explosion
  50% (1 splinter per m²) at 9 m from the point of explosion
- very small radius danger area (20 m)
- uniform dispersion of fragments in every case
- weight (235 g) representing the best throwing range/accuracy ratio

"Tested and approved by the Belgian Army"

PRB also stands for

- military explosives
- powder for small-arms ammunition
- powder for artillery ammunition
- ammunition for cannon, howitzers and mortars
- air-ground and air-air rockets
- hand and rifle-launched grenades
- anti-personnel and anti-tank mines
- "turn-key" facilities

Sa PRB - Defense Department
Avenue de Broqueville 12
B-1150 Bruxelles, Belgium
Tel. 71.00.40
Telex 21624 (Robur bru)

Introduction

'Train hard, fight easy' was Marshal Suvorov's succinct advice to his Russian soldiers. It applies to any army. But the technology behind the weapons with which an army trains and fights becomes more complex every year. Likewise the capability of the weapons available improves. This is particularly true of the infantry and is the reason why Brassey's—established as a defence Annual as long ago as 1886—has decided to produce this completely new reference book on Infantry Weapons.

Our aim is simply to provide readable and well-illustrated descriptions of as many of the world's infantry weapons as possible for the benefit of everyone—from journalist to military adviser—who needs accurate information at short notice.

Inevitably, this compilation was not an easy task. The first matter for decision was to agree on the definition of an infantry weapon. Small arms, mortars, grenades, some missiles and certain combat aids are clearly infantry weapons and some are clearly not. Some combat aids and mines, for example, are not strictly infantry weapons, but are so inextricably bound up with infantry operations that we decided to include them—though only some. There is such a plethora of, for example, grenades and pyrotechnics, that we have deliberately excluded many. Nonetheless we believe we have presented the reader with a comprehensive selection of some weapons and a fully representational selection of many others.

Now, for the reader. I would hope that readers who feel like commenting upon the book will not hesitate to do so. All constructive comments will be welcomed. In this way, we may be able to improve the content of the book, and possibly its presentation in the next edition.

What of the men (and women) who use these weapons? I will not attempt a full definition of infantry, save to say that the term for me includes all those who are recruited, trained and organised into properly and legally constituted units of foot-soldiers. I include most parachute units and commandos but exclude para-military police. In particular, I exclude all subverters and guerillas who, though they may call themselves commandos, use infantry and other weapons and move well on foot, are not infantry in the traditional sense. They do not have that indefinable stoic integrity of the average infantryman. So I am describing those excellent and gallant men who carry out those truly nasty, uncomfortable and often thankless tasks given them, with uncommonly good fortitude and remarkable intelligence and skill. They suffer more than most, the rigours of the elements, the physical burden of the weapons, ammunition, equipment, food and clothing they carry on their back. They climb in and out of aeroplanes and armoured boxes, they live underground, they lie for hours in the jungle swamps, they struggle up hills, they walk down the 'murder miles' of urban battlefields and they guard palace gates and it is they, the infantry, who more than any other arm are close enough to see the fear in their adversaries' eyes, or feel that awful fear themselves, as they close in for the kill. It is for the infantry a very personal battle.

Fortunately, in most countries, the infantrymen are still the *élite* arm, for it is the infantry who are supported by the cavalry, the gunners, the engineers and all the other arms including the navies and the air forces. Unquestionably, the infantry, light or heavy, on foot, in helicopters or in armoured carriers, are the premier arm whom all other support on to the ground that must be captured and won, if a war is to be brought to a successful military conclusion.

It would, perhaps, be pertinent here to question whether the weapons with which the infantry are equipped measure up to the task. We believe this is a matter the reader must judge for himself. There are a number of most interesting developments taking place in infantry weapons, but probably neither as many as are desirable nor being achieved as quickly as they should be. The main areas of improvement which I would like to see are those of personal mobility and communication and lethality. I know the infantryman is being asked to carry too much. This is partly due to the inability of many to live off 'a bit of fish and bag of rice', but it is primarily due to the complexity and weight of weapons, equipment and ammunition. On the second point, communication, I believe that the weight and accuracy of the fire power covering the battlefield today demands that the infantry must be able to operate singly or in pairs—in other words, to skirmish commando-fashion. To be successful, this requires amongst other things the capability of the junior commander to talk easily to every man. In other words, personal radio.

So far as lethality is concerned, I, like many others, am surprised at the poor standard of shooting that exists in the armies of today. Despite remarkable developments in the areas of increased range, sighting and weapon stability and weapon manufacture, the accuracy has generally deteriorated badly. The answer may lie in the adoption of better training methods, even better ammunition or better sights (perhaps all sights should seem the same to the soldier looking through them instead of varying with almost every weapon), or perhaps it is just a case of making shooting interesting.

So much for the aim and the background, now for the book itself. We are extremely grateful to the host of manufacturers, large and small, who have helped make this book possible by providing facts, figures and pictures (with permission to reproduce them). I hope the information given is faithfully reflected in the descriptions. In some cases, we have had to assess or calculate some fact or figure. I hope readers will bear with us if we have got it wrong.

I am grateful, too, to the researchers, compilers, publishers, printers, secretaries, friends, acquaintances and families whose patience, knowledge and endurance have made the book possible. I thank the various organisations who have helped with advice and encouragement and, above all, we all thank you who have read thus far.

JOHN OWEN

INFANTRY WEAPONS OF THE WORLD

Pistols and Revolvers

Like most new inventions, the automatic pistol, which first began to appear in the late 1890s, was not considered a serious competitor to the established revolver. The early Borchardt, Bergmann and Mauser were considered to be over complex, and were bought by some officers more for gimmick value and show than for practical reasons. Winston Churchill, however, highly praised his 7·63 mm Mauser military model, which he put to practical and successful use at the Battle of Omdurman in 1898.

At the beginning of this century, the American John Browning was starting to design and produce a series of automatic pistols and, in the case of the ·38 in Colt automatic, cartridge ammunition to fit. These pistols were still not being seriously considered by the military, but when it began to dawn on soldiers that the automatic pistol had possibilities, trials were begun in 1907 in the United States to confirm or reject the theory.

As these trials got under way, Browning submitted the pistol which was later to become the basic design for the majority of military pistols up to the present day. A short recoil-locked breech weapon, this pistol was finally adopted as the M1911 in ·45ACP. Also entered in the trials was a ·45 model of the Luger pistol. The Luger, based on an earlier American design the Borchardt, utilised the same toggle lock, and was originally designed to fire the powerful 7·65 mm bottleneck cartridge. Though unsuccessful in the United States trials, the Luger was in 1908 adopted in 9 mm by the German army. An expensive weapon to produce, the Luger was unreliable in adverse conditions due to the close machining tolerances not allowing a wide enough margin to avoid being affected by small quantities of dirt. The pistol, nevertheless, remained in service until well after production ceased in 1943.

By 1910, several countries had designed, produced and adopted a wide variety of patently unusual weapons in a selection of calibres, some firing totally ineffectual cartridges. Most of these automatics, however, were only introduced as additions rather than as replacements for the revolver.

Provided that any particular automatic pistol has proved itself to be reliable, its advantages over the revolver are fourfold. First, the automatic pistol holds more rounds than the revolver, and can be reloaded more quickly, provided that a supply of magazines is readily available. Secondly, the automatic retains all the gas pressure of the cartridge, whereas in the revolver a certain amount is lost through the gap between cylinder and barrel. Thirdly, most automatics fire single action having been cocked by the slide. Thus a higher rate of fire combined with greater accuracy are available which are important factors in close range combat. Lastly, pointing characteristics of the automatic are generally accepted as being better than the revolver.

On the other hand, the revolver is basically accurate and more reliable. It does not have to rely on the self-loading mechanism of the automatic, which requires good ammunition and a sound magazine to function correctly. It is therefore less prone to jamming and it is for this reason that the majority of police forces still prefer the revolver. On many occasions, the police officer has no one to back him up should his weapon malfunction. It is also interesting that, since the widespread introduction of the sub machine gun, the number of pistols in military use has decreased considerably and the weapon is carried more for psychological than practical reasons.

From the great variety of calibres used in pre-war weapons the 9 mm parabellum has been accepted almost universally for pistol use (as well as for the SMG). However, the heavier ·45ACP is still in wide use, and is certainly a better cartridge in terms of stopping power, but requires a proportionately heavier action to handle it. The Russians, as ever, feeling the need for a round which cannot be accepted by any other than native weapons, have produced the 9 mm Makarov which is a compromise between 9 mm parabellum and 9 mm short.

For the future, it would appear that, unless some entirely new form of ignition is introduced, automatic pistol design will not progress a great deal, as the short recoil system has proved to be the most effective for use with a 9 mm parabellum or similar round. However, though the inertia factor must dictate a minimum basic weight, experiments in metallurgy will continue to result in lighter, but durable, weapons.

Although few, if any, regular armies are currently equipped with revolvers, those that are use mostly the Colt or Smith & Wesson types. The most common calibres are the ·38 in Smith & Wesson, the ·38 in special or ·357 in magnum, the ·45 in rimmed cartridge being considered obsolete. The heavier frame and military models are favoured, the lighter alloy frame guns being considered unable to take the punishment liable to be incurred in military use.

James Dowdall

Luger (PO8 model) pistol.

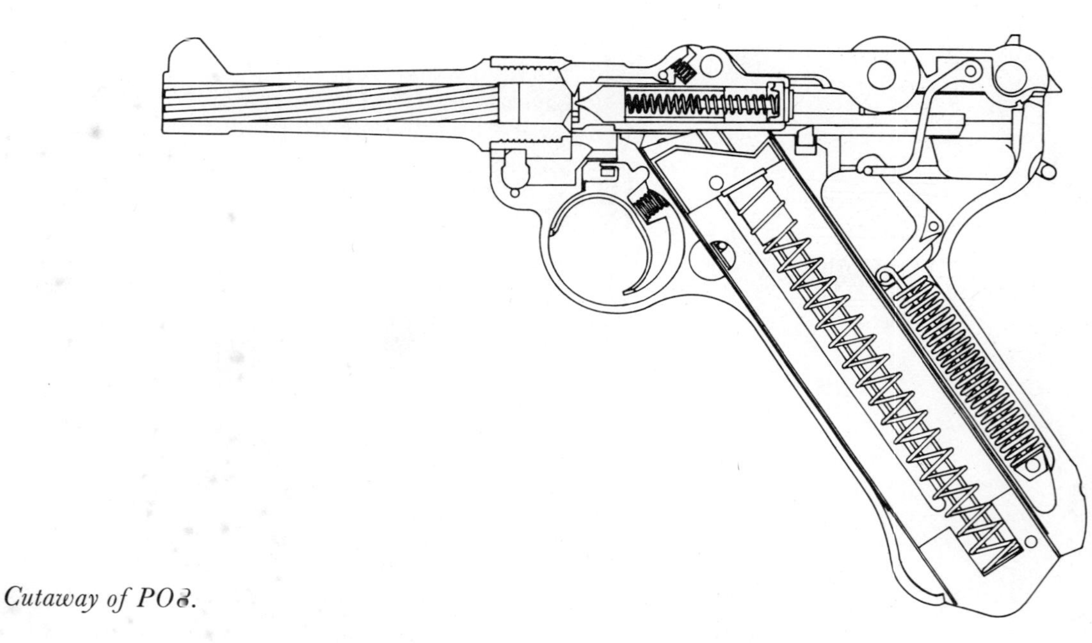

Cutaway of PO8.

Smith & Wesson (military and police) revolvers. Most police forces prefer revolvers to pistols.

Colt 1911A1 (Spanish version) pistol, one of many variants of the Colt manufactured outside the United States.

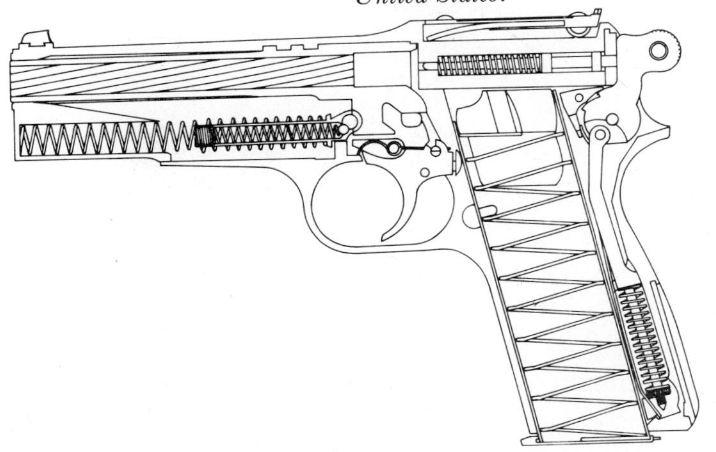

Cutaway of Browning HP 35.

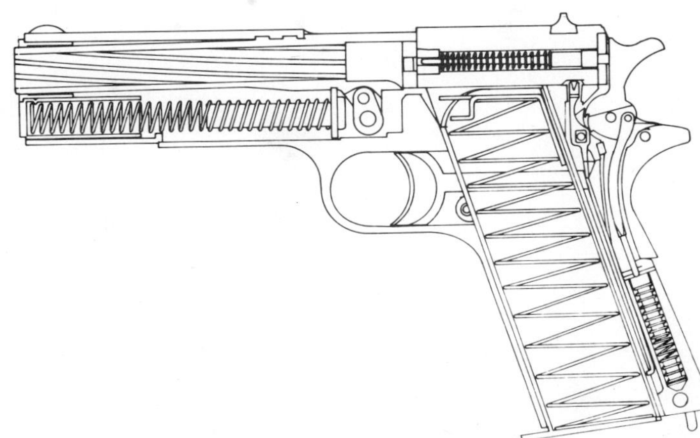

Cutaway of Colt 1911A1.

M1927 (Ballester Mollina) pistol

Manufacturer: **Ministry of Defence (Argentina)**

See the Colt M1911A1.

In service with the Argentinian forces.

Browning HP 35 pistol

Manufacturer: **FN Herstal (Belgium) and Inglis (Canada)**

Calibre	9 mm parabellum
Dimensions	Length 20·3 cm Barrel length 12 cm
Weight	0·8 kg
Effective range	70 m
Operation	Recoil
Muzzle velocity	450 m/sec
Sight	Front—blade Rear—U notch
Magazine	13 round detachable box type

The last pistol to be designed by John Moses Browning, the HP35 or GP (Grande Puissance) was introduced in 1935. At that time two models were produced by FN, one with fixed sights and the other with a tangent type rear sight and capable of being fitted with a shoulder stock. The GP saw extensive service during World War II in both British and Canadian hands, as the pistol was produced under licence in Canada. Although similar in design and function to the locked breech system of the Colt (1911A1), the GP differs from it in several respects. The front barrel bearing is integral with the slide as opposed to the separate unit of the Colt, and a camming wedge on the underside of the barrel locks the barrel to the slide in place of the swinging link system of the Colt. The double staggered line box magazine takes 13 rounds, a useful feature in a military handgun. On post-war weapons, the trigger system has been so designed that removal of the magazine disconnects the trigger.

In service with the Belgian, Canadian, Danish, Dutch, Indonesian, Taiwanese and United Kingdom forces.

Browning HP35 pistol.

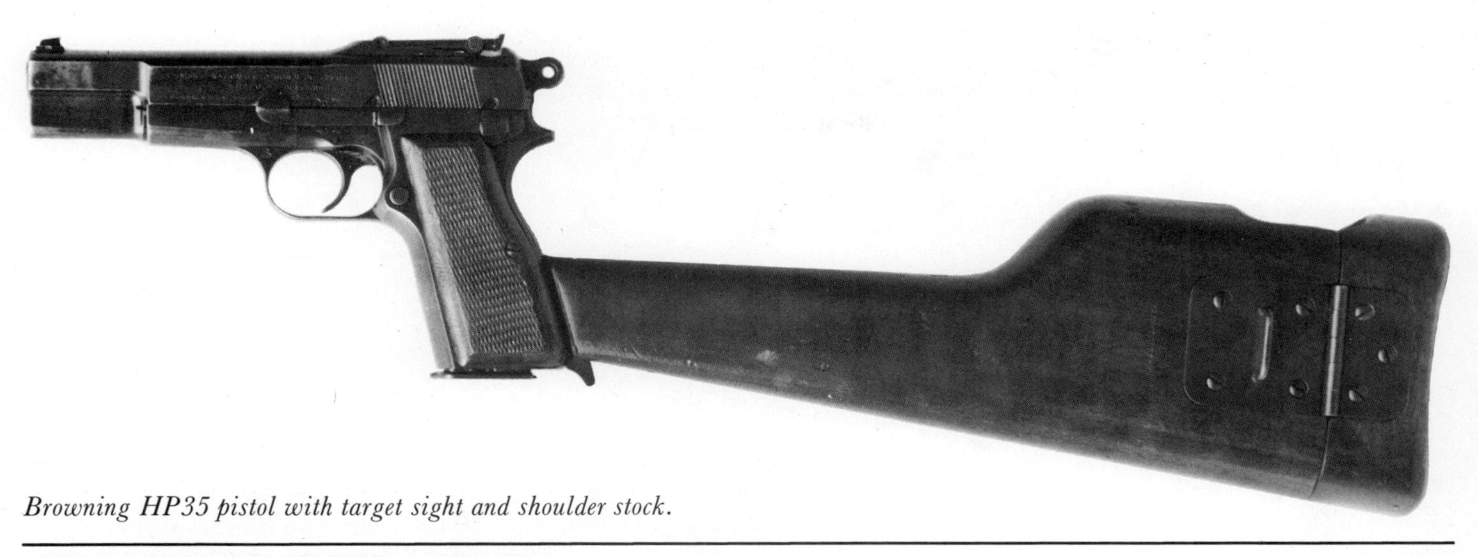

Browning HP35 pistol with target sight and shoulder stock.

M51 and type 54 pistols

Manufacturer: **State factories (People's Republic of China)**

See the Tokarev TT33.

In service with the communist Chinese forces.

Type 59 pistol

Manufacturer: **State factories (People's Republic of China)**

See the Makarov.

In service with the communist Chinese forces.

Vz61 Skorpion machine pistol

Manufacturer: **Ceska Zbrojovka (Czechoslovakia)**

Calibre	7·65 mm
Dimensions	Length 27·6 cm stock folded, 52·2 cm stock extended Barrel length 11·4 cm
Weight	1·31 kg
Effective range	50–75 m
Operation	Blowback, selective fire
Muzzle velocity	305 m/sec
Sight	Front—protected post Rear—flip over notch graduated for 75 or 150 m
Magazine	10 or 20 round detachable box type

The Vz61 Skorpion is a machine pistol in the true sense. A basic blowback weapon firing the relatively weak

Vz61 Skorpion machine pistol, stock extended

Vz61 Skorpion machine pistol (with stock folded).

7·65 mm round, the Skorpion is fitted with a cyclic rate reducer. This is in fact an inertia mechanism fitted in the pistol grip. On completing its rearward stroke, the bolt strikes an actuator causing it to pivot on its pin. The actuator then strikes a spring-loaded plunger compressing the unit downwards. As the actuator pivots downwards the top part catches in the bolt thus holding it back until the spring plunger returns upwards to trip the actuator and thus release the bolt. This reduces the rate of fire from approx 1000 rpm to 800 rpm. The weapon fires from a closed bolt and has a three position selection lever giving safe, repetition and automatic. A folding wire stock should be used when the weapon is fired on automatic. The weapon was basically designed for use by armoured vehicle crews. Also available for the Skorpion is a night sighting device, a silencer, bayonet hip holster and even a shoulder holster.

In service with the Czechoslovak forces.

M52 pistol

Manufacturer: **State factories (Czechoslovakia)**

Calibre	7·62 mm M48
Dimensions	Length 21 cm
	Barrel length 12 cm
Weight	1 kg
Effective range	50 m
Operation	Recoil
Muzzle velocity	420 m/sec
Sight	Front—blade
	Rear—square notch
Magazine	8 round detachable box type

Unusual in that it uses a roller locking system based on that of the German MG42, the M52 fires an unnecessarily powerful cartridge. The Czech 7·62 mm M48 round is some 20% more powerful than the Soviet 7·62 mm Type P which may also be fired in this pistol. The roller locking system, though giving great strength, is expensive to produce and rather impractical as the weapon is harder to strip than most. Unless the trigger is pulled, the weapon is prevented from firing by an automatic safety mechanism on the firing pin. The finish of the weapon is rather rough and, due to the extra power involved when using the M48 round, the gun has a heavy recoil and sharp muzzle blast. The M52 is in limited service in the Czech army as it is being replaced largely by the Vz 61 Skorpion and the Wz 63 machine pistols. It may, however, be encountered in Africa, South America and some of the Arab countries.

In service. See text.

M52 pistol.

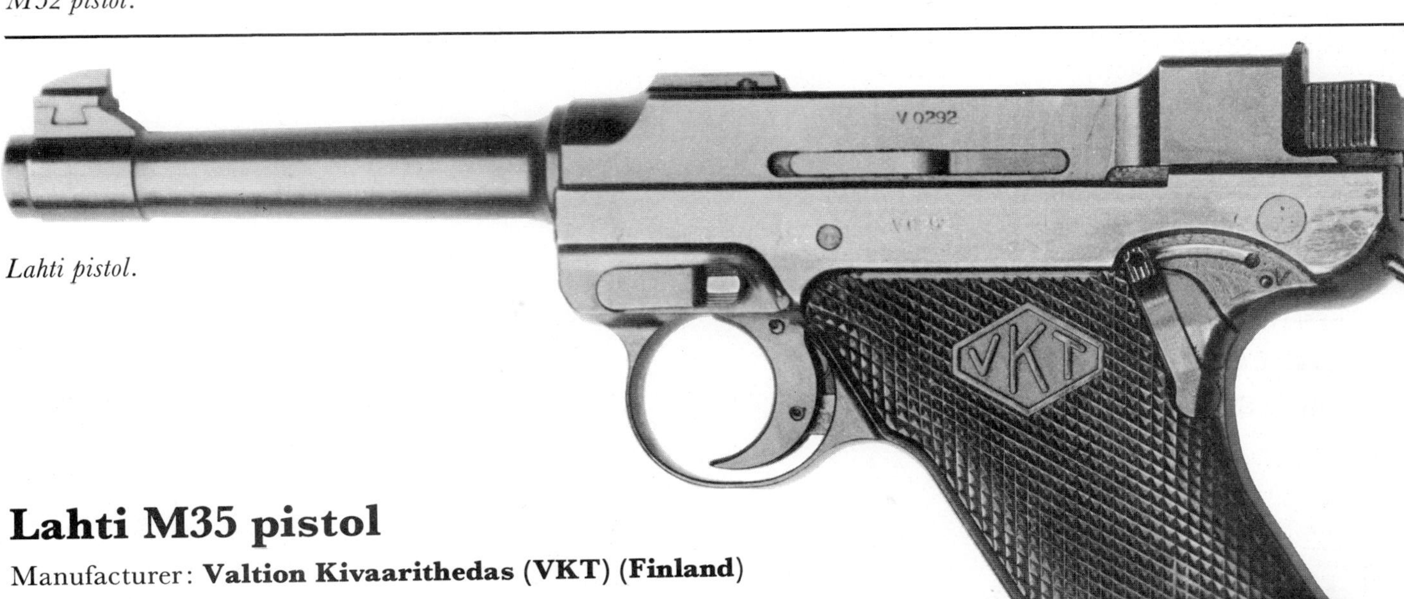

Lahti pistol.

Lahti M35 pistol

Manufacturer: **Valtion Kivaarithedas (VKT) (Finland)**

Calibre	9 mm parabellum
Dimensions	Length 27·2 cm Barrel length 14 cm
Weight	1·1 kg
Effective range	50 m
Operation	Recoil
Muzzle velocity	370 m/sec
Sight	Front—barleycorn Rear—U notch
Magazine	8 round detachable box type

The Lahti pistol was adopted by Finland in 1935. The M35 is a short recoil arm using a modified Bergmann–Bayard lock. Externally the M35 resembles the Luger. The weapon is well made and was designed with a view to operating in sub-zero temperatures. To this end, a pivoting accelerator, positioned on the front underside of the sub-receiver, imparts added drive to the breech-block in rearward motion, thus decreasing the likelihood of malfunction due to the lubricant freezing. The slide of the Lahti is enclosed, apart from the ejection port, and is thus well sealed against the ingress of dirt. The pistol has also been adopted and produced by Sweden at their Husqvarna Plant as the M40. This model differs only in minor respects; for example, external differences are the omission of the loaded chamber indicator as fitted to the Finnish model and the pistol grips of the Finnish model are stamped VKT, the Swedish model having the Husqvarna trademark. Although rather heavy for a modern pistol, both weapons are aptly suited for use in the prevailing cold conditions.

In service with the Finnish and Swedish forces.

M50 pistol

Manufacturer: **Manufacture d'Armes de Saint-Etienne (France)**

Calibre	9 mm parabellum
Dimensions	Length 19·3 cm
	Barrel length 11·2 cm
Weight	0·8 kg
Effective range	50 m
Operation	Recoil
Muzzle velocity	360 m/sec
Sight	Front—blade
	Rear—U notch
Magazine	9 round detachable box type

M50 pistol.

Superior to any pistol which the French had previously designed, the M50 is basically a copy of the Colt 1911A1. The same swinging link locking system is used with dual lockings lugs. The safety catch, however, is mounted on the rear of the slide probably to save re-familiarising with a safety in a different position, as the earlier French Model 1935 A & S had slide-mounted safeties. A loaded chamber indicator is mounted in the slide and the packaged hammer/sear assembly may be removed as one unit. Like the later Browning Hi Power pistols, the M50 cannot be fired with the magazine removed.

In service with the French forces, but may be encountered elsewhere.

Pistole M pistol

Manufacturer: **State factories (German Democratic Republic)**

See the Makarov.

In service with the DDR forces.

Walther PP and PPK pistols

Manufacturer: **Carl Walther Waffenfabrik AG (Germany)**

Calibre	7·65 mm, 9 mm short, 6·35 mm and ·22 in LP
Dimensions	Length 17·2 cm
	Barrel length 10 cm
Weight	0·7 kg
Effective range	35 m
Operation	Blowback
Muzzle velocity	290 m/sec (7·65 mm)
Sight	Front—blade
	Rear—U notch
Magazine	8 round detachable box type

The Walther PP, and its smaller edition the PPK, were first introduced in 1929 and 1931 respectively and were one of the first automatic pistols to feature a double action trigger mechanism. The pistols were well designed and manufactured with simple blowback actions. Featuring not only a double action trigger, but also a loaded chamber indicator which protruded out of the rear of the slide, the PP and PPK have not only been sold in their more common calibres of 7·65 mm and 9 mm short but also in ·22 in and 6·35 mm. Used in large quantities by the German Army and Police during World War II, the Walther pistols are being mass produced again and have sold widely abroad, especially to police forces. France, Hungary and Turkey have copied or produced the weapons under licence and a number of countries have manufactured copies based almost exactly on the originals.

In service with the French, German, Hungarian and Turkish forces.

Walther PP pistol.

Walther PPK pistol.

Walther P38 (P1) pistol

Manufacturer: **Carl Walther Waffenfabrik AG (Germany) and others**

Calibre	9 mm parabellum
Dimensions	Length 21·8 cm
	Barrel length 21·[illegible] cm
Weight	0·9 kg
Effective range	50 m
Operation	Recoil
Muzzle velocity	340 m/sec
Sight	Front—blade
	Rear—rounded notch
Magazine	8 round detachable box type

A refinement of the earlier AP pistol and introduced in 1938 to replace the Luger, the Walther P38 has several outstanding features. A wedge-shaped locking block with projections at the top is hinged below the barrel and engages in corresponding lugs in the slide to lock the action. When struck against the receiver, a plunger mounted in the barrel lug pushes the locking block down and out of engagement. The pistol can be easily reassembled after stripping, omitting the locking block, in which case the pistol may be seriously damaged if fired. Like the earlier Walther PP and PPK pistols, the P38 features a loaded chamber indicator in the slide, and the weapon may be fired using a single or double action trigger pull. Over 1 million were produced during World War II and manufacture began again shortly after war ended. World War II versions with the eagle or swastika stamped on them are still around. The P38 is now standard in the German army as the P1 and has been bought by several countries including Sweden (M39).

In service with the German and Swedish forces.

Walther P38 pistol.

48M pistol

Manufacturer: **State factories (Hungary)**

See the Tokarev TT33.

In service with the Hungarian forces, but obsolescent.

PA-63 pistol

Manufacturer: **State factories (Hungary)**

Calibre	9 mm
Dimensions	Length 17·5 cm Barrel length 8·7 cm
Weight	0·66 kg (loaded)
Effective range	50 m
Operation	Blowback
Muzzle velocity	315 m/sec
Sight	Front—blade Rear—notch
Magazine	7 round detachable box type

The 9 mm pistol PA-63 is the latest of several lightweight pistols to be introduced into the Hungarian armed forces, all resembling to some extent the German Walther PP pistol. A standard blowback-operated, double action weapon with very little bulk, the PA-63 is light and manageable for close quarters work, but the claimed effective range of 50 m appears to be optimistic and the small capacity of the magazine is a disadvantage.

There are several slightly different versions of the PA-63, varying mainly in the material of the grip and the body finish, but all carry the same thumb-operated safety catch on the left side near the external hammer and on the same side the magazine release catch forward of the top of the grip.

In service with the Hungarian forces.

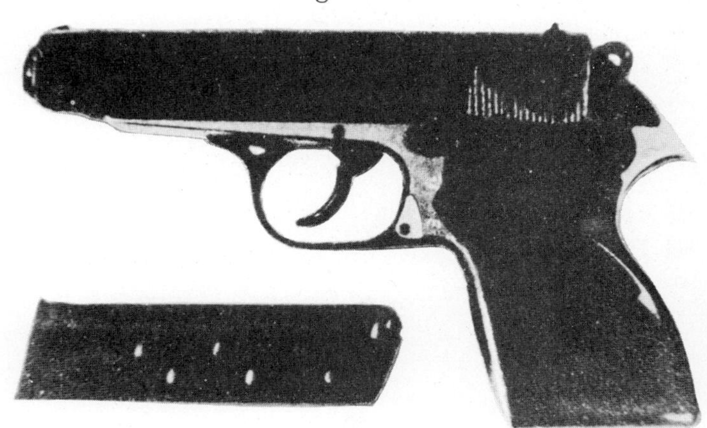

PA-63 pistol.

Beretta M51 pistol

Manufacturer: **Pietro Beretta (Italy)**

Calibre	9 mm parabellum
Dimensions	20·3 cm Length 20·3 cm Barrel length 11·4 cm
Weight	0·8 kg
Effective range	50 m
Operation	Recoil
Muzzle velocity	360 m/sec
Sight	Front—blade Rear—V notch
Magazine type	8 round detachable box

The Beretta Modello 51 first appeared in 1957. A recoil-operated weapon, the pistol uses the same pivoting wedge system as the Walther P38. The safety catch is placed unusually at the rear of the grip near the spur and is a push button type. Unlike earlier Italian pistols, the M51 features a slide stop which retains the slide to the rear when the magazine is empty.

In service with the Italian, Egyptian, and Israeli forces.

Beretta M51 pistol.

Obregon pistol

Manufacturer: **Fabrica de Armas (Mexico)**

Calibre	·45 ACP
Dimensions	Length 20·8 cm
	Barrel length 12·2 cm
Weight	1·1 kg
Effective range	50 m
Muzzle velocity	260 m/sec
Sight	Front—blade
	Rear—dovetailed bar with notch
Magazine	7 round detachable box type

Externally resembling the Colt 1911A1, the Mexican Obregon operates on an entirely different principle. Using an adaptation of the old Steyr–Hahn system, the barrel is rotated into and out of engagement by a helical cam engaging with a locking lug on the frame. Potentially, this type of action should give greater accuracy due to the axial unlocking action, whereas the Colt–Browning type of swinging barrel tends to lift the weapon on firing.

Although still standard with the Mexican army, the Obregon has not been produced for some years.

In service with the Mexican forces.

M1914 pistol

Manufacturer: **Ministry of Defence (Norway)**

See the Colt M1911A1.

In service with the Norwegian forces.

Pistolet TT pistol

Manufacturer: **State factories (Poland)**

See the Tokarev TT33.

In service with the Polish forces, but obsolescent.

Model 64 pistol

Manufacturer: **State factories (Poland)**

Calibre	9 mm Makarov
Dimensions	Length 15·5 cm
	Barrel length 7·9 cm
Weight	0·596 kg
Effective range	35 m
Operation	Blowback
Muzzle velocity	305 m/sec
Sight	Front—blade
	Rear—notch
Magazine	8 round detachable box type

The M64 pistol now replaces the old Pistolet TT in the Polish army. The pistol outwardly resembles the Makarov and has some features copied from the Walther PP. A double action weapon, the trigger mechanism differs from either the Makarov or Walther designs. An internal slide stop is fitted and the safety catch is situated at the rear of the slide on the left-hand side.

In service with the Polish forces.

Radom Wz35 pistol

Manufacturer: **State factories (Poland)**

Calibre	9 mm parabellum
Dimensions	Length 19·8 cm
	Barrel length 11·9 cm
Weight	1 kg
Effective range	50 m
Operation	Recoil
Muzzle velocity	340 m/sec
Sight	Front—blade
	Rear—V notch
Magazine	8 round detachable box type

The Polish Radom Wz35 is another weapon based on the Colt–Browning design and was produced under the direction of experts from the FN plant before the war. The gun uses the same swinging barrel locking action of the later type Brownings. However, the safety catch is mounted at the rear of the slide and, if applied when the weapon is cocked, will first block the striker and then release the hammer forward. Two slides are fitted, the forward one being a hold-open device for when the last shot is fired. The rear one (mounted in the same place

Radom Wz35 (Rear Slide Catch missing.)

as the safety catch on the 1911A1) is merely a slide hold to assist in dismantling. A grip safety is also fitted. The Wz35 is a robust weapon and can handle all types of 9 mm round.

In service with the Polish forces and elsewhere.

Radom WZ35 pistol.

M63 machine pistol

Manufacturer: **State factories (Poland)**

Calibre	9 mm
Dimensions	Length 33·3 cm (with butt 60·7 cm) Barrel length 15 cm
Weight	1·8 kg (loaded)
Effective range	50 m (200 m with butt)
Operation	Selective fire, blowback operated
Muzzle velocity	325 m/sec
Sight	Front—blade Rear—protected notch
Magazine	25 or 15 round detachable box type

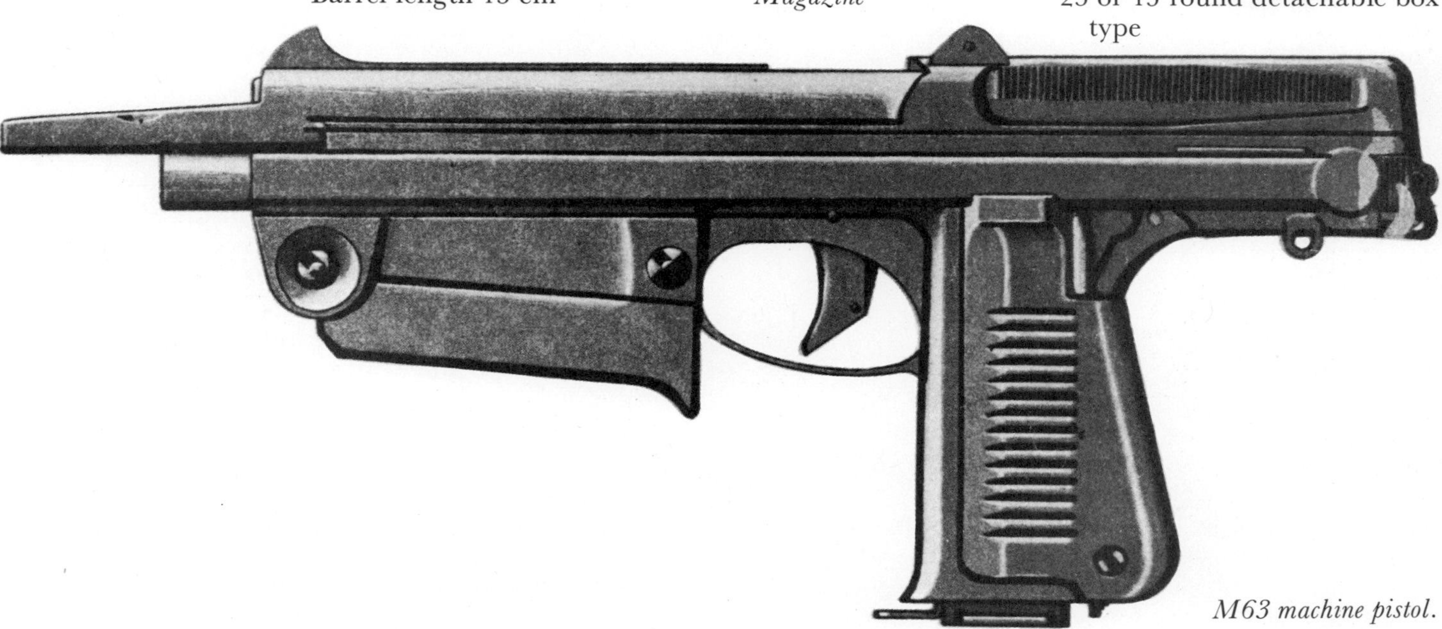

M63 machine pistol.

The Polish M63 machine pistol was produced to utilise the new Soviet 9 × 18 mm round and follows the same design ideas as the Soviet Stechkin (APS) and Czech Skorpion machine pistols. While the butt and forward grip are still folded, the weapon can, in spite of its ungainly appearance, be used accurately as a normal pistol and is usually carried in a holster. To be used as a sub machine gun, the forward grip should be lowered until it locks at 90° to the barrel and the butt, normally folded on either side of the pistol body, should be retracted to the rear and the butt plate revolved into position. If required, the attached leather strap can be used as a brace support. The M63 fires from the open bolt position and fire is selected by the different finger pressure on the trigger, not by selector switch. The distinctive semi-circular extension below the muzzle is a compensator to reduce the amount of kick when firing on automatic. The smaller 15 round magazine is designed to be used when the weapon is employed purely as a pistol. The main purpose of the M63 is to act as the personal weapon of troops operating in a very confined space as, for instance, an armoured vehicle.

In service with the Polish forces.

Super Star pistol

Manufacturer: **Bonifacio Echeverria SA (Spain)**

Calibre	9 mm largo
Dimensions	Length 20 cm
	Barrel length 12·7 cm
Weight	1 kg
Effective range	50 m
Operation	Recoil
Muzzle velocity	370 m/sec
Sight	Front—blade
	Rear—V notch
Magazine	8 round detachable box type

The Spanish Super Star pistol is again of a basic Colt 1911A1 design using the Browning type of barrel cam. A two-piece slide stop is fitted and the Colt-type grip safety is not featured. Weapons used by the Spanish army are in 9 mm largo, but the Super Star is also sold commercially in 9 mm parabellum, ·45 ACP and ·38 in super auto.

In service with the Spanish forces.

M40 pistol

Manufacturer: **Husqvarna plant (Sweden)**

See the Lahti M35.

In service with the Swedish forces.

M39 pistol

See the Walther P38.

In service with the Swedish forces.

SIG M49 pistol

Manufacturer: **Schweizerische Industrie-Gesellschaft (Switzerland)**

Calibre	9 mm parabellum or 7·65 mm
Dimensions	Length 21·6 cm
	Barrel length 12·0 cm
Weight	0·9 kg
Effective range	60 m
Operation	Recoil
Muzzle velocity	340 m/sec
Sight	Front—blade
	Rear—V notch
Magazine	8 round detachable box type

The SIG 210 series of pistols are based on the Colt–Browning actions using a cam attached to the barrel, engaging with the slide lock pin to unlock the action. The slide in this weapon, however, is carried inside the frame as opposed to the other Colt–Browning types where the slides wrap around the outside of the frame. A slide stop is also fitted. The SIG is extremely well made and is consequently more expensive to produce, giving it only limited treasury appeal. Several versions are offered in 9 mm parabellum and 7·65 mm. The SIG 210–1 and 210–2 differ only in finish, the latter being sand-blasted to provide a non-reflecting surface. A target version is also produced with tangent sights as the 210–6. All models may be adapted to fire either cartridge by merely changing the barrel and recoil spring. A ·22 LR conversion kit is also available.

In service with the Swiss and Danish forces.

SIG 49 (210-2) pistol.

SIG 49 (210) pistol (for enthusiasts).

SIG 49 (210-5) pistol.

Tokarev TT33 pistol

Manufacturer: **State factories (USSR)**

Calibre	7·62 mm Type P
Dimensions	Length 19·3 cm Barrel length 11·4 cm
Weight	0·8 kg
Effective range	50 m
Operation	Recoil
Muzzle velocity	420 m/sec
Sight	Front—blade Rear—U notch
Magazine	8 round detachable box type

The Tokarev pistol first appeared during the early 1930s. Again of the basic Colt–Browning design, the TT33 has some interesting features. A removable sub-assembly block containing the trigger mechanism and forming part of the frame has its inside surfaces machined to act as a cartridge guide. Most feed malfunctions are due to weak or damaged magazine lips but this feature of the TT33 almost eliminated this problem. The gun has no safety catch but the slide and trigger may be locked by a half-cock position on the hammer. The barrel locking lugs run the complete circumference of the barrel for ease of manufacture on later models.

Used extensively by Soviet forces during World War II, the Tokarev has been produced throughout the Warsaw Pact countries and communist China. Hungary manufactured a version for Egypt called the Tokagypt in 9 mm parabellum. The Tokarev types differ only in the motif on the grips and the slide serrations.

In service with many communist forces, but obsolescent.

Tokarev TT33 pistol.

Makarov pistol

Manufacturer: **State factories (USSR)**

Calibre	9 mm Makarov
Dimensions	Length 16 cm Barrel length 9·5 cm
Weight	0·8 kg
Effective range	35 m
Operation	Blowback
Muzzle velocity	420 m/sec
Sight	Front—blade Rear—square notch
Magazine	8 round detachable box type

Although based on the Walther PP, the Makarov (PM) pistol differs in some respects. The main differences are an externally mounted slide stop, a spring type magazine catch and the lack of a loaded chamber indicator. The trigger is a double action type.

Now standard in most major Euro-Asian communist armies, the Makarov is also manufactured in East Germany as the Pistole M and in communist China as the Type 59 pistol.

In service with the Warsaw Pact and other communist forces.

Makarov pistol.

Enfield revolver No 2 Mk 1

Manufacturer: **Royal Small Arms Factory (United Kingdom)**

Calibre	·38 in, ·380 in S&W and ·38 in Webley
Dimensions	Length 25·9 cm Barrel length 12·7 cm
Weight	0·5 kg
Effective range	40 m
Muzzle velocity	180 m/sec
Sight	Front—blade Rear—U notch

First issued to the British Army as the Pistol No 2 Mk 1 in 1932, the Enfield revolver went through two modifications to become the No 2 Mk 1**, the single or double action feature of the earlier models being removed in favour of the simpler to produce double action. This reduced the potential accuracy of the weapon due to the increased trigger pressure needed to fire a double action type of revolver. Standard issue throughout World War II, the gun remained in service until replaced by the Browning HP 35. The revolver is robustly built and is reliable. Though not thought to be in first line use by any army, this weapon is likely to be encountered in ex-British territories and countries supplied with arms by the United Kingdom.

Obsolescent. See text.

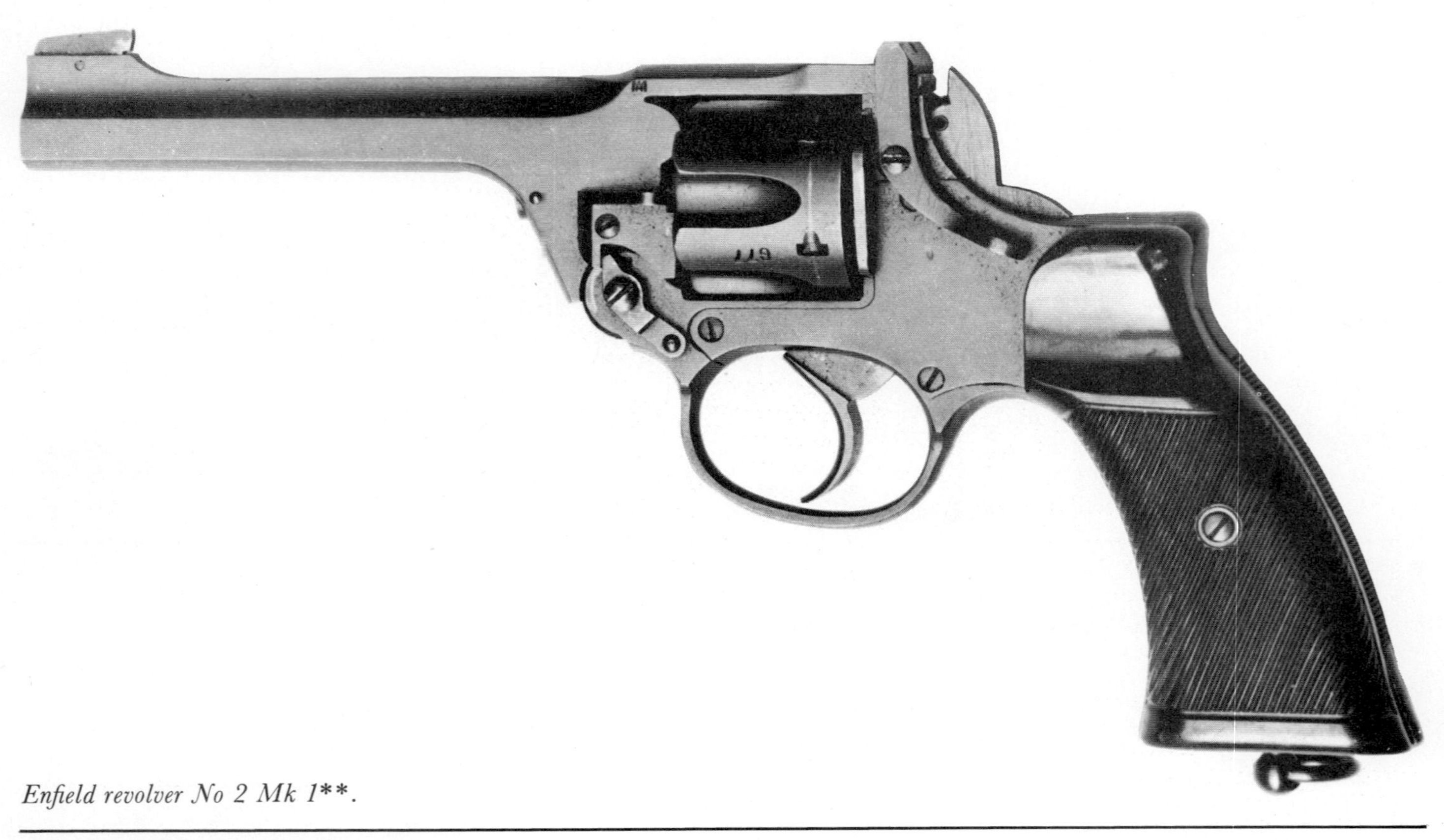

*Enfield revolver No 2 Mk 1***.

Colt M1911A1 pistol

Manufacturer: **Colt's PTFA and Ithaca, Remington, Springfield Armory and Union Switch and Signal (United States)**

Colt M1911A1.

Calibre	·45 ACP
Dimensions	Length 21·8 cm
	Barrel length 12·7 cm
Weight	1·1 kg
Effective range	50 m
Operation	Recoil
Muzzle velocity	250 m/sec
Sight	Front—blade
	Rear—square notch
Magazine	7 round detachable box type

This forerunner of most modern military pistols has been copied more than any other single design. First designed by John Moses Browning and adopted by the United States in 1911, the gun saw considerable service during World War I. Modified in the 1920s, the gun became the M1911A1 and has remained almost unchanged since. The action is locked using two locking lugs in the top of the barrel engaging in corresponding lugs in the slide. Engagement and disengagement are affected by a pivoting link attached to the underside of the barrel which swings on the slide retaining pin to pull the barrel downwards on firing. A detachable front barrel bearing also serves to retain the return spring and cup situated below the barrel. A safety catch is situated on the frame just forward of the spur and a grip safety is also fitted.

The 1911A1 has also been produced under licence in Norway (M1914) and Argentina (M1927 Ballester Mollina).

In service with the Argentinian, Taiwanese, Greek, Indonesian, Iranian, Japanese, Mexican, Norwegian, United States, South Vietnamese and other forces.

M57 pistol

Manufacturer: **State factories (Yugoslavia)**

See the Tokarev TT33.

In service with the Yugoslav forces, but obsolescent.

M67 pistol

Manufacturer: **State factories (Yugoslavia)**

Calibre	7·65 mm, 9 mm
Dimensions	Length 16·5 cm
	Barrel length 9·4 cm
Weight	0·8 kg (loaded)
Effective range	50 m
Operation	Blowback operated, semi-automatic only
Muzzle velocity	310 m/sec
Sight	Front—blade
	Rear—notch
Magazine	6 round detachable box type

The Yugoslav M67 pistol is the latest to be added to the wide variety of pistols used by the armed forces of that country. It is manufactured in two different calibres to take the 9 × 17 mm and the 7·65 × 17 mm SR rounds. The M67 is a very small, lightweight pistol with only a limited magazine capacity, weighing only 0·7 kg empty. The safety catch is located, for thumb operation, in the cut-away angle of the top of the left-hand grip, while the magazine release catch is also on the left of the grip behind the base of the trigger guard. Unlike most pistols produced by the Warsaw Pact countries, the slide assembly is retained and released by a similar slide stop unit and pin to that of the 9 mm Browning pistol located on the left above the trigger.

In service with the Yugoslav forces.

BRASSEY'S DEFENCE PUBLICATIONS

Royal United Services Institute
and
BRASSEY'S

DEFENCE YEARBOOK

The 85th issue of the famous Brassey's Annual appeared in October 1974 in a new guise under the aegis of The Royal United Services Institute for Defence Studies as a Defence Year Book, and continues to make an authoritative contribution to the study of strategy, international relationships and related subjects. The first "Naval Annual" edited by Lord Brassey appeared in 1886. He gave as its aims the study of the events of the year, to draw lessons for the future and to provide knowledge of defence matters by stimulating discussion. This continued to be the aim as "Brassey's" evolved from a purely naval annual and extended in scope to the broader aspects of defence in 1950. It is equally appropriate now for the latest edition, still under the title of Brassey's, in which key questions of defence are viewed in an international context – the relations of the super powers, the world energy crisis, arms control and reductions, the Arab-Israeli war. An innovation is the section on weapon systems, providing data essential to the study of current strategic problems.

The Royal United Services Institute for Defence Studies was set up by Royal Charter for the study of British defence and overseas policy. It is the oldest institute of its kind in the world, having been established in 1831 and given its first charter in 1860, but its outlook is international, contemporary and forward-looking; as it must be, it being no longer possible to view defence exclusively from a national standpoint. As well as strategy, the economics of defence and the influence of science and technology on the development of weapons, it studies nuclear deterrence, disarmament, peace-keeping, arms control, the role of the military in modern society, the utility of armed force as a political instrument and the prevention of war. The Institute publishes a quarterly Journal, reports of its seminars and defence monographs, all of which are widely read, and is admirably fitted to supply the direction and editorship of this important Defence Year Book.

Price: £7.50

ISBN 0 902726 14 5

Published by Brassey's Naval and Shipping Annual Ltd. (in association with Thornton Cox Ltd.,) 15 Cavendish Square, London W1MOHT.

Distributed by Seeley Service and Cooper Ltd., 196 Shaftesbury Avenue, London WC2H 8JL.

1974

Sub machine Guns

Although the earliest SMG design dates back to the 1890s, the first practical examples did not appear in any numbers until after the start of World War I. In April 1914, an Italian named Bethel Revelli took out a patent on a weapon originally designed for use in aircraft. First produced at the Villar–Perosa plant, and later by Fiat and under licence for the Italian Government in Canada, the Villar Perosa (VP) as it is universally known, was later adapted for use by infantry and was mounted on motor cycles and bicycles. The VP consisted basically of two weapons held together by a crossbar and used a form of retarded blowback in that the bolt was cammed to turn slightly during the forward motion. Either mechanism could be fired individually, or both together, using 25 or 50 round magazines. A mounting was also available by which the weapon could be slung around the firer's neck and operated on the move.

At the battle of Caporetto in 1917, large numbers of VPs were captured by the Germans who sent a number back to Germany for evaluation. Earlier in the same year, the Germans, realising the need for a light automatic weapon to fill the gap between rifle and pistol, had begun issuing larger numbers of the heavy 7·63 mm and 9 mm Mauser pistols, the holsters of these weapons being able to double as a shoulder stock. In addition, production of a longer barrelled version of the P08 Luger pistol was increased. Fitted with a tangent rear sight and optional stock, the artillery model, as it was known, could also be fitted with a specially designed and unique 32 round snail drum magazine which gave it considerably increased firepower. Although this magazine was awkward and required a heavy and expensive loading tool, it nevertheless fulfilled the basic requirement for a SMG—a lighter weapon with more fire-power than a rifle, yet firing the same cartridge as a standard pistol.

The realisation of the usefulness of this type of weapon led to the acceleration of design work started in 1916 by Hugo Schmeisser, later joined by Theodore Bergmann. By June 1918, the Bergmann MP181 was being issued to front line units. The MP181 was a basic blowback weapon which also took the 32 round snail drum magazine, though this had to be fitted with a removable sleeve to allow for the shorter magazine housing of the SMG. The gun fired full automatic only, had a wooden stock, a ventilated barrel jacket and at 4·1 kg was heavier than the standard rifle.

The Treaty of Versailles required, inter alia, that the German Army should not hold any SMGs and the MP181 was relegated to use by the police. The gun was later modified by changing the magazine housing to take a straight box type magazine, and provision was made for firing single shots. This was the MP2811.

The Americans, likewise feeling the need for a weapon in the hands of an infantryman which was capable of putting down concentrated fire, began to inaugurate ideas for a truly unique system, though this cannot really be classed as a SMG. Rather than go to the lengthy and expensive process of designing a special weapon, a unit was produced which could be fitted to the ·03 Springfield rifle. Known as the Pedersen device (official secrecy shrouding it under the designation 'Automatic Pistol Cal ·30 Model 18'), the unit could be inserted into the rifle in place of the turn bolt. A 40 round magazine containing ·30 pistol type cartridges was then inserted and the blowback operated action fired the weapon semi-automatically.

Although 500,000 Model 18s were eventually ordered, only 65,000 units were produced and none saw service as it was felt that the extra weight (1 kg and 10 magazines at 0·5 kg each), together with the likelihood of the soldier losing the ordinary bolt, considerably outweighed any advantages.

John Taliaferro Thompson's famous series of SMGs began in 1917 with the belt fed persuader in ·45ACP. Using a retarded blowback system which incorporated the Blish hesitation lock (a sliding H-piece straddling the bolt to retard it until the pressure dropped), the gun failed miserably. However, as developments continued, so matters improved, and the Annihilator fitted with a box magazine reached prototype form just too late to be of use to the US forces in World War II. The first production model appeared in 1921 and, though the tests by the US Marine Corps were favourable, the gun did not sell. The 1921 model featured a choice of box or drum magazines, the latter being dispensed with when the weapon was modified for pure military use to become the M1 in 1942. By the time the M1 was adopted, it had been proved that the Blish piece was unnecessary and, along with several other expensive features, was done away with thus making the gun pure blowback-operated.

In the period between the wars, several countries experimented with SMG designs, but few realised the potential of this type of weapon. Consequently, experimentation and trial costs were mostly kept to a minimum. Blowback operation was now being accepted as the most efficient system although some other types had been introduced including a toggle action by Furrer.

Having seen the effects of SMG use at first hand during the Spanish Civil War, the Germans then went on to design and manufacture their MP38 prior to World War II. This weapon was the first SMG produced with the salient features now incorporated in most modern SMGs. A simple turned bolt, combined with a steel tube receiver with exterior milled slots for lightness, made the gun relatively easy to produce. The firing pin and operating spring were manufactured as a telescoping unit preventing spring kinkage and the entry of dirt. The most revolutionary feature, however, was the fitting of a folding stock, the gun being primarily designed for use by parachute and armoured troops which required the gun to be stored and operated in confined spaces. Although no fire selection button was fitted, the weapon had a low enough rate of fire to permit single shots to be tapped off by a trained operator. The later version, MP40, cut down production costs even further by using a stamped steel receiver and by the modification of other parts. The magazines were also strengthened by the addition of two ribs to either side.

Both the British and Americans, slow to realise the potential of a new arm, began ordering vast numbers of the heavy and expensive Thompsons at the start of World War II, even though the Americans had adopted the weapon in 1938.

Finally, the British began to design their own SMG. Deciding to make their own copy of the German MP2811, manufacture of the Lanchester began in early 1941, later being issued to the Royal Navy. At the same time, it was felt that a lighter and cheaper model was required and this led to the Sten gun. Manufactured using a maximum of stampings and spot welding, the Sten in its various marks went on to become the cheapest SMG ever put into mass production. The stock was removable and thousands, including silenced versions, were issued to Allied soldiers or dropped to resistance fighters. The Germans even produced a copy of the Sten during the closing months of the war.

The Russians, showing slight pre-war interest in the SMG, had also manufactured a copy of the German MP2811 but in 7·62 mm Type P as opposed to the 9 mm parabellum of the original. The change in calibre was due to the fact that the Russian barrel makers had been producing the 7·62 mm Nagant rifle for many years and the adoption of the same bore size did not necessitate re-tooling. Their later PPD and PPSH designs were cheap and easy to produce and featured a 71 round drum magazine giving greater firepower, but they were difficult to load at night and not very rugged.

The advantages of the Sten and similar weapons, in terms of production costs, soon became apparent to the Americans who proceeded to design one capable of being manufactured with similar ease and having the advantage of firing either the ·45ACP or the 9 mm parabellum cartridges with a minimum change of parts. Designated the M3, the weapon was popularly known as the Grease Gun and first appeared in December 1942.

Today's weapons are basically only refinements of the designs laid down 30 or 40 years ago, though in peacetime the standard of manufacture tends to rise.

The most advanced feature to come out of post-war SMG design is the wrap-around bolt. This type of bolt has the advantage, not only of allowing the weapon to have a much shorter and compact receiver, but also of displacing the weight of the bolt more towards the muzzle. This eliminates a great deal of muzzle climb on full automatic fire and thus reduces the need for a compensator, previously the accepted way of reduction. In general these weapons are also more accurate.

With few exceptions, the universally accepted SMG cartridge is the 9 mm parabellum. The drum magazine has now been completely superseded by the box type which, on some weapons, is located inside the pistol-grip most notably in the wrap around bolt type guns. The box magazine has advanced considerably and with most modern types a loading tool is no longer necessary. Nonetheless the Warsaw Pact countries, and particularly Russia, have phased out a great number of their SMGs in preference to their assault rifles which they use as both rifle and SMG. The future of the SMG within NATO, however, like the LMG, is now dependent on the new calibre which is yet to be decided on. If, as in the case of the USA, the calibre is to be of 5·56 mm or similar, then it is likely that the SMG will be gradually phased out in preference to a dual purpose weapon, or system, except for special operations or for use by men working in cramped surroundings, such as radio operators. Whatever the case, the SMG will be found in use for many years to come in many armies, and particularly by revolutionary and similar groups or by police forces.

It is worthy of note that, since the SMG first appeared, almost every country with the engineering capacity has produced a SMG of some description, though the majority never progressed beyond the prototype stage.

James Dowdall

Owen Mk1 sub machine gun

Manufacturer: **Lysaghts Newcastle Works (Australia)**

Calibre	9 mm parabellum
Dimensions	Length 81·3 cm Barrel length 25 cm
Weight	4·2 kg
Effective range	120 m
Operation	Blowback
Type of fire	Select
Muzzle velocity	420 m/sec
Sight	Front—barleycorn Rear—aperture
Magazine	32 round detachable box type
Cyclic rate	700 rpm

Adopted in 1941, the Mk1/42 Owen gun was designed and produced owing to the slow response from the United Kingdom and the United States to Australia's request for large numbers of SMGs (either Sten or Thompson) with which to equip her troops.

The Owen has several unusual features, the most marked being that the ejector is an integral part of the gun's top-mounted magazine, thus simplifying production of the basic weapon. The barrel, part of which was ribbed on early versions and fitted with a compensator, could be easily removed by use of a top-mounted spring plunger release. All models had detachable butts and the late production Mk1/44s were fitted with a bayonet mount. Early models had a solid steel frame which was later modified to lose a lot of the unnecessary weight.

Refinished and modified in the early 50s by Australian Ordnance, all models were then fitted with a new wood stock, and a rear-mounted sheet metal cover was added to the rear of the receiver which, when slid downwards would block the cocking handle, thus acting as an extra safety catch.

Although now obsolete in the Australian regular army, the Owen is still in use by reserve units and may be encountered in South East Asia.

In service, but obsolescent.

9 mm Owen Mk 1

F1A1 sub machine gun

Manufacturer: **Small arms factory (Australia)**

Calibre	9 mm parabellum
Dimensions	Length 71·3 cm Barrel length 20·3 cm
Weight	3·26 kg
Effective range	120 m
Operation	Blowback
Type of fire	Automatic
Muzzle velocity	381 m/sec
Sight	Front—blade Rear—folding aperture
Magazine	34 round detachable box type (interchangeable with the Sterling)
Cyclic rate	600 rpm

The Australian F1 is the successor to the very popular

Owen SMG. A simple blowback weapon, the F1 retains the top-loading feature of its predecessor. However, the magazine is now of the curved variety, and is interchangeable with the Sterling or Canadian CI SMGs. The pistol-grip and butt-plate are standard L1A1 rifle components. This simplifies manufacture and has advantages in terms of handling familiarity. A cover attached to the cocking handle prevents dirt entering through the cocking-slot. The cocking-handle, which is non-reciprocal with the bolt, may be locked to the bolt to facilitate clearance of excess dirt in the action. The foresight is mounted on the magazine housing, and the high rearsight (necessitated by the straight line stock configuration) folds flush with the receiver when not in use. Provision is made for a bayonet, though the F1 does not retain the compensator of the Owen.

Introduced originally as the X3, the F1 entered series production in late 1962 and has replaced the Owen, except in some reserve units.

In service with the Australian forces.

9 mm F1A1

Steyr MP69 sub machine gun

Manufacturer: **Steyr–Daimler–Puch Aktiengesellschaft (Austria)**

Calibre	9 mm parabellum
Dimensions	Length 63·5 cm (stock extended), 46 cm (stock folded)
Weight	2·7 kg
Effective range	100 m
Operation	Blowback
Type of fire	Select
Muzzle velocity	410 m/sec
Sight	Front—post with protecting ears Rear—L type with aperture
Magazine	25 or 32 round detachable box type
Cyclic rate	550 rpm

Recently introduced into the Austrian Army, the Steyr M69 uses the Uzi system of a wrap-around bolt giving a reasonable barrel length combined with a good general compactness. Like the Uzi, the M69 utilises a combined pistol-grip magazine housing. A telescopic stock is fitted and the type of fire is selected by different trigger pressures. The safety catch may be operated from either side, and the weapon may be cocked using the forward part of the sling which is attached to the cocking-piece.

In service with the Austrian forces.

Vigneron sub machine gun

Manufacturer: **SA Précision Liègeoise (Belgium)**

Calibre	9 mm parabellum
Dimensions	Length 88·5 cm Barrel length 30·5 cm
Weight	3·2 kg
Effective range	150 m
Operation	Blowback
Type of fire	Select
Muzzle velocity	370 m/sec
Sight	Front—blade Rear—aperture
Magazine	32 round detachable box type
Cyclic rate	620 rpm

A simple blowback operated select fire SMG, the Vigneron is a weapon of unremarkable design, but nevertheless well made with one or two features unusual in a modern SMG. The barrel, part of which is ribbed, is fitted with a compensator. The wire stock has three length adjustments and is 7·6 cm longer on one side, having a loop at its end to facilitate use as a cleaning rod.

Although a 3-position change lever is fitted, slight pressure on the trigger will give single shots when 'full auto' is selected. Automatic fire is obtained only when the trigger is fully depressed. An integral pistol-grip safety device is also featured. The cocking-handle is non-reciprocal with the bolt and an ejection port cover is also added. First issued in 1953, the gun saw considerable service in the then Belgian Congo and a number were issued to Congolese troops when the Belgians left and may still be encountered there. The Belgians still hold the Vigneron in reserve for use by second line troops.

In service with the Belgian forces.

9 mm Vigneron

INA 953 sub machine gun

Manufacturer: **Ordnance factory (Brazil)**

Calibre	·45 in ACP

See the Madsen M46.

In service with the Brazilian forces.

C4 (Sterling) sub machine gun

Manufacturer: **Canadian Arsenals Limited (Canada)**

See the Sterling (L2A3).

In service with the Canadian forces.

M23 and M25 sub machine guns

Manufacturer: **State factories (Czechoslovakia)**

Calibre	9 mm parabellum
Dimensions	Length 68·6 cm (stock extended), 44 cm (stock folded) Barrel length 28·4 cm
Weight	3·1 kg
Effective range	200 m
Operation	Blowback
Type of fire	Select
Muzzle velocity	380 m/sec
Sight	Front—hooded barleycorn Rear—rotary V notch
Magazine	24 or 40 round detachable box type
Cyclic rate	600 rpm

(text on facing page)

M24 and M26 sub machine guns

Manufacturer: **State factories (Czechoslovakia)**

Calibre	7·62 mm M48
Dimensions	Length 67·5 cm (wooden stock), 68·6 cm (metal stock extended), 44 cm (stock folded) Barrel length 28·4 cm
Weight	4·1 kg
Effective range	200 m
Operation	Blowback
Type of fire	Select
Muzzle velocity	550 m/sec
Sight	Front—hooded barleycorn Rear—rotary V notch
Magazine	32 round detachable box type
Cyclic rate	600 rpm

The Czech M23 and M25 are blowback-operated weapons, the distinction being that the M23 has a fixed stock and the M25 a folding stock. Like the Uzi, the barrels of the M23 and M25 are extended well into the receiver and the recessed bolt 'wraps around' the barrel in the forward position. An ejection port is cut out of the side of the bolt, thus the receiver ejection port is closed to dirt whether the weapon is cocked or not. The butt-piece of the M25 may be used as a fore pistol-grip when the stock is folded. The pistol-grip, like the Uzi, also serves as a magazine housing. A magazine-loader is attached to the right-hand side of the foregrip and is used with 8 round stripper clips. To prevent the weapon from accidentally discharging should it be dropped, the cocking-handle is locked into its slot in the receiver by a tilting process, thus the handle may only be withdrawn manually.

Now obsolete in the Czech army, large numbers were sold to Syria and Cuba where they may still be encountered. The current SMGs of the Czech army are the M24 and M26 which are very similar to the above, except for a change of calibre to 7·62 mm M48, the powerful Czech pistol cartridge. The main exterior difference is that the pistol-grips of the M24 and M26 point slightly forward and a phosphated finish is applied, as opposed to the black finish of the M23 and M25.

In service with the Czech (M24 and M26) and, possibly, with the Cuban and Syrian (M23 and M25) forces.

7·62 mm M23

7·62 mm M25, stock folded

7·62 mm M25, stock extended

Type 36 sub machine gun

Manufacturer: **State factories (People's Republic of China)**

Calibre	·45 in or 9 mm

See the M3A1.

In service with the communist Chinese forces.

Type 43 sub machine gun

Manufacturer: **State factories (People's Republic of China)**

See the PPS43.

In service with the communist Chinese and some Far Eastern communist forces.

Type 50 sub machine gun

Manufacturer: **State factories (People's Republic of China)**

See the PPSh41, but the Type 50 SMG uses only a box magazine.

In service with the communist Chinese forces.

M49 (Hovea) sub machine gun

Manufacturer: **Haerens Vabenarsenalat (Denmark)**

Calibre	9 mm parabellum
Dimensions	Length 80·6 cm (stock extended), 54·8 cm (stock folded) Barrel length 21·6 cm
Weight	3·4 kg
Effective range	150 m
Operation	Blowback
Type of fire	Full automatic
Muzzle velocity	365 m/sec
Sight	Front—blade Rear—U notch L type
Magazine	36 round detachable box type. Also Swedish M45B and Suomi box type
Cyclic rate	600 rpm

Designed at the Swedish Husqvarna arms plant, the

Hovea was the direct competitor to the Carl Gustav SMG, at trials in the late 1940s, to find a suitable SMG for the Swedish army. Although the Swedes finally accepted the Carl Gustav weapon, the Danish government preferred the Hovea, and so bought a number of these weapons together with the licence to manufacture them in Denmark. Adopted as the M49, the Hovea was originally designed to take the 50 round Finnish Suomi magazine, but it has now been replaced by the standard Carl Gustav 36 round magazine. Fitted with a sideways-folding stock, the Hovea is similar in looks and design to the Swedish M45B, and is essentially made up of spot-welded or riveted steel stampings.

In service with the Danish forces.

Madsen M46, M50 and M53 sub machine guns

Manufacturer: **Dansk Industri Syndikat AS Madsen (Denmark)**

Calibre	9 mm parabellum
Dimensions	Length 80 cm (stock extended), 53 cm (stock folded) Barrel length 20 cm
Weight	3·2 kg
Effective range	150 m
Operation	Blowback
Type of fire	M46, M50 and M53 full automatic, M53 Mk II select
Muzzle velocity	375 m/sec
Sight	Front—blade Rear—aperture
Magazine	32 round curved detachable box type (Earlier models had straight box type)
Cyclic rate	550 rpm

(Statistics are for the M53)

Introduced in 1946, the Madsen SMG model 46 deviates in several respects from previous conventional SMG designs. The receiver is made in two stamped steel sections hinged at the rear of the weapon. By unscrewing and removing the barrel-retaining nut, the receiver can be unfolded to remove the barrel, bolt and operating spring and guide. The retracting handle consists of a plate, the milled grip flanges of which are folded down to lie on each side of the receiver. A very necessary magazine loading-tool is issued with each gun. This is carried in the pistol-grip along with an extra firing-pin, safety-button and extractor.

The Madsen features an added safety system in the form of a lever positioned to the rear of the magazine housing. This lever must be squeezed when grasping the magazine housing to fire the weapon. If the gun is handled incorrectly, this lever will block the forward

9 mm Madsen M46

9 mm Madsen M53 stock folded, note bayonet lug on barrel jacket

movement of the bolt. The normal safety catch located on the left-hand side of the receiver will lock the bolt in in the open or closed position.

The Madsen was modified in 1950, the main difference being the introduction of a milled cocking handle which was integral with the bolt. The final model, the M53, differs in several respects. A curved magazine replaces the earlier straight magazine, and the barrel locking-nut has been altered to screw on to the barrel rather than the receiver. A Mk II version of the M53 is offered with a removable slatted barrel-jacket which can also take a bayonet. A change lever for selective fire is also fitted, and the gun is turned out with a better finish than previous models.

The Madsen was given close scrutiny in the United Kingdom and the results of extensive trials were favourable. Indeed, it is often considered that the gun would have entered service in British forces had the EM2 rifle been adopted. The Madsen M46 was also produced, with slight modifications, in ·45 in ACP in Brazil. Originally designated as the MB50, the weapon was improved later, and is now known as the INA 953. The main modification apart from the change in calibre was the addition of a metal loop to the lower end of the magazine housing to ensure tightness. The retracting handle was also relocated to the right-hand side of the receiver.

In service with the Brazilian (INA 953), Columbian, El Salvadoran, Guatemalan, Indonesian, Paraguayan, Thai and Venezuelan forces and the Danish police.

Cristobal Model 2 sub machine carbine

Manufacturer: **Armeria Fabrica de Armas (Dominica)**

Calibre	·30 in carbine
Dimensions	Length 94 cm Barrel length 40·6 cm
Weight	3·5 kg
Effective range	300 m
Operation	Delayed blowback
Type of fire	Select
Muzzle velocity	560 m/sec
Sight	Front—hooded blade Rear—V notch adjustable
Magazine	25 or 30 round box type
Cyclic rate	580 rpm

Unusual in that it fires the ·30 in US carbine round, the Cristobal is almost in a class of its own which could be termed as a sub machine carbine. Designed and produced with the assistance of technicians from the Beretta plant in Italy, the Cristobal outwardly looks like the Beretta SMG. Internally, however, the Cristobal differs considerably. The weapon has a delayed blowback action using a unique system in that an arm, pivoting inside the bolt, engages in a slot in the receiver when the bolt is fully forward. When the gun is fired, the inertia of this lever (the top of which engages in a heavily sprung striker) has to be overcome before the bolt can travel rearwards, thus providing the necessary delay. The weapon will not fire, therefore, until the action is fully closed, thus allowing the striker to be released by the forward motion of the top of the lever.

A later model, the M1926, is produced with a folding stock; the fixed stock version differing only by the addition of a perforated barrel-jacket. Both early and late models have two triggers, instead of a change lever, to select the type of fire required.

In service with the Dominican forces.

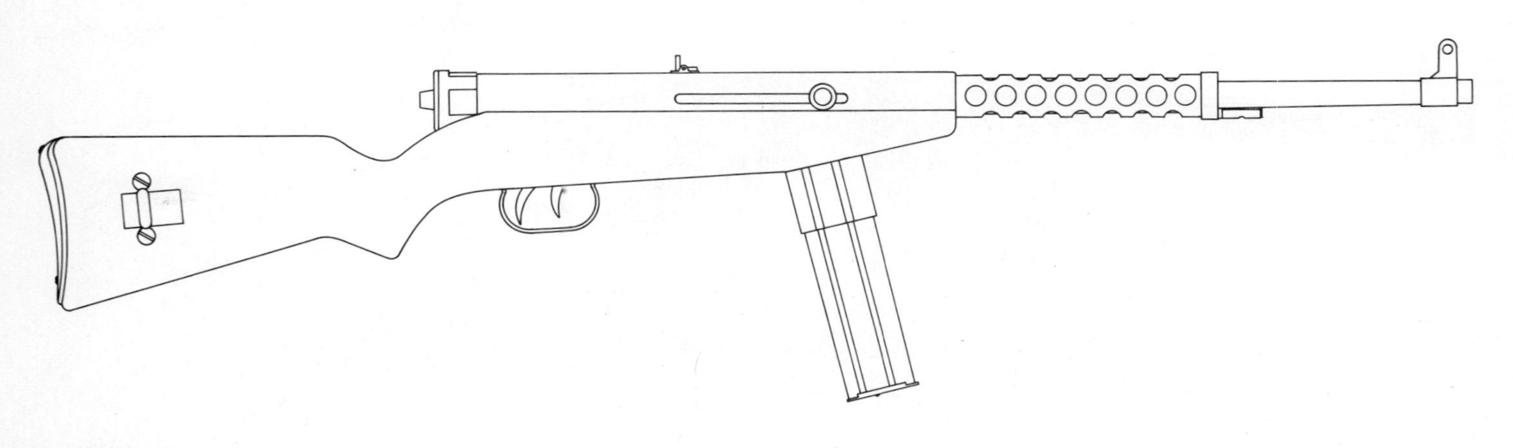

·30 in Cristobal Model 2

MAT49 sub machine gun

Manufacturer: **Manufacture d'Armes de Tulle (France)**

Calibre	9 mm
Dimensions	Length 71 cm (stock extended), 46 cm (stock folded) Barrel length 25 cm
Weight	3·6 kg
Effective range	150 m
Operation	Blowback
Type of fire	Full automatic
Muzzle velocity	380 m/sec
Sight	Front—hooded blade Rear—L type aperture
Magazine	32 round detachable box type
Cyclic rate	600 rpm

Adopted by the French Army in 1949, the MAT49 SMG saw considerable service in Indo–China and Algeria. A conventional blowback design, the weapon has, nevertheless, several unusual, but useful, features. When not required for use, the magazine-housing, with magazine attached, may be folded forward to clip beneath the barrel merely requiring to be swung back and down for instant readiness. This feature, combined with a telescopic steel stock makes the MAT49 particularly suitable for use by parachute troops. A pistol-grip squeeze safety is fitted, thus preventing accidental discharge by dropping etc, and the ejection port dust-cover is released on cocking, or on discharge.

A large number of MAT49s were captured in Indo–China by the Viet Mihn and they were later converted to the Soviet 7·76 mm Type P round, and the cyclic rate was increased to 900 rpm. These weapons are easily recognised by their longer barrel and 35 round magazine.

In service with the French forces and with the Viet Cong.

9 mm MAT49

MP40 sub machine gun

Manufacturer: **CG Haenal Waffen und Fahrradfabrik AG (Germany) and others**

9 mm MP40, stock extended

9 mm MP40, stock folded

Calibre	9 mm parabellum
Dimensions	Length 83 cm (stock extended), 63 cm (stock folded) Barrel length 25 cm
Weight	3·9 kg
Effective range	100 m
Operation	Blowback
Type of fire	Full automatic
Muzzle velocity	400 m/sec
Sight	Front—hooded barleycorn Rear—notched flip-over leaf
Magazine	32 round detachable box type
Cyclic rate	500 rpm

First produced in 1938, the earlier MP38 was originally designed for use by German parachute and armoured troops, but was later issued to all arms. The forerunner of modern SMG design, the MP38 and its later version the MP40 were one of the first SMGs to feature a folding stock. The MP38 may be distinguished by its ribbed receiver, aluminium grip-frame, and lack of a bolt-lock safety device. This model is unlikely to be encountered today.

The MP40 differs in its non-ribbed receiver and numerous other minor aspects, including the addition of a two-piece bolt-handle which is able to lock the bolt to the receiver, thus preventing accidental discharge. The combined striker and return-spring is contained within a telescopic tube, which is common to both versions. Two variants of the MP40 were produced, the MP40/II being adapted to take two magazines which could be slid across the magazine housing as required. The MP41 or MP41/I differed only in substituting the folding stock for a fixed wooden stock. Neither version was produced in large numbers. However, over one million MP40s were produced, and examples may still be encountered in many small countries.

In service with the Austrian forces.

HK5A2 and HK5A3 (or MP5) sub machine guns

Manufacturer: **Heckler and Koch GmbH (Germany)**

Calibre	9 mm parabellum
Dimensions	Length HK5A2 (MP5AL) 67 cm, HK5A3 (MP5A3) 66 cm (stock extended), 49 cm (stock folded) Barrel length 22 cm
Weight	HK5A2 2·4 kg HK5A3 2·5 kg
Effective range	150 m
Operation	Delayed blowback
Type of fire	Select
Muzzle velocity	400 m/sec
Sight	Front—hooded post Rear—rotary aperture
Magazine	10, 15 or 30 round box type
Cyclic rate	650 rpm

The Heckler and Koch MP5 is derived basically from the HK rifle series, using the same roller-locking system. The weapon comes in two versions, the MP5A2 with fixed stock and the MP5A3 with telescopic stock. Both versions may be fitted with the 10, 15 or 30 round magazine. Heckler and Koch also produce a 5·56 mm version of the MP5, known as the HK53, though the gun has so far failed to sell. All these weapons fire from a closed bolt, thus producing a 'cook off' hazard which is an unusual aspect in a modern SMG.

Due to its perhaps unnecessarily high grade of manu-

9 mm HK5A2, fixed stock

facture, the HK5 series of SMGs are expensive to produce and so far only the German police have adopted the MP5A2, though a few are believed to be in service with the Bundeswehr.

In service with the West German police and, possibly, the West German forces.

M48 sub machine gun

Manufacturer: **State factories (Hungary)**

See the PPSh41.

Obsolescent in Hungary.

M22 sub machine gun

Manufacturer: **Ordnance factory (Iran)**

See the PPSh41.

In service with the Iranian forces.

Uzi sub machine gun

Manufacturer: **Israel Military Industries (Israel) and Fabrique Nationale Herstal (Belgium)**

Calibre	9 mm parabellum
Dimensions	Length 63·7 cm (wooden or metal stock)
	Barrel length 26 cm
Weight	3·5 kg
Effective range	200 m
Operation	Blowback
Type of fire	Select
Muzzle velocity	390 m/sec
Sight	Front—truncated cone with protecting ears
	Rear—aperture battle
Magazine	25, 32 or 40 round detachable box type
Cyclic rate	600 rpm

One of the most prolific SMGs in the Western World today, the Uzi is produced in its native country of Israel and under licence at FN Herstal in Belgium. Designed in the late 1940s by Uziel Gal, the Uzi incorporates features within its design which, at the time of its conception, were considered revolutionary. The old problem of bad feed, often caused by the magazine not being held firmly enough in its housing, was almost eliminated by making the magazine-housing integral with the pistol-grip into which is also incorporated a grip safety. Magazine changing, particularly at night, is thus allegedly simpler because of the 'hand finds hand' principal. The Uzi achieves a reduction in muzzle climb on automatic fire, compactness, and the retention of a reasonable barrel length by machining the bolt to permit a recess for the barrel which is extended into the receiver. The top-mounted cocking-handle is non-reciprocal with the bolt and is fitted with a sliding dust-cover. Later models have 'cuts' in the top cover to prevent the bolt going forward in the event of the cocking-lever being accidentally released during bolt retraction. The Uzi may be found with a variety of stocks. Early models were fitted with long wooden stocks which were later shortened and were detachable. Nowadays, the more common stock to be found is the folding metal-type.

The Uzi has provision for a bayonet, and a grenade launcher may be screwed to the front of the receiver in place of the barrel locking-nut. A blank firing device is also available. Standard in numerous armies, the Uzi is renowned for its durability, compactness and reliability under adverse conditions.

In service with the Belgian, Dutch, Israeli, West German and numerous other African, European and South American forces.

9 mm Uzi, later version with metal stock

9 mm Uzi, wooden stock on early model

38/49 (Model 4) sub machine gun

Manufacturer: **Pietro Beretta (Italy)**

Calibre	9 mm parabellum
Dimensions	Length 80 cm Barrel length 21·5 cm
Weight	3·2 kg
Effective range	150 m
Operation	Blowback
Type of fire	Select
Muzzle velocity	375 m/sec
Sight	Front—blade Rear—L type flip over with U notch
Magazine	20 or 40 round detachable box type
Cyclic rate	550 rpm

The Beretta 38/49 is merely a modified version of the

9 mm Beretta 38/49 (Model 4) with 20 round magazine

earlier Model 38 series of SMGs whose development started before World War II.

Of a conventional blowback design, the 38/49 is unusual in being fitted with a full wooden stock, although a folding stock version is also produced. Type of fire is selected by the use of two triggers and muzzle climb is reduced by the fitting of a compensator. The ejection port is on the left-hand side, an almost unique innovation found in this series of weapons. A cross bolt-type safety catch is fitted to the 38/49 Model 4. However, a grip safety is featured on the folding stock version and the later Model 5 is fitted with a fore-end squeeze safety.

In service with the Costa Rican, Dominican, Egyptian (with a folding bayonet), West German, Indonesian, Tunisian, Thai and Yemeni forces.

Model 12 sub machine gun

Manufacturer: **Pietro Beretta (Italy)**

Calibre	9 mm parabellum
Dimensions	Length 64·5 cm (stock extended), 42 cm (stock folded) Barrel length 20 cm
Weight	3 kg (folding stock), 4 kg (wooden stock)
Effective range	100 m
Operation	Blowback
Type of fire	Select
Muzzle velocity	365 m/sec
Sight	Front—hooded blade Rear—L flip over with U notch
Magazine	20, 30 and 40 round detachable box type
Cyclic rate	550 rpm

Adopted by the Italian Army in 1961, the Model 12 features a wrap-around bolt similar to the Uzi SMG, giving compactness and greatly reduced muzzle climb.

Deep grooves running the length of the cylindrical body allow for a large amount of dirt and foreign matter to be absorbed before malfunctioning takes place. Though normally fitted with a sideways folding stock, the weapon may also be found with a detachable wooden stock. The type of fire is selected by means of a button located in front of the rear pistol-grip which also incorporates a grip safety.

In service with the Italian forces.

9 mm Beretta Model 12

Type 49 sub machine gun

Manufacturer: **State factories (North Korea)**

See the PPSh41, but the Type 49 uses only a drum magazine.

In service with the North Korean forces.

K50m sub machine gun

Manufacturer: **State factories (North Vietnam)**

Calibre	7·62 mm (Russian or Chinese)

See the PPSh41 (especially the last paragraph).

In service with the North Vietnamese forces and the Viet Cong.

FBP M/48 sub machine gun

Manufacturer: **Fabrica de Braco de Prate (Portugal)**

Calibre	9 mm parabellum
Dimensions	Length 81 cm (stock extended), 63·5 cm (stock folded) Barrel length 25 cm
Weight	3·7 kg
Effective range	100 m
Operation	Blowback
Type of fire	Automatic
Muzzle velocity	390 m/sec
Sight	Front—blade Rear—fixed aperture
Magazine	32 round detachable box type
Cyclic rate	500 rpm

Designed by Major Goncalves Cardoso of the Portuguese artillery, the FBP M/48 is basically a weapon incorporating the best features of the German MP40 and the United States M3A1 SMGs. The ERMA originated bolt and telescopic operating spring housing, differ from the MP40 only in the use of a fixed firing-pin. The pullout wire stock, stamped receiver design, trigger housing and sights are the same as the United States M3A1. Although of unremarkable design, the FMB is, nevertheless, well made.

In service with the Portuguese forces, but obsolescent.

Z62 Star sub machine gun

Manufacturer: **Bonafacio Echeverria y Compania SA (Spain)**

Calibre	9 mm parabellum or 9 mm largo
Dimensions	Length 69·5 cm (stock extended), 48 cm (stock folded) Barrel length 20 cm
Weight	2·8 kg
Effective range	100 m
Operation	Blowback
Type of fire	Select
Muzzle velocity	360–550 m/sec
Sight	Front—blade Rear—L type aperture
Magazine	20, 30 or 40 round detachable box type
Cyclic rate	550 rpm

The standard SMG of the Spanish Army, the Z62 has replaced the earlier Z45 which was basically a copy of the German MP40, but with some modifications. The Z62 is a conventional blowback-operated weapon incorporating some unusual features. A bolt inertia safety is mounted behind the spring-loaded firing-pin to prevent accidental discharge due to dropping. The stock, when folded, allows the shoulder-piece to be used as a fore-end grip. The folding cocking-handle is non-reciprocal with the bolt and is located at the front of the perforated barrel-jacket. Three magazine sizes are available and the weapon is produced in either 9 mm parabellum or 9 mm largo.

In service with the Spanish forces.

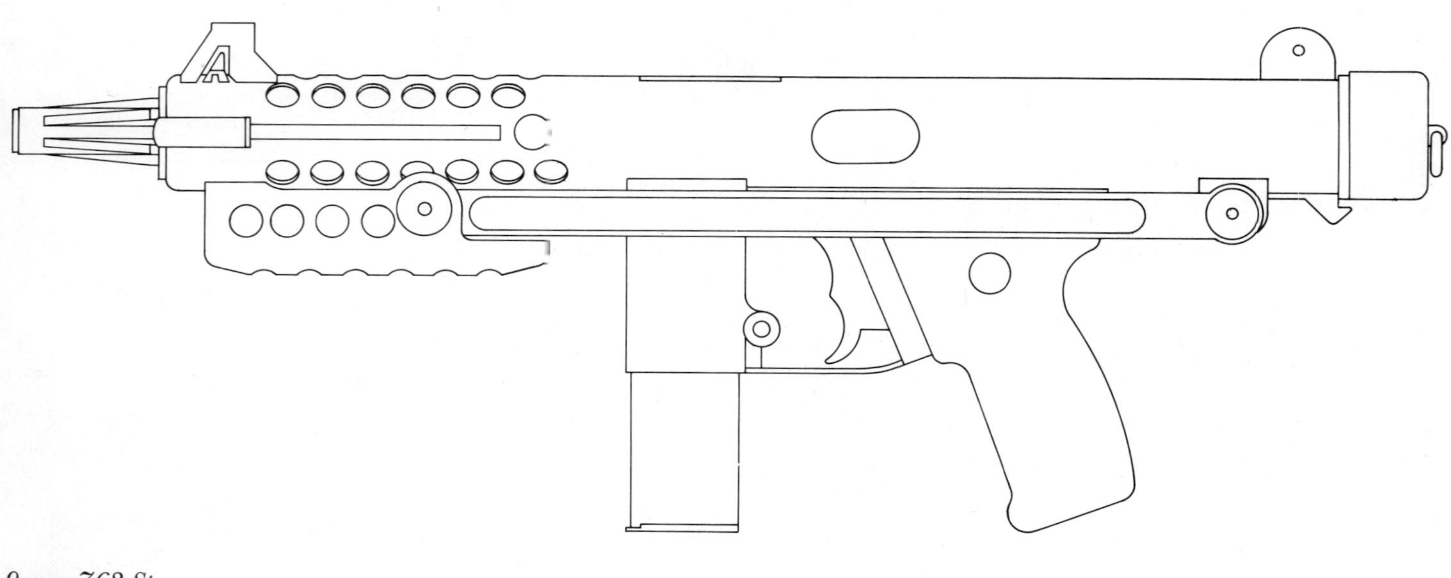

9 mm Z62 Star

Carl Gustav M45B sub machine gun

Manufacturer: **Carl Gustav Stads Gevarfactori (Sweden)**

Calibre	9 mm parabellum
Dimensions	Length 81 cm (stock extended), 55 cm (stock folded) Barrel length 17·8 cm
Weight	3·4 kg
Effective range	150 m
Operation	Blowback
Type of fire	Full automatic
Muzzle velocity	365 m/sec
Sight	Front—protected post Rear—L type
Magazine	36 round detachable box type
Cyclic rate	550–600 rpm

Designed during the closing months of World War II, the M45, with minor modifications, has remained the standard Swedish SMG. The first model was designed originally to take the 50 round Suomi drum magazine. When the 36 round box magazine was introduced in the early 1950s, a removable magazine housing was added in order that the gun, now the M45B, could be used with both magazines. From 1951, as the 36 round magazines became more plentiful, the magazine housing was permanently attached to the receiver. A conventional blowback design, the M45B is well made and, due to its construction of pressed-steel parts riveted together, is relatively cheap to produce.

The gun has been manufactured under licence in Egypt as the Port Said SMG, and large numbers have been sold to Indonesia.

In service with the Egyptian, Indonesian and Swedish forces.

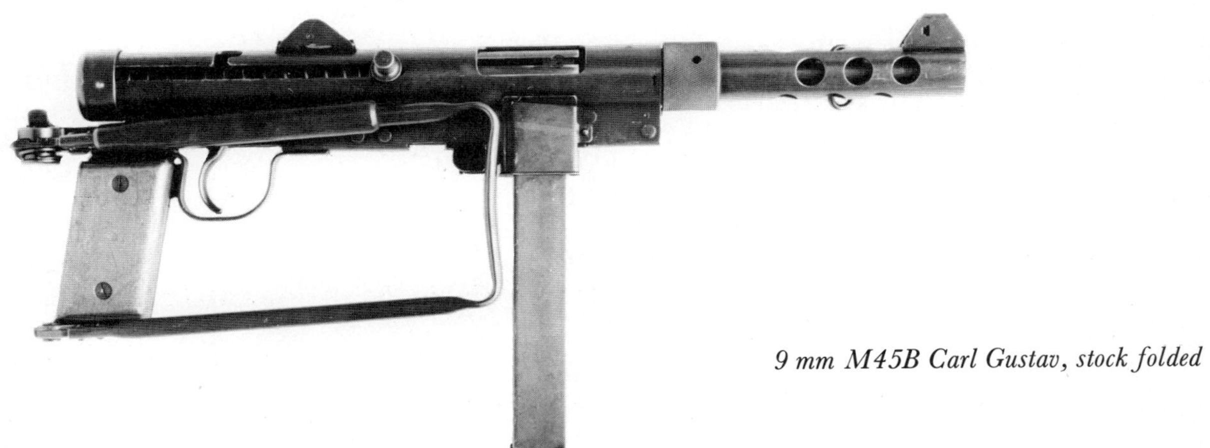

9 mm M45B Carl Gustav, stock folded

PPSh41 sub machine gun

Manufacturer: **State factories (USSR)**

Calibre	7·62 mm type P
Dimensions	Length 82·2 cm Barrel length 26·5 cm
Weight	3·9 kg
Effective range	150 m
Operation	Blowback
Type of fire	Select
Muzzle velocity	500 m/sec
Sight	Front—hooded post Rear—tangent leaf or L type with U notch
Magazine	71 round drum or 35 round box type
Cyclic rate	700–900 rpm

7·62 mm PPSh41, with 71 round drum magazine

Designed by George Shpagin in 1940, the PPSh41 met the need for an easily mass produced, but rugged, SMG.

The receiver and barrel-jacket are stamped out, the main milled parts being the bolt and the barrel, the bore of which is chrome-plated. The PPSh41 has a select fire lever positioned in front of the trigger and the rather elaborate tangent sight on the early models was replaced by a simplified L type. The two-piece bolt handle allows the bolt to be locked in either the forward or the rear position. A 71 round drum, or a 35 round box, magazine may be fitted, the former giving the gun a great advantage over its German World War II counterpart, the MP40. Moreover, the Germans even went so far as to convert a number of captured PPSh41s to 9 mm parabellum. Although the PPSh41 is obsolete in the USSR and Soviet bloc, a large number is probably being held in reserve as there were over 5 million produced during World War II alone.

The weapon has also been produced in large numbers in China as the Type 50 SMG (taking only the box magazine), North Korea as the Type 49 (drum magazine only), Hungary as the M48 and in Iran as the M22.

A North Vietnamese version known as the K50m is merely a Chinese Type 50 with the barrel-jacket shortened and the wooden stock replaced by a pistol-grip and metal housing incorporating a wire stock similar to that used on the French MAT49. This weapon may also be found in either 7·62 mm Russian or 7·62 mm Chinese.

Obsolete, but in service in various parts of the world (see text)

PPS43 and 43/52 sub machine guns

Manufacturer: **State factories (USSR)**

Calibre	7·62 mm Type P
Dimensions	Length 82 cm (stock extended), 61·5 cm (stock folded) Barrel length 23 cm
Weight	3·6 kg
Effective range	75 m
Operation	Blowback
Type of fire	Automatic
Muzzle velocity	490 m/sec
Sight	Front—post with ears Rear—L type
Magazine	35 round detachable box type
Cyclic rate	650 rpm

7·62 mm PPS43, stock extended

7·62 mm PPS43, stock folded

Primarily made of sheet metal stampings, the PPS43 is a modified version of the PPS42 which was designed, built and field-tested during the siege of Leningrad.

Cheaper to produce than the PPSh41, the PPS43 fires fully automatic only and has no fixed ejector. The main operating spring guide-rod acts as an ejector when the bolt is in the rearward position. The 35 round curved box magazine, although similar to that of the PPSh41, is not interchangeable. The stock is unusual in that, when folded, it lies on top of the receiver.

Although obsolete in the Soviet army, the PPS43 is still in use in Poland as the model 43/52 and fitted with a wooden stock. Also produced in China as the Type 43 copy.

In service with the Polish and other Warsaw Pact sponsored forces.

Sten Mark II sub machine gun

Manufacturer: **British Small Arms Company, the Royal Small Arms Factory and others (United Kingdom)**

Calibre	9 mm parabellum
Dimensions	Length 76·2 cm Barrel length 19 cm
Weight	3 kg
Effective range	75 m
Operation	Blowback
Type of fire	Select
Muzzle velocity	390 m/sec
Sight	Front—inverted V blade Rear—aperture
Magazine	32 round detachable box type
Cyclic rate	540 rpm

Designed during the latter part of 1940, the Sten met the United Kingdom's urgent need for a cheap and easily mass-produced SMG.

Based loosely on the German MP38/40, the Sten utilised the minimum amount of production time and materials. During World War II, a total of five different models were produced, all with different modifications within those models. A basic blowback weapon, the Sten featured a detachable butt, and on some models, a detachable barrel. The magazine housing of the Mark II could be swivelled around the receiver to form a dust cover for the ejector-port. A silenced version of the Mark II also saw service. Other variations such as wooden stocks, forward pistol-grips, flash-hiders and bayonet-mounts came and went with different marks and, as a lot of these parts were interchangeable between models, some examples may be found with parts from other marks. Although rugged and extremely cheap to produce, the gun is not renowned for its reliability due to a badly designed and fitted magazine which also has the disadvantage of needing to be loaded with a special loading-tool, though this is not uncommon in other makes.

With over 4 million built during World War II in the United Kingdom, Canada and New Zealand, it is likely that the Sten will be encountered for some years to come in the hands of irregulars. Indeed, many countries are believed to hold large stocks in reserve, though the weapon is no longer in front-line use in any regular force.

Obsolete, but in reserve.

9 mm Sten Mark II

Sterling (L2A3) sub machine gun

Manufacturer: **Sterling Engineering Company and Royal Small Arms Factory (United Kingdom)**

Calibre	9 mm parabellum
Dimensions	Length 71 cm (stock extended), 48 cm (stock folded) Barrel length 19·8 cm
Weight	2·7 kg
Effective range	200 m
Operation	Blowback
Type of fire	Select

Muzzle velocity	430 m/sec
Sight	Front—blade with protecting ears Rear—aperture battle
Magazine	34 round detachable box type
Cyclic rate	550 rpm

The Sterling SMG is a further development of the Patchett machine carbine which was designed during World War II, some early models seeing action at the Normandy landings. Designed by William Patchett and produced and developed at Sterling Engineering, the early Patchett took the same magazine as the Sten and Lanchester SMGs, but the gun itself was of a considerably better design than either of its predecessors. Later models were adapted to take a magazine specially designed by Patchett which featured two rollers instead of the usual follower. The next model to appear was the L2A1 which was also produced at the Royal Ordnance Factory Fazakerly and was adopted in August 1953 by the British army. Limited numbers were sold to over 40 countries, and Canada and New Zealand officially adopted the weapon, the Canadians producing it under licence in modified form at Canadian Arsenals where it is now known as the C4. By now, the weapon was known as the Sterling, and featured an arctic trigger (facilitated by removing the trigger guard) and a bolt having four special sharpened ribs machined out of its side which cut

9 mm Sterling L2A3 with bayonet, bayonet scabbard, magazine and sling

Sterling L2A3, stock folded

through accumulated fouling and drove the dirt out through a slot below the barrel and through holes in the receiver.

Several slight modifications served to redesignate the weapon as the L2A2 which was the first mass-produced model. The final and current version is the L2A3 which again differs only slightly—in the sights and the butt. All models of the Sterling may be fitted with a bayonet. A silenced version, the L34A1, was introduced to replace the Mk6 silent Sten.

In service with the Canadian (C4), New Zealand, United Kingdom and other forces.

Sterling L2A3 with silencer

Thompson M1A1 sub machine gun

Manufacturer: **Savage Arms Corporation (United States)**

Calibre	·45 in
Dimensions	Length 81·3 cm Barrel length 26·6 cm
Weight	4·7 kg
Effective range	100 m
Operation	Blowback
Type of fire	Select
Muzzle velocity	280 m/sec
Sight	Front—blade Rear—fixed aperture
Magazine	20 or 30 round detachable box type
Cyclic rate	700 rpm

First manufactured in series production in 1928, the Thompson went on to become the most common of the Allied SMGs of the early World War II years.

A device known as the Blish hesitation lock combined to make the early 1928 model a delayed blowback weapon. An optional variety of box magazines was available, as was a 50 round or a 100 round drum-magazine. The wooden butt stock was quickly detachable and this, combined with a heavily ribbed barrel, Cutts compensator and a high quality Lyman rearsight, made manufacture a very lengthy and expensive operation. As production increased at the beginning of World War II, the need for a cheaper and easier-to-produce model became apparent. In April 1942, the SMG Cal ·45 M1 appeared. This model did away with the ribbed barrel, detachable stock, Blish lock, compensator and several other expensive refinements and provision was no longer made for the fitting of the drum-magazine. Slightly modified later that year, the gun became the M1A1 and remained as such until production

·45 in Thompson M1A1

ceased in 1944. Over 1½ million were produced. Though accurate and reliable, the Thompson was heavy and still expensive to manufacture even in its M1A1 form. The gun later saw service in the Korean War and a number were taken out of mothballs for the Vietnam conflict

Copies of the Thompson have been manufactured in China and Egypt, and a number were turned out in the jungle workshops of North Vietnam. The Thompson may still be encountered worldwide, particularly in the hands of irregular forces, and is still also used by many police forces and law enforcement agencies.

In service (see text).

M3A1 sub machine gun

Manufacturer: **General Motors Corporation (Guide Lamp Division) and Ithaca Gun Company (United States)**

Calibre	·45 in or 9 mm parabellum
Dimensions	Length 75 cm (stock extended), 57 cm (stock folded) Barrel length 20·3 cm
Weight	3·6 kg
Effective range	100 m
Operation	Blowback
Type of fire	Automatic
Muzzle velocity	280 m/sec
Sight	Front—blade Rear—aperture
Magazine	30 round detachable box type
Cyclic rate	350–450 rpm

The need for a cheap and rugged weapon, similar to the Sten gun, to replace the heavy and expensive Thompson, became apparent soon after America's entry into World War II.

The M3 SMG, nicknamed the 'Grease Gun' due to its similar shape, entered service in late 1942. Made mostly from stampings, the M3 can be adapted to 9 mm by changing the barrel, bolt, magazine housing and magazine. The gun features an unusual, but reasonably foolproof, safety system. The ejection port-cover is fitted with a projecting lug which, when the cover is closed, locks the bolt in either the cocked or battery position, thus eliminating the danger of accidental discharge and keeping the action free of dirt. The rather complex cocking mechanism of the M3 was later simplified by the addition of a hole in the bolt allowing the bolt to be withdrawn by the use of a finger, thus eliminating the cocking mechanism.

Redesignated M3A1, the gun was also modified by the addition of a magazine loading device attached to the wire stock. The capacity of the oil bottle carried inside the pistol grip of both models was increased and a guard was added to the magazine catch. An optional flash-hider could also be fitted to both models. A number of 9 mm M3s were fitted with silencers for use by special forces and a small number were supplied with curved barrels. The M3 series saw extensive service during World War II and in Korea. It is also produced by the communist Chinese.

In service with some South American and communist Chinese forces.

·45 in M3A1, stock folded, note cocking handle

Ingram MAC10 sub machine gun

Manufacturer: **Military Armament Corporation (United States)**

Calibre	·45 in and 9 mm parabellum
Dimensions	Length 54·8 cm (stock extended), 26·7 cm (stock folded)
	Barrel length 14·6 cm
Weight	2·8 kg
Effective range	75 m
Operation	Blowback
Type of fire	Select
Sight	Front—blade with ears
	Rear—leaf
Magazine	30 round box type (32 round for 9 mm)
Cyclic rate	1090 rpm (M 10/9)
	1145 rpm (M 10/45)

Ingram MAC11

Manufacturer: **Military Armament Corporation (United States)**

Calibre	9 mm short
Dimensions	Length 46·0 cm (stock extended), 22·2 cm (stock folded)
	Barrel length 12·9 cm
Weight	1·6 kg
Effective range	50 m
Operation	Blowback
Type of fire	Select
Sight	Front—blade with ears
	Rear—leaf
Magazine	16 and 32 round box type
Cyclic rate	1200 rpm

The Ingram M10 and M11 are a series of very light, compact, durable and accurate SMGs. Compactness is obtained by using the wrap-around bolt system similar to that of the Uzi, the bolt being made of 8620 heat treated steel. The pistol-grip doubles as a magazine housing and, as there is no fore-end, a web strap is attached to a swivel mounted on the barrel. The sliding stock, when extended, has a two position shoulder-piece for use from the hip or the shoulder or to be hooked behind the elbow. When folded, the shoulder piece folds over the top of the receiver. As well as a change lever and safety catch, the bolt may be locked by twisting the cocking-handle through 90°. Offered in three calibres, ·45, 9 mm parabellum and 9 mm short, the Ingram may also be fitted with a suppressor.

Adapted with sound and flash suppressors, the Ingram is an ideal personal weapon for clandestine operations. As well as being in service throughout the world, it has been purchased by several Law enforcement agencies.

In service with the forces of Chile, Colombia, the Dominican Republic, Saudi Arabia, the USA and the United Kingdom.

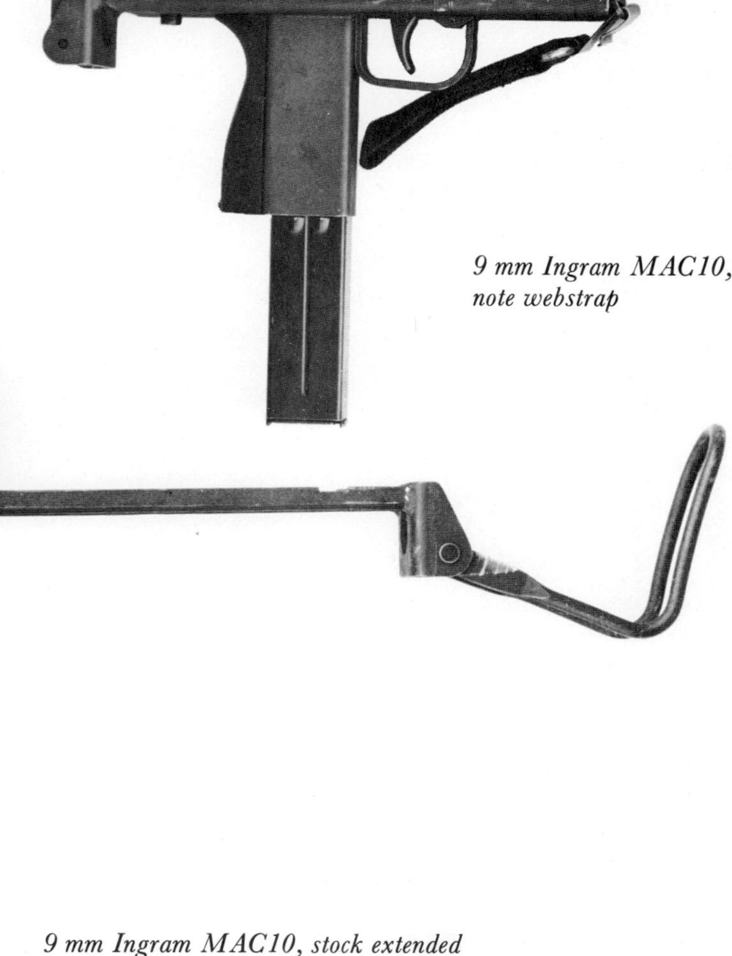

9 mm Ingram MAC10, note webstrap

9 mm Ingram MAC10, stock extended

·45 in Ingram MAC11 with silencer

M56 sub machine gun

Manufacturer: **Crvena Zastava (Yugoslavia)**

Calibre	7·6 mm Type P
Dimensions	Length 87 cm (stock extended), 59 cm (stock folded) Barrel length 24·7 cm
Weight	3 kg
Effective range	75 m
Operation	Blowback
Type of fire	Select
Muzzle velocity	520 m/sec
Sight	Front—hooded blade Rear—L type U notch
Magazine	32 round detachable box type
Cyclic rate	570–620 rpm

Introduced to replace the earlier M49 (basically a copy of the Soviet PPSh41), the M56 uses the best points of the M49 and the German MP40.

The lower body, pistol-grip and folding stock are almost direct copies of the MP40, but the bolt is very similar to that of the M49. The M56 is a select fire weapon and may be fitted with a bayonet. The magazine is interchangeable with that of the M49.

In service with the Yugoslav forces.

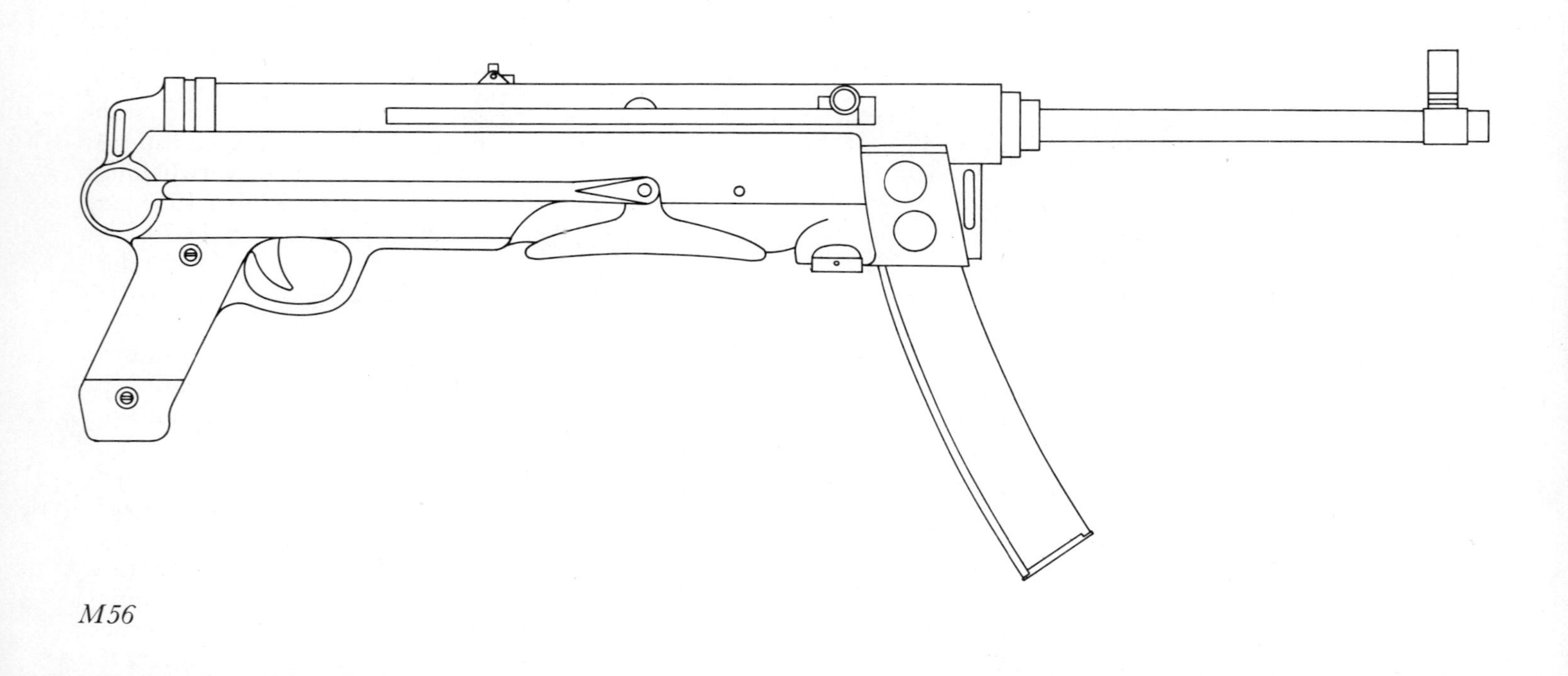

M56

Rifles and Carbines

Serious discussion on rifles continues to be hinged around the question of the bullet and its calibre. There is, of course, the overriding need to reduce the infantryman's load, and, as it is often argued, ammunition must be light. This will help to give the soldier a weapon that is easy to handle in the confines of an armoured personnel carrier or operate in the urban or rural jungles—in other words, a rifle of the light carbine type. On the other hand, the argument continues, the bullet must be capable of being fired from the light machine gun (LMG) and remain lethal at ranges up to 800 m, and there lies the conflict and dilemma.

During World War II, both Germany and Russia developed an intermediate cartridge, described as being midway between a rifle and a submachine gun (SMG) round. Both countries used their standard rifle bullet size with a smaller case. The Russian cartridge (designated 7·62 mm × 39 mm M43) was first used in the SKS rifle and the round remains standard today in the AK47, AKM and the earlier model LMGs, although it is worthy of note that the new PK general purpose machine gun (GPMG) returns to the old rimmed 7·62 mm M1908 cartridge, which gives ranges in excess of 900 m.

When in 1945 the British set up their ideal small arms calibre panel, they were under the impression that they would be developing information mutually with the USA. In 1947, when they visited the USA with the results of their tests, they learned for the first time of the US T65 cartridge and the T25 rifle. The competitive demonstrations in 1950 between the T65 cartridge (later destined to become the 7·62 mm (NATO) round) and the British ·280 in or 7 mm round were held using the US T25 rifle and the British-designed EM2 (Bull Pup) rifle. With a muzzle velocity of 700 m/sec (comparing well with the Soviet M43 round at 675 m/sec), the early loadings of the British cartridge were somewhat handicapped when pitted against the 30–06 ballistics of the T65. Yet, although the British EM2 rifle outperformed the T25, the excellent performance of the ballistically superior ·280 in cartridge at longer ranges went unnoticed. Finally, due to overwhelming pressure from the USA, the T65 was adopted as NATO standard in December 1953, and the British finally abandoned their EM2 rifle and ·280 in cartridge in favour of the 7·62 cm cartridge and the Belgian FN rifle. The 7·62 mm cartridge has since remained the standard round for all NATO countries and the French still retain their 7·5 mm round for their standard rifle the M49/56 and their AAT 52 LMG.

The subsequent adoption by the USA of the 5·56 mm round was in direct contrast to their earlier insistence on a full rifle calibre, in preference to an intermediate type originally proposed and in use by the Soviet block, China and other European countries, and caused a great deal of controversy. This very high velocity round was developed by the Armalite Company in 1957. It has an approximate muzzle velocity of 980 m/sec (using the standard AR18) and the makers claim that: '*Impact results in a hydrostatic effect and corresponding extensive rupture of flesh in the immediate bullet path and displacement of fluids which are driven into body tissue over a wide area. This causes a major shock and a high percentage of fatalities when compared with any present 7·62 mm (·30 cal) service load.*' At ranges exceeding 550 m, however, when the round has decelerated appreciably, the velocity effectiveness is almost lost. Many military commentators consider, however, that 400 m–450 m is the maximum killing range required of a military rifle, and so the 5·56 mm has much in its favour, especially as a rifle produced in this calibre need not normally weigh more than 3 kg. More ammunition may be carried by the soldier and, if using a breech-locking system similar to that of the M16 or AR18, the weapon becomes cheaper and easier to produce.

It is odd that, at frequent intervals, infantry pundits claim on various grounds that they will be satisfied with a maximum range for the rifle of some 350 m. The same strange thinking is often extended to denigrating the value of the sniper. Certainly, such views have been prevalent in the USA and UK at intervals over the years but, fortunately, military history has repeatedly shown that such thinking is fallacious. In simple terms, every rifleman should be capable of hitting his target at all ranges up to 500 m and, with a sniper's rifle, to 700 m–800 m.

A disadvantage of the 5·56 mm round is that, due to the low muzzle energy, gas-fouling problems increase. These were prevalent on the M16 when first used in Vietnam, as the cartridges were loaded with WC846, a slower burning powder than the IMR4475, with which the rifle mechanism was carefully balanced to function. This resulted in a high degree of separated case malfunctions combined with a higher rate of fire.

The findings of the Ichord Committee investigations conducted in the field in 1968 led to the M16A1. The main modifications were the addition of a heavy buffer (to slow down the cyclic rate) and the chrome plating of the chamber (to reduce friction and protect against corrosion). These modifications appear to have cured the problems and, combined with regular and thorough cleaning, make the rifle reliable. With the fleetingly glimpsed targets and short distances involved in jungle and urban warfare, the 5·56 mm round seemed to prove relatively satisfactory.

Indeed, most major European arms companies are experimenting with, or have produced rifles for sale in 5·56 mm, eg FN, Beretta, SIG, H&K and MAS. None of these weapons has been sold in large numbers but, if NATO adopts the 5·56 mm cartridge, most countries will probably equip with their own native-designed weapon. Most of these rifles are capable of launching grenades and taking a bayonet, the retention of which appears to be more of a tradition and for ceremonial than as a practical requirement, except as a knife or combination wire cutter. A folding or telescopic stock version is also

T48 heavy barrel FN rifle produced for US trials 1952

EM2 rifle—the British cal ·280 design

Modified T48 which became FAL in 7·62 calibre

offered for use by parachute troops and for carriage in helicopters and armoured vehicles. Extras include a three round burst capability, telescopic sights, night sights and bipods.

It is depressing to note that, due to the effects of capillary action and surface tension, barrels of smaller calibres tend to hold condensation. If a weapon is fired with even a small amount of water closing the bore, the enormous chamber pressure generated can blow up the rifle. Furthermore, the degree of penetration, compared to the 7·62 mm (NATO), is cut down by equipment, thick brush or other cover due to the light (55 grain) bullets being easily mutilated on contact. In a European-type action, there would seem to be little doubt that the increased depth of penetration, combined with the capability of being interchangeable with LMGs and sniper rifles at ranges up to, say, 800 m, all emphasise the basic advantages of the intermediate round (and the basic weight increase would be less than 1 kg per man).

It is probable that the next decade will see a new calibre adopted by NATO, though whether or not the 5·56 mm round will be chosen is still open to conjecture. Although considerable military opinion seems to revolve around this calibre at present, many ballistics experts and experienced infantrymen still feel that the intermediate round —the British ·280 in or the German World War II 7·92 mm 'kurz' cartridge—is the answer for the next generation assault rifle.

* * * * *

Since the end of World War II, arms manufacturers have made increasing use of steel stampings wherever possible. With their obvious cost and weight advantages, they enable some of the simpler types to be produced under licence in countries lacking the more sophisticated types of milling, cutting and boring machines. The wooden stock, so long a standard material in most small arms, is now disappearing in favour of the plastic or composition type. In comparison with cost of replacement or the time-consuming repair of a cracked or chipped stock instead, the plastic stock needs merely to be replaced. Moreover, during the Vietnam war it was found that the wooden stocks of the M14 rifles were becoming so warped as to make stripping almost impossible.

* * * * *

In most countries, the sniper rifle has merely meant the 'accurizing' of an old standard bolt-action rifle with the addition of a telescopic sight. However, the Russians have gone against this trend by introducing the semi-automatic Dragunov. Using the basic Kalashnikov action, this rifle, specifically designed for sniping, is chambered for the old, but well proven, 7·62 mm M1908 rimmed cartridge which, as previously stated, has also been reintroduced for the PK GPMG. The Dragunov also features an unusual skeleton stock with pistol grip. The rifle was introduced to replace the M1890/30 Moisin Nagant sniper model, although this rifle is probably still in second line use by Warsaw Pact countries.

The French also have a special sniper rifle, the FRF1. Although a conventional bolt-action type, it was specially designed and features a folding bipod and a stock, the length of which may be altered to suit the individual. Some countries like Belgium and Germany merely add a telescopic sight to their standard rifle although they undoubtedly hold stocks of bolt-action weapons in reserve.

James Dowdall

Type D Browning automatic rifle

Manufacturer: **Fabrique Nationale Herstal (Belgium)**

Calibre	7·92 mm and ·30–06
Dimensions	Length 114·5 cm Barrel length 50 cm
Weight	9·2 kg
Effective range	1400 m
Operation	Gas
Muzzle velocity	730 m/sec
Sight	Front—post type Rear—tangent
Magazine	20 round detachable box type
Cyclic rate	Slow 350–450 rpm Fast 500–650 rpm

The type D BAR is a gas-operated automatic weapon which fires from an open bolt, and takes a 20 round magazine. It has a quick-detachable flanged barrel to which a carrying handle is attached. A variable gas port is fitted to facilitate the correct amount of gas used to meet varying conditions. Although not a selective fire weapon, there are, nevertheless, 3 positions for the change lever. Normal automatic fire is obtained when the change lever is switched to 'M'. However, when the lever is pushed to 'R', this actuates a decelerator which slows down the forward travel of the moving mechanism. This reduces the rate of fire to approximately 350–450 rpm and also enables single shots to be fired by manual tapping of the trigger.

The Type D is fitted with a bipod and can be used with a butt monopod, but there is no provision for a bayonet or grenade launcher. Dust covers are provided for the ejection and magazine ports. Unlike its United States counterpart (M1918A2), the Type D's action can be easily stripped by removing the trigger group and hingeing down the butt to remove the operating mechanism.

An expensive weapon, the Type D was supplied to Egypt in 7·92 mm where it is now second-line service, having been replaced by Soviet weapons. It was supplied to Belgium in ·30–06, but is now obsolete there.

In service with Egyptian second-line troops.

Type D BAR

SAFN Model 49 rifle

Manufacturer: **Fabrique Nationale Herstal (Belgium)**

Calibre	·30 in, 7 mm, 7·65 mm, 7·92 mm
Dimensions	Length 120·1 cm Barrel length 58·9 cm
Weight	4·5 kg
Effective range	680 m
Operation	Gas
Muzzle velocity	730 m/sec
Sight	Front—shielded post Rear—tangent aperture
Magazine	10 round charger loaded
Cyclic rate	Semi-automatic

Developed in the 1930s, the Model 49 replaced the earlier bolt action rifles of some nine countries and was produced in 4 calibres. It is also interesting to note that this weapon formed the basis for the highly successful FAL rifle.

A gas-operated, semi-automatic rifle, the M49 utilises the Tokarev tilting bolt-locking system in which the bolt locks on a bar set in the bottom of the receiver. The gas-operated return system uses a piston rod to return the action. Gas regulation is adjusted by removing the front hand guard and turning the gas adjusting sleeve

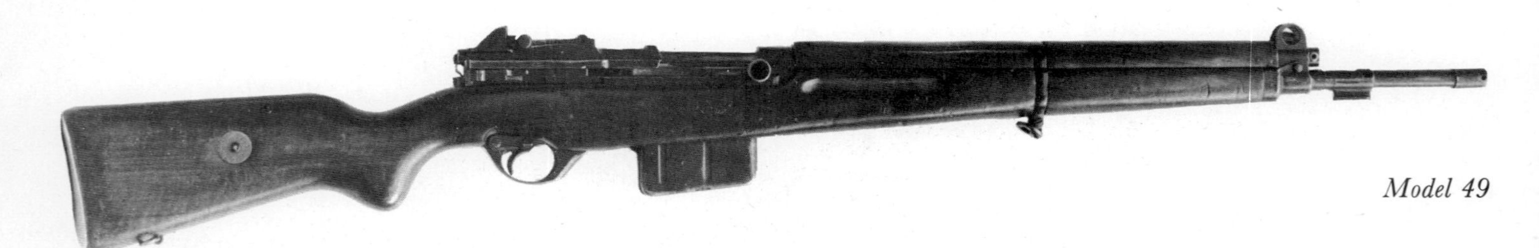

Model 49

accordingly to suit conditions.

Fitted with a 10 round magazine, the rifle is loaded using 5 round chargers (called 'stripper clips' in the USA) or individual rounds. The magazine may be removed by using a cartridge to actuate the magazine catch. When the hammer is cocked, the hammer spring guide, projecting from the trigger guard, acts as a cocking-indicator. The action remains open after the last shot has been fired. A manual hold-open device for loading single rounds is another feature.

A bayonet lug is fitted and some models are fitted with a muzzle break. The tangent-type aperture rear-sight is adjustable for elevation and windage. Also supplied in sniper version, the M49 is no longer in service as a first-line weapon

In service with the Argentinian, Brazilian, Columbian, Egyptian, Indonesian, Luxembourg, Turkish, Venezuelan and Zairen forces.

FN FAL (FAR) rifle

Manufacturer: **Fabrique Nationale Herstal (Belgium)**

Calibre	7·62 mm (NATO) and ·30–06, 7 mm, 7·65 mm, 7·92 mm
Dimensions	Length 105·3 cm with variations Barrel length 53·3 cm
Weight	4·3 kg
Effective range	500 m
Operation	Gas
Muzzle velocity	850 m/sec
Sight	Front—protected post Rear—folding aperture (see text)
Magazine	20 round detachable box type
Cyclic rate	650 rpm

The FAL, with minor modifications, is the most successful and widely used of the post-war developed combat rifles and is currently in service with some 70 countries. It is not intended to comment on the many minor modifications ordered by individual nations since, with the exception of the British version (SLR L1A1), no modifications have been made to the basic mechanism. Only the existing FN designs are, therefore, presented.

The FAL is a selective-fire weapon firing from a locked bolt and using a gas regulation system for reloading. Two basic variations of the rifle are available—one with a fixed stock and one with a folding tubular stock and both have a carrying handle. There is also a heavy-barrelled version for use as a section support weapon.

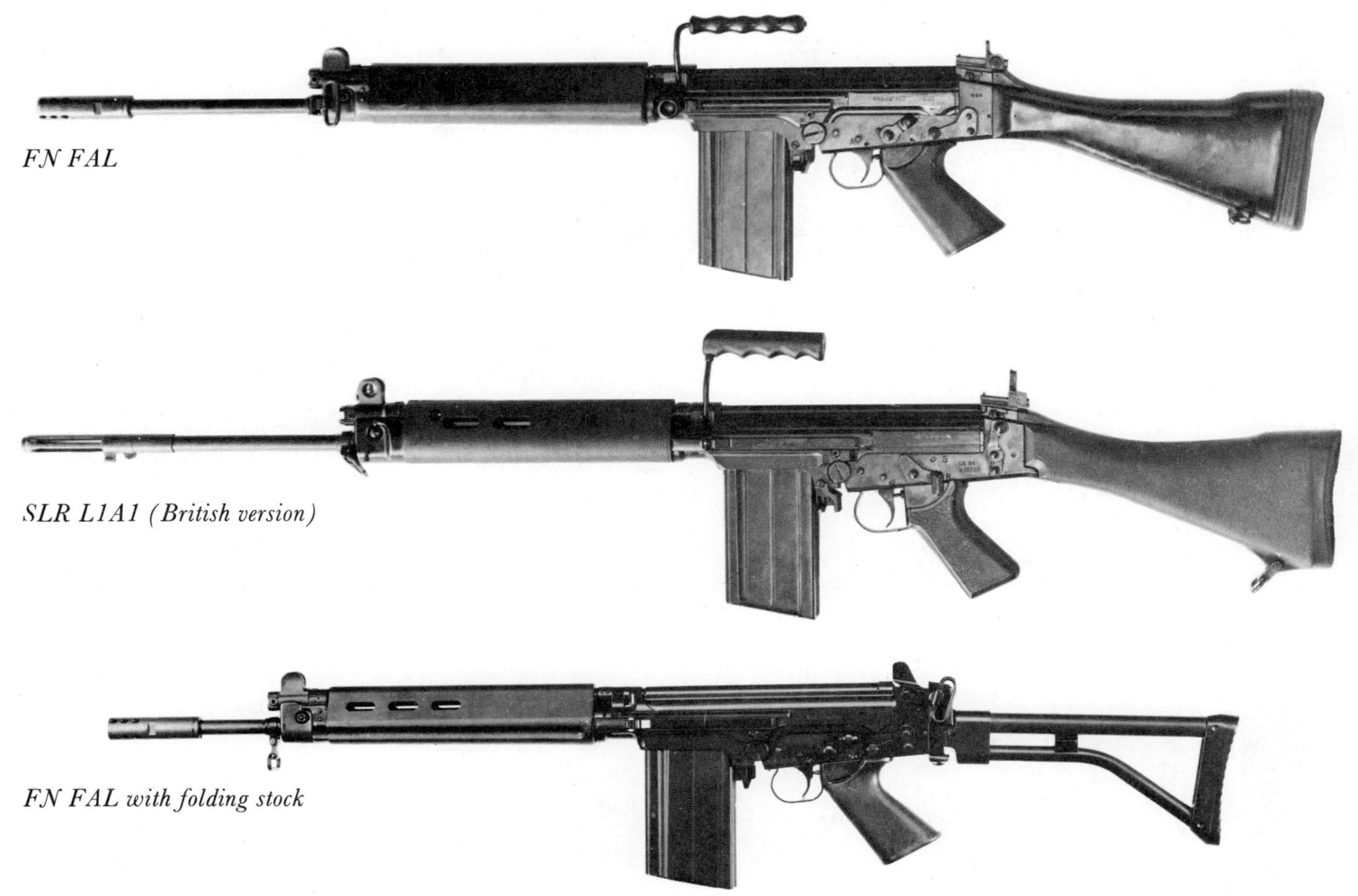

FN FAL

SLR L1A1 (British version)

FN FAL with folding stock

FN FAL with heavy barrel and telescopic sight

The sights differ, however. In the fixed-stock version they are of the protected post foresight and folding rear aperture types. The backsight is graduated in 100 m stages from 200 m to 600 m. In the folding stock version, the sights are similar to those in the CAL, the foresight being of the protected post type and the rear of the apertured L type set for 150 m and 250 m. Both versions can be equipped with telescopic sights simply by changing the receiver cover.

The field stripping of the FAL can be done without tools since, like the CAL, it breaks open rather like a shotgun and the entire bolt assembly can be withdrawn, or replaced, quickly and easily. The gas piston can be taken out by squeezing the studs on the gas regulator and twisting it so that it unlocks. The piston and return spring are then withdrawn.

The flash suppressor is the area where most modifications have been made by the user nations. The basic FN versions have a flash suppressor which also serves other purposes. It forms a grenade launcher of 22 mm diameter, a support for the FN tubular bayonet (which is also used on the FN CAL), and it also accepts a blank firing device if required.

Two 20 round box magazines are available for the FAL, one in steel and the other in light alloy. In addition, when the British converted their Bren guns (see light machine guns) to fire the NATO 7·62 mm cartridge, they designed its magazine, holding 30 rounds, to be interchangeable with the magazine of the L1A1.

In service with the forces of over 70 countries.

FN CAL (5·56) rifle

Manufacturer: **Fabrique Nationale Herstal (Belgium)**

Calibre	5·56 mm
Dimensions	Length 97·8 cm Barrel length 47 cm
Weight	3·3 kg
Effective range	400 m
Operation	Gas
Muzzle velocity	765 m/sec
Sight	Front—protected post Rear—aperture battle
Magazine	20 or 30 round, detachable box type
Cyclic rate	650–700 rpm

It is believed that Fabrique Nationale Herstal, formerly Fabrique Nationale d'Armes de Guerre, started development of a 5·56 mm calibre rifle in about 1963. It was originally intended to scale down the well-known FN FAL to fire 5·56 mm ammunition, but it was finally decided to produce a new rifle. The CAL is the result of subsequent research and development.

The CAL is a gas-operated weapon employing the same gas return system as the FAL, and can be field stripped in a similar manner. The main design difference between the two weapons is in the bolt-locking system. Whereas the FAL employs a rear-locking tilting block, the CAL uses a rotating bolt which locks into a barrel extension. This system of locking means that the stresses of firing are passed into the barrel extension. Thus, although high-grade steel is needed for the bolt head, the rest of the weapon, other than the barrel, does not.

FN CAL

FN CAL with folding stock

The CAL has a four-setting selector giving: safe, semi-automatic, a three-round burst and fully automatic. The burst capability is ingenious and worthy of comment. Two sears, operating on an escapement system, enable the rifle to fire three rounds on each trigger squeeze, and, if set on burst, when a new magazine is inserted, the next squeeze of the trigger will always fire a three-round burst initially.

The CAL is available in two basic configurations: a fixed-stock version and a folding-tubular stock version. Various extras are available for either version, and are mentioned below.

Sights on both versions are of the protected post fore-sight and L type aperture rearsight. The rearsight is set at two ranges–250 m and 400 m. An optical scope sight can also be fitted to the top of the receiver for fine shooting. A removable bipod is available, and the bayonet is the same as that of the FAL, which is a useful costing feature.

The flash suppressor/grenade launcher is designed to take all rifle grenades with a tail boom diameter of 20 mm. In addition, a separate 40 mm grenade launcher can be fitted, though it is understood that FN are re-working their original designs in this field.

On trial with the Belgian forces.

Vz58 rifle

Manufacturer: **Ceskoslovenská Zbrojovká (Czechoslovakia)**

Calibre	7·62 mm	*Operation*	Gas
Dimensions	Length 84·3 cm (Vz58p) and 63·5 cm (Vz58v stock folded)	*Muzzle velocity*	700 m/sec
	Barrel length 40 cm	*Sight*	Front—protected post Rear—tangent leaf
Weight	3·1 kg	*Magazine*	30 round detachable box type
Effective range	400 m	*Cyclic rate*	700–800 rpm

Vz58

Vz58 with folding stock

Replacing the earlier M52/58, the Czech Vz58 is externally similar to the Soviet AK47 though it differs internally in several aspects.

The gas system utilises a short-stroke piston to drive the action rearwards, whereas the piston and bolt carrier of the AK47 are machined in one piece. There is no facility for gas adjustment. The action is locked by a tilting bolt system, whereas the AK47 uses a rotating bolt. A simpler trigger mechanism than the AK47, combined with an axial hammer, serve to make this part of the weapon more efficient than its Soviet counterpart. Although this weapon will use all standard Warsaw Pact 7·62 mm × 39 mm ammunition, Czech-manufactured ammunition should normally be used.

Supplied in two versions, the Vz58p with either wood or fibre compound stock, fore-end and pistol grip (earlier versions used wood) and the Vz58vp with a folding metal stock (for parachute and armoured troops), the Vz58 can be fitted with a bayonet and flash hider. A bipod is also available but, when fitted, prevents the use of the bayonet. A tangent leaf rearsight is graduated to 800 m in 100 m increments. The front sight is of the protected post type.

Some 1·4 kg lighter than the AK47, the Vz58 will tend to climb rapidly on fully automatic fire, but is nevertheless a well-designed and manufactured weapon.

In service with the Czechoslovak forces.

MAS36 and M1936CR39 (folding stock) rifles

Manufacturer: **Manufacture d'Armes de Saint-Etienne (France)**

Calibre	7·5 mm
Dimensions	Length 101·8 cm (M1936CR39—88·64 cm (or 61·7 cm with stock folded))
	Barrel length 57·4 cm (M1936 CR39—44·95 cm)
Weight	3·8 kg (M1936CR39—3·6 kg)
Effective range	500 m (M1936CR39—450 m)
Operation	Bolt
Muzzle velocity	820 m/sec
Sight	Front—barley corn with guards
	Rear—ramp with aperture
Magazine	5 round integral staggered-row box type

Introduced in 1936, using the then new 7·5 mm M29 cartridge, the MAS36 uses a modified Mauser type of bolt action. The main difference lies in the position of the locking lugs which, in the MAS36, engage into the receiver directly above the trigger. Although this allows a shorter bolt stroke, it sacrifices the strength of the Mauser, which lies in its breech-locking lugs.

The 5 round magazine is loaded by using clips, or cartridges inserted singly. A bayonet can be fitted into a slot below the barrel, and when not in use is taken out, reversed, and replaced in the slot in a similar fashion to a cleaning rod.

A parachute version (designated M1936CR39) was produced with folding aluminium stock and shorter barrel. A postwar version (the M1936M51) has a built-in grenade launcher.

Although no longer in first-line service in France, the MAS36 is still used for training and may be encountered in many of the ex-French colonies.

In service with the French and French ex-colonial forces.

MAS 36

M49 and M49/56 rifles

Manufacturer: **Manufacture d'Armes de Saint-Etienne (France)**

Calibre	7·5 mm
Dimensions	Length 110 cm
	Barrel length 58 cm (M49/56—52·6 cm)
Weight	4·7 kg (M49/56—3·9 kg)
Effective range	540 m
Operation	Gas
Muzzle velocity	825 m/sec (M49/56—820 m/sec)
Sight	Front—blade with protecting ears
	Rear—ramp with aperture
Magazine	10 round detachable box type
Cyclic rate	Semi-automatic

Developed to replace the MAS36 bolt-action rifle, the M49 and the updated semi-automatic M49/56 utilise main design features from other well-proven weapons.

M49/56

M49/56, stripped

The gas system is similar to that of the Swedish Ljungman M42 in that, instead of the usual piston, the gas is tapped off through the gas port in the barrel and then passes down a tube, the other end of which protrudes slightly into the bolt carrier. The gas hits the carrier, forcing it to the rear and allowing the reloading cycle to take place. The weapon's tilting bolt-locking system is also that of the Ljungman and Tokarev rifles. The action remains open when the last round has been fired, and the weapon is easily field stripped.

Both the M49 and 49/56 have grenade launchers permanently attached, the sights for these being mounted on the left-hand side and top of the barrel respectively. A rubber butt cushion is issued for use with the grenade launcher. The M49/56, but not the M49, has provision for a bayonet.

The detachable magazine (the release catch of which is mounted on the magazine itself) may be filled with single rounds or with 5 round charges (called 'stripper clips' in the USA). Both models have grooves cut in the left-hand side of the receiver to accommodate a telescopic sight. Normal sights are blade type front, and ramp with aperture rear. A luminous night sight may also be fitted.

The weapon saw considerable service with the French Army in Indo-China.

In service with the French and ex-French colonial forces.

FRF1 rifle

Manufacturer: **Manufacture Nationale D'Armes de Saint-Etienne (France)**

FRF 1

Calibre	7·5 mm and 7·62 mm (NATO)
Dimensions	Length 114 cm Barrel length 55 cm
Weight	3·7 kg
Effective range	850 m
Operation	Bolt
Muzzle velocity	850 m/sec
Sight	Telescopic, fixed battle
Magazine	10 round detachable box type

Specially designed for sniping purposes, the FRF1 (Fusil Repetitif Fusil 1) is unusual in that it is not an adaptation of a standard military weapon as most sniper rifles are. Using a bolt action with a 10 round detachable box magazine (fitted with a rubber pad on the base) the F1 is really a militarized competition rifle.

The stock length may be altered by using extension pieces and the rifle incorporates a folding bipod adjustable for height, a pistol-grip and a padded cheek-rest. A telescopic sight is fitted, and a night sight is also available. A number of foresight fittings are supplied with the rifle. Trigger pull is adjusted by use of a micrometer screw. There is no provision for the fitting of a bayonet. Open sights are fitted but need rarely be used.

Although a telescopic sight may be fitted to all models of the French Army's M49/56, this rifle is the standard sniper rifle of the French Army.

In service with the French forces.

FAMAS 5·56 mm rifle

Manufacturer: **Groupement Industriel des Armements Terrestres (France)**

Calibre	5·56 mm
Dimensions	Length 75 cm Barrel length 48 cm (rifled section only)
Weight	3·25 kg
Effective range	300 m
Operation	Delayed blowback
Muzzle velocity	960 m/sec
Sight	Integral within carrying handle
Magazine	25 round detachable box type
Cyclic rate	850–950 rpm

The FAMAS (Fusil Automatic Manufacture Nationale d'Armes de Saint-Etienne) is the French answer to the growing requirement for a small-calibre combat rifle. There is so far little manufacturer's information on this rifle, which, it could be argued, is really a sub machine carbine.

The basic design appears to be of the 'Bull Pup' type—similar to the ill-fated British EM2 of 1949. The magazine is to the rear of the trigger mechanism and the shooter's face therefore rests immediately to one side of the receiver.

Apart from its outward similarity to the EM2, this weapon has a number of other interesting features. One of the most useful is the ability to change ejection to either side as the firer wishes, thus eliminating one of the major problems of the left-handed soldier. The FAMAS 5·56, unlike the EM2 which was gas-operated, is a delayed blowback weapon making considerable use of plastic materials. This has resulted in an assault rifle weighing about 4–5 kg, though at the time of writing no precise figures are available.

The weapon is equipped with only one sight of the adjustable ring variety, encased in the fixed carrying handle. The manufacturer claims that this system

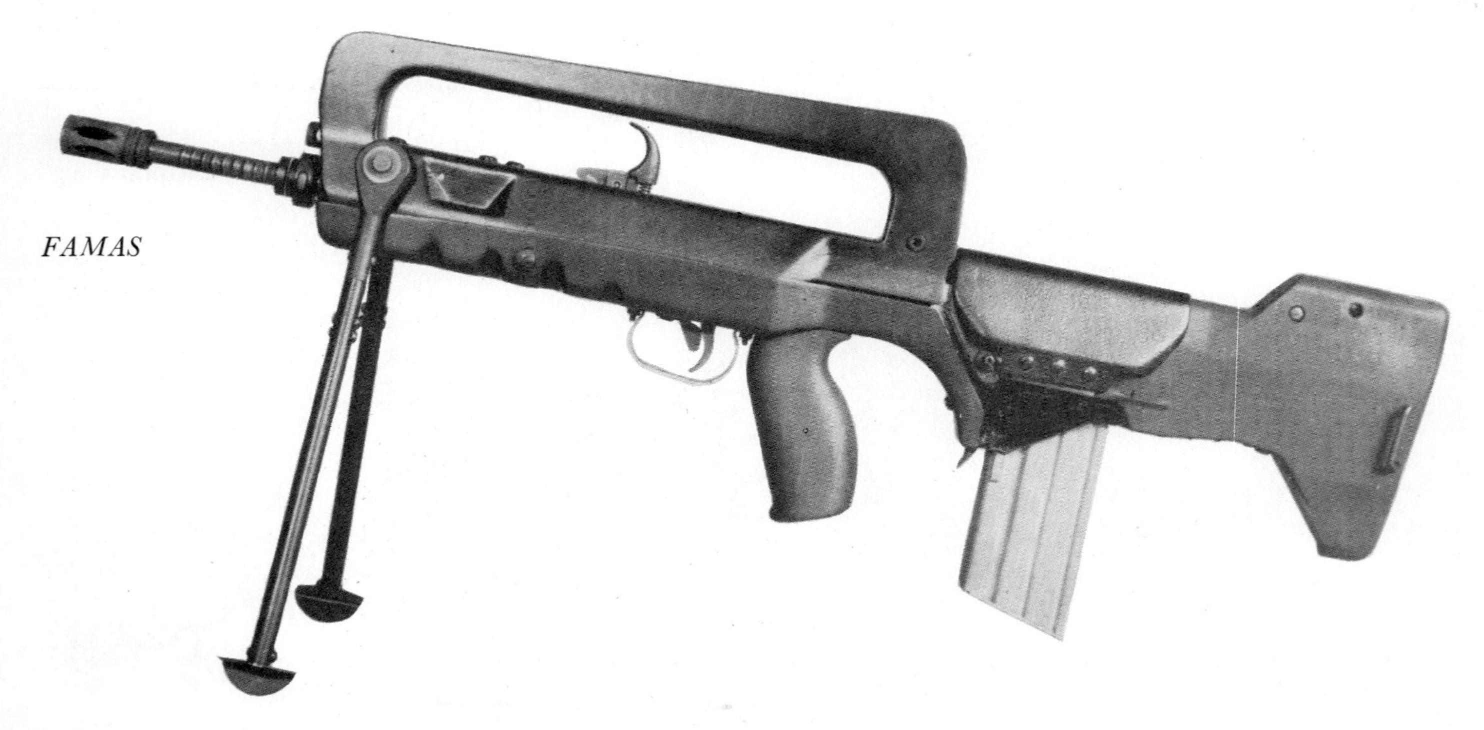

FAMAS

permits it to be as accurate as any conventional weapon. As far as is known firing can be semi-automatic, controlled burst or fully automatic, and a bipod is provided for greater stability.

The flash suppressor/grenade launcher is designed to enable the weapon to launch 500 gm anti-personnel grenades up to 400 m or 500 gm and 'Grafac' grenades out to about 80 m using an appropriate ballistite cartridge. Since the 'Garfac' grenade has an interior tail-boom diameter of 22 mm, it is assumed that this weapon can launch any rifle grenade with the same tail-boom characteristics.

Not yet in service.

Mauser Kar 98k rifle (and variants)

Manufacturer: **Mauser Werke AG (Germany)**

Calibre	7·92 mm
Dimensions	Length 110·7 cm Barrel length 60 cm
Weight	3·9 kg
Effective range	550 m
Operation	Bolt
Muzzle velocity	755 m/sec
Sight	Front—blade Rear—tangent
Magazine	5 round staggered fixed box type

The Mauser action rifle is the most prolific bolt action design ever produced.

Using front locking lugs which give enormous strength to the action, the rifle was first produced during the 1880s and has survived to the present day, having been the standard rifle of the German and other armies for over 50 years. Most examples were capable of taking a bayonet and, on some, a grenade launcher. The safety is a thumb-operated lever mounted on the bolt plug.

Produced under licence in many different countries and in a wide variety of calibres, the rifle is still in use by some countries, eg Turkey and Indonesia, some South American and African countries, and large numbers are in second line or sniper use, with large stocks held in reserve in many major countries.

In service with the Turkish, Indonesian and some South American and African forces.

Mauser Kar 98K

G3 rifle (and variants)

Manufacturer: **Heckler & Koch, and Rheinmetall GmbH (Germany)**

Calibre	7·62 mm (NATO)
Dimensions	Length 102 cm (G3A3); 80 cm (G3A4) Barrel length 45 cm
Weight	4·3 kg
Effective range	500 m
Operation	Recoil
Muzzle velocity	780 m/sec
Sight	Front—protected post Rear—rotary aperture
Magazine	20 round detachable box type
Cyclic rate	500–600 rpm

The G3 is the standard weapon of the West German armed forces and has recently gone into production, under licence, in both the UK and France. Considerable attention has been given to designing a weapon that is easy to manufacture and to maintain. Current models of the G3 make extensive use of stampings and plastic. It is understood that only the barrel and bolt components are machined.

Work on assault rifles like the Stg 45(M) during World War II supplied much of the design information for the G3. The latter rifle is a recoil operation weapon with a delayed blowback locking mechanism, otherwise called

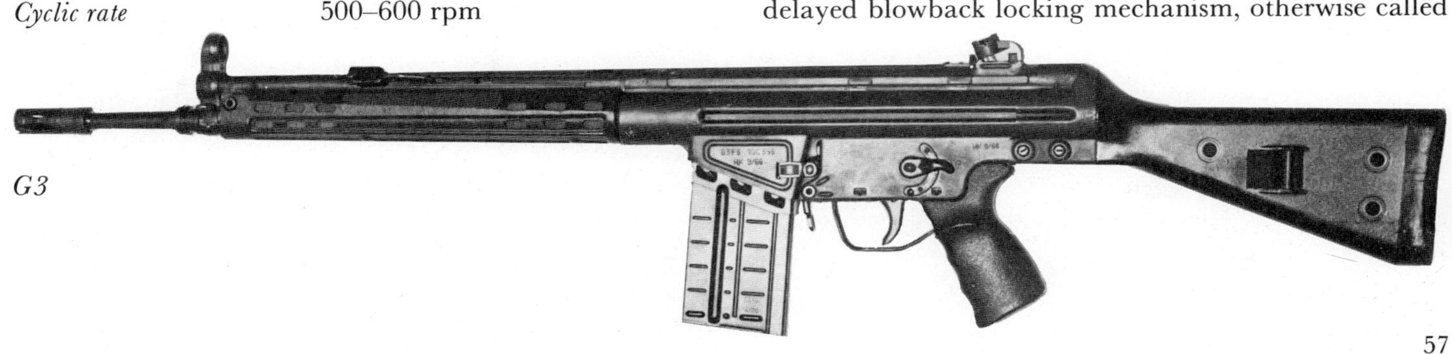

G3

G3 with telescopic sight

G3 (early French version)

G3A4 with folding stock

a recoil-operated, roller-locked system. See also the CETME.

The weapon is designed for semi- and fully-automatic fire and has a three-position selector/safety lever which is situated on the left side above the pistol-grip. There is also a position indicator on the right. The most unusual feature of this rifle is the design of the rearsight, which is a rotary-type sight, adjustable for elevation and windage, consisting of an open V and three diopter holes for ranges from 100 m–400 m. The foresight is of the protected post type. Infra-red sights can be fitted without modification.

There are relatively few variations of the G3. However, a folding stock version (G3A4) is available parts of which are interchangeable with the fixed stock version and vice versa. Early models were fitted with forestocks of wood or of stamped steel. The standard models produced today have plastic stocks and forestocks. A bipod can be fitted which, in the case of the French production version, is standard. With the attachment of a 4-power scope, the G3 can be used in the sniper role. This sight, which is graduated for ranges from 100 m–600 m, can be attached to the rifle without any special preparations.

The flash suppressor/grenade launcher permits the launching of any rifle grenade having an interior tail boom diameter of 22 mm. In order to fire blank cartridges the flash suppressor has to be replaced by a blank firing attachment, and a special bolt must be used. In addition, Heckler and Koch have recently produced a detachable independent 40 mm grenade launcher (see grenade launchers).

In service with the Austrian, Danish, Dominican, French, Indonesian, Norwegian, Portuguese, Pakistani, Swedish, Turkish and West German forces.

HK33 rifle (and variants)

Manufacturer: **Heckler & Koch GmbH (Germany)**

HK33

HK33 with telescopic sight

HK33 with bipod

HK33 with folding stock

Calibre	5·56 mm
Dimensions	Length 92 cm } HK33A2 Barrel length 38·2 cm }
Weight	3·5 kg
Effective range	400–500 m (estimated)
Operation	Delayed blowback
Muzzle velocity	960 m/sec
Sight	Front—hooded post Rear—rotary with 4 apertures. Adjustable for windage and elevation
Magazine	20, 30 or 40 round detachable box type
Cyclic rate	600 rpm

The HK33 series was designed to compete in the military market for a weapon to fire the increasingly popular 5·56 mm cartridge.

Three versions are currently offered by Heckler and Koch. The standard version is the HK33A3 and could be classified as a sub machine carbine.

All these weapons work on the same recoil action with a delayed roller locking system, as does their larger counterpart the G3. The full-length models only are capable of launching grenades as standard.

Like the G3, the HK33 series use the same rotary rear sight with 4 apertures, as well as utilising stampings for the majority of the weapon.

Not yet in service.

Galil (ARM) rifle

Manufacturer: **Israel Military Industries (Israel)**

Calibre	5·56 mm
Dimensions	Length 97 cm Barrel length 46 cm
Weight	3·9 kg
Effective range	600 m
Operation	Gas
Muzzle velocity	980 m/sec
Sight	Front—protected post Rear—aperture battle
Magazine	35 or 50 round detachable box type
Cyclic rate	650 rpm

Galil (SAR) rifle

Manufacturer: **Israel Military Industries (Israel)**

Calibre	5·56 mm
Dimensions	Length 84·5 cm Barrel length 33 cm
Weight	3.5 kg
Effective range	400 m
Operation	Gas
Muzzle velocity	920 m/sec
Sight	Front—protected post Rear—aperture battle
Magazine	35 or 50 round detachable box type
Cyclic rate	650 rpm

Galil ARM

Galil ARM with bipod

Galil SAR

Designed by Israel Military Industries, the Galil ARM (automatic rifle and LMG) and SAR (short assault rifle) are almost pure Kalashnikov in design, but scaled down to take the 5·56 mm cartridge. The weapon utilises the same rotating-bolt locking system with the bolt-carrier and piston machined as one piece. The cocking handle is top-mounted and the change lever may be operated from either side of the weapon, thus making the weapon suitable for use by either left- or right-handed troops. When set to 'safe', the change lever automatically closes the ejection port to prevent the entry of dirt.

A robust aperture battle sight is fitted with settings for 300 m or 500 m. These sights, combined with the use of the bipod (also serving as a wirecutter) and the 50 round magazine, make the ARM version suitable for use as a LMG. Folding luminous night sights, effective up to 100 m, are fitted, as standard, on both versions. A flash-suppressor acts as a mount for both bayonet or grenade launcher. Grenade-launching cartridges are normally used with a special 12 round magazine. Both versions are fitted with a folding-stock thus making them suitable for armoured and paratroop use.

The Galil has been in service with Israeli forces for some 12 months. Initial designs were produced from weapons captured during the Six Day War.

In service with the Israeli forces.

BM59 Standard rifle

Manufacturer: **Pietro Beretta (Italy)**

Calibre	7·62 mm (NATO)
Dimensions	Length 109·5 cm Barrel length 49·1 cm
Weight	4·4 kg
Effective range	500 m
Operation	Gas
Muzzle velocity	812 m/sec
Sight	Front—protected post Rear—adjustable aperture
Magazine	20 round detachable box type
Cyclic rate	800 rpm

BM59 Paratroop rifle

Manufacturer: **Pietro Beretta (Italy)**

Calibre	7·62 mm (NATO)
Dimensions	Overall length 122·5 cm Length (with stock) 72·5 cm (without grenade launcher) Barrel length 46·8 cm
Weight	4·5 kg
Effective range	400 m
Operation	Gas
Muzzle velocity	800 m/sec
Sight	Front—protected post Rear—adjustable aperture
Magazine	20 round detachable box type
Cyclic rate	800 rpm

BM59 Alpine rifle

Manufacturer: **Pietro Beretta (Italy)**

Calibre	7·62 mm (NATO)
Dimensions	Overall length 111 cm Length (with stock) 85·5 cm Barrel length 49·1 cm
Weight	4·5 kg
Effective range	500 m
Operation	Gas
Muzzle velocity	812 m/sec
Sight	Front—protected post Rear—adjustable aperture
Magazine	20-round detachable box type
Cyclic rate	800 rpm

Beretta made large numbers of Garand M1 rifles for NATO use after the war, and they have put this experience to good use in the BM59 assault rifle. Although Beretta manufacture the BM59 as an independent weapon, they are also able to modify the Garand M1 to the same specifications, since the BM59 mechanism is essentially an updated Garand mechanism.

There are four current versions of the BM59, including the LMG version which is dealt with in the LMG section. In all configurations the BM59 is a gas-operated selective fire weapon loading from a 20 round magazine. The gas regulator is of the two-position spindle type. For normal firing it is hinged back to lie flat along the barrel. Gas is tapped from the barrel through the valve into a return tube where the pressure of the expanding gas drives a piston rearwards and initiates the reloading cycle.

BM59

BM59 with bayonet fixed and bipod folded

All current versions of the BM59 include the following features. A bipod which folds back under the forestock, a bolt stop which holds the bolt open after the last round is fired, a winter trigger, a cartridge-clip guide for loading magazines on the rifle, a two-position selector for semi- or fully automatic fire, an independent safety catch located in front of the trigger guard, and the Beretta grenade launcher tri-compensator which is detachable on the paratroop version. This last device serves four purposes. To launch grenades with tail booms of 22 mm diameter, to cut down recoil, to limit climb on automatic fire and to act as a flash suppressor. The BM59 has a protective post foresight and fully adjustable aperture rearsight.

The main difference between standard version and the paratroop and alpine versions is the stock. The standard version has a straight wood butt and no separate pistol grip, while the two specialist versions have collapsible folding stocks and plastic pistol grips.

In service with the Italian forces.

Model 70/223 rifle (and variants)

Manufacturer: **Pietro Beretta (Italy)**

Calibre	5·56 mm
Dimensions	Length 94 cm (AR); 93·5 cm (SC) Barrel length 45 cm
Weight	3·7 kg (AR); 3·8 kg (SC) includes magazine
Effective range	400 m
Operation	Gas
Muzzle velocity	970 m/sec
Sight	Front—protected post Rear—adjustable aperture
Magazine	30 round detachable box type
Cyclic rate	630 rpm

The Model 70 is the Beretta contribution to the 5·56 mm assault rifle requirement, and is of post–1968 design and production. There are three configurations available, an assault rifle (AR), a special carbine (SC) and a LMG. The LMG is dealt with under light machine guns.

The rigid stock of the assault rifle is easily detached and a tubular folding stock can be fitted with equal ease, thus making a carbine. It is only the type of stock which denotes whether the weapon is an assault rifle or a special carbine.

The Model 70 is a gas -operated weapon firing from a locked rotating bolt. A bolt stop holds the bolt open after the last round is fired. The gas regulator is similar to that of the BM 59, being of the spindle valve type. This form of gas return has only two settings, open for normal firing and closed for grenade launching. When open, the control lever is hinged forward on top of the barrel. As long as it remains in this position a grenade cannot be properly fitted. A three-position selector on the left-hand side above the pistol grip gives the choice of safe, semi-

70/223 AR

70/223 SC

automatic and fully automatic fire.

Field stripping requires no tools, except the point of a bullet, and the entire operation of stripping and re-assembly takes about one and a half minutes. The weapon has been designed for a minimal number of components (85) and, for field stripping, breaks into three groups. The cleaning kit is carried in a recess in the pistol-grip.

The battle sights consist of a protected post foresight and an adjustable aperture rearsight. In addition, a grenade-launching sight with three range graduations of 50 m, 75 m and 100 m folds down behind the rearsight.

A telescopic sight is available for the weapon which can be easily attached or detached. The flash-suppressor serves as a support for the bayonet and couples as a 40 mm Mecar grenade launcher. In order to launch a grenade the firer must unload the rifle, put the spindle valve lever to its upright position, place the grenade on the launcher and insert an appropriate cartridge.

Not yet in service. If NATO standardises on the 5·56 mm round, it seems probable that the Italian armed forces, currently equipped with a BM59 of Beretta manufacture, would adopt the Model 70 as an alternative weapon.

Model 64 rifle

Manufacturer: **Howa Kogyo Kyokai (Japan)**

Calibre	7·62 mm
Dimensions	Length 98·5 cm Barrel length 44·9 cm
Weight	4·3 kg
Effective range	450–500 m
Operation	Gas
Muzzle velocity	807 m/sec (NATO cartridge), 715 m/sec (reduced charge)
Sight	Front—hooded with folding blade
Sight	Rear—folding aperture adjustable for windage
Magazine	20 round detachable box type
Cyclic rate	450–500 rpm

Designed for use by the Japanese Ground Self-Defence Force to replace their United States-made rifles, the Type 64 is the end result of a number of designs submitted by Howa Kogyo Kyokai of Tokyo.

The weapon fires a low-powered version of the 7·62 mm

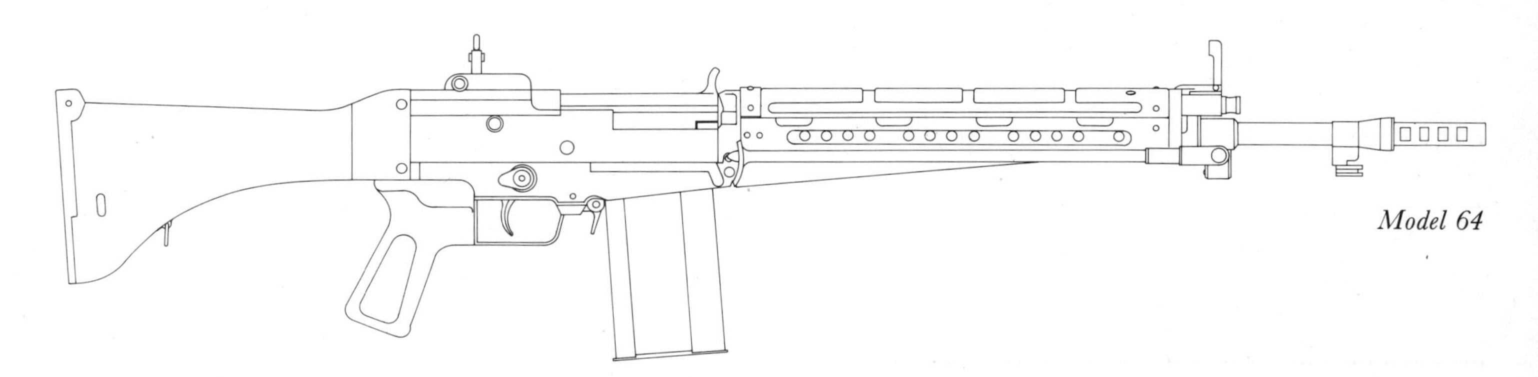

Model 64

(NATO) cartridge, although provision is made on the gas regulator for adjusting the gas flow to accommodate the full-powered cartridge. The gas system is operated by a spring-returned piston similar to that of the FAL rifle. The tipping-type bolt is similar to that of the Soviet SKS carbine in that the bolt is cammed down into and up out of the locked position by the bolt carrier.

The Type 64 features a permanently attached folding bipod and a folding shoulder-rest fitted to the butt. The muzzle break serves as a grenade launcher and there is provision for a bayonet.

It is interesting to note that this rifle was specifically designed for the shorter Asiatic soldier, and is in complete contrast to the extraordinary length of the Japanese World War II rifles.

In service with the Japanese Ground Self-Defence Force.

CETME rifle

Manufacturer: **Centro de Estudios Tecnicos de Materiales Especiales (Spain)**

Calibre	7·62 mm (NATO)
Dimensions	Length 100 cm Barrel length 45 cm
Weight	4·1 kg
Effective range	500 m (reduced charge), 550 m (full charge)
Operation	Delayed blowback
Muzzle velocity	790 m/sec (reduced charge), 890 m/sec (full charge)
Sight	Front—hooded blade Rear—tangent, aperture battle
Magazine	20 round detachable box type
Cyclic rate	600 rpm

The majority of the design work for the CETME rifle was done by L Vorgrimmler, an ex-Mauser Werke engineer, who emigrated from Germany to Spain at the end of World War II. He adapted the basic roller-locked retarded blowback principle of the wartime Stg45 rifle, which was produced in very small numbers, to a modern assault rifle, but still used the same wartime 7·92 mm Kurz round. The weapon was modified later to handle a low-powered 7·62 mm (NATO) cartridge although, provided that a different bolt head is fitted, the full-powered cartridge may be used.

An uncommon feature of the CETME is that it fires automatically from an open bolt, and semi-automatically from a closed bolt. The operating handle is non-reciprocal with the bolt. The chamber is fluted to prevent case separation due to the lack of allowance for slow initial extraction. Using less than 20 parts which require machining, the CETME (designated M58 in Spain) is composed mainly of stampings, and the makers claim that less than 9 hours are required for series production. It is supplied with, or without, a bipod. The rifle is produced under licence in Germany, with modifications, as the G3 and has been supplied to several countries including Norway, Sweden, Denmark, Portugal and Pakistan.

In service with the Spanish, Norwegian, Swedish, Danish, Portuguese and Pakistani forces.

CETME (M58)

AG42 rifle

Manufacturer: **Carl Gustafs Stads Gevärsfactori (Sweden)**

Calibre	6·5 mm
Dimensions	Length 121·4 cm Barrel length 62·2 cm
Weight	4·7 kg
Effective range	580 m
Operation	Gas
Muzzle velocity	746 m/sec
Sight	Front—hooded post Rear—tangent
Magazine	10 round box type
Cyclic rate	Semi-automatic

Designed by Erik Eklund in 1941, the AG42, or Ljungman, was the first mass-produced rifle to use a direct gas system, which was considered rather unorthodox at the time. Instead of the usual piston arrangement, the gas was tapped from the barrel whence it travelled down a tube to hit the face of the carrier which was then driven

AG42 (Egyptian model)

to the rear. This direct gas system has since been adopted into the successful United States M16 rifle, the French M49/56 and others. The action is locked by the rear of the bolt being forced into lugs in the receiver by cams on the bolt carrier in a similar fashion to the Russian SKS carbine.

The rifle can be fitted with a bayonet, and a muzzle break helps to hold the muzzle down during firing.

The Ljungman was adopted and produced under licence in Egypt, but in 7·92 mm. Known there as the Hakim, it was also adapted to fire the Soviet 7·62 mm M43. Madsen in Denmark also produced small numbers of this weapon in several calibres and modified it by encircling the barrel with the gas tube.

The AG42, originally intended to replace the old Mauser bolt-action rifles, is now being phased out by the Swedish Army and is now being superseded by the Swedish-made copy of the G3.

In service with the Swedish, and Egyptian (in 7·62 mm), forces.

SIG510-4 rifle (and variants)

Manufacturer: **Schweizerische Industrie-Gesellschaft (Switzerland)**

Calibre	7·62 mm (NATO)
Dimensions	Length 101·5 cm Barrel length 50·5 cm
Weight	4·3 kg
Effective range	500 m
Operation	Delayed blowback
Muzzle velocity	780 m/sec
Sight	Front—post with protecting ears Rear—aperture
Magazine	20 round detachable box type
Cyclic rate	450–620 rpm

This is a selective fire weapon utilising a delayed blowback roller-locking system. It has a loading indicator, situated in the forward part of the breech-housing, which protrudes when there is a round in the chamber. This device can be invaluable in the dark. A bipod is attached to the weapon behind the foresight and can be folded and swivelled so that it lies along the top of the barrel casing.

The sights are of the protected post and graduated-aperture type. Ranges are set in 100 m steps from 100 m to 600 m with elevation and windage adjustments being possible. In addition, the weapon is equipped to mount an optical sight which does not interfere with the fixed sights.

This rifle makes considerable use of stampings. Field stripping is very simple and no tools are required. It is so designed, the maker claims, that the individual parts will only fit in the right place.

The muzzle of the 510-4 incorporates a grenade launcher of 22 mm diameter and doubles as a flash suppressor and bayonet mount. The SG510-4 is one of the SG510 range of weapons which all operate on the same principles, but are chambered for a wide range of ammunition.

Other versions are, briefly, as follows:

510-1 is the commercial version of the Stg57 in 7·5 mm. It has a rubber composition butt.

510-2 is similar to the 510-1 (in 7·5 mm).

510-3 is similar to the 510-1, but is in 7·62 mm, and uses the 7·62 mm × 39 mm round which itself is a development of the Russian standard M43 round.

The 510-1, 2 and 3 have modified muzzles, and a different sighting system—a folding protected post foresight and an adjustable folding cylinder aperture rear sight. Lastly, the 510-2 and 3 have no bipods.

In service with the Chilean and Bolivian forces.

SIG510-4

Stg57 rifle

Manufacturer: **Schweizerische Industrie-Gesellschaft (Switzerland)**

Calibre	7·5 mm	*Muzzle velocity*	760 m/sec
Dimensions	Length 100 cm Barrel length 58 cm	*Sight*	Front—folding blade with protecting ears
Weight	5·6 kg		Rear—folding aperture
Effective range	450 m	*Magazine*	24 round detachable box type
Operation	Delayed blowback	*Cyclic rate*	450–500 rpm

Stg57

Stg57 with bipod forward

Stg57 with bipod back

Stg57 with winter trigger

The basic design of the SIG Stg57 action is similar to that of the CETME, using a blowback design delayed by rollers. This system again results in the need for a fluted chamber to make up for the lack of slow initial extraction. The action differs from the CETME in that the Stg57 fires on both fully automatic and single shot from a closed bolt, whereas the CETME fires from an open bolt on fully automatic. (The disadvantage of a closed bolt is the danger of rounds 'cooking off' or self-igniting in a hot chamber.) A bipod is fitted, and may be slid along to fix at either end of the barrel-jacket. The rifle has provision for a bayonet, and the rubber butt helps to absorb shock when grenades are fired from the built-in launcher. A folding winter trigger is fitted as standard.

All the weapons in the series are made with a high degree of precision and are consequently rather more expensive to produce than some other assault rifle counterparts.

The Stg57 is the standard rifle of the Swiss Army; it is also sold commercially as the SIG 510 series with slight modifications in 7·62 mm (NATO) and 7·62 mm × 39 mm.

In service with the Swiss armed forces.

SIG530 rifle

Manufacturer: **Schweizerische Industrie-Gesellschaft (Switzerland)**

Calibre	5·56 mm
Dimensions	Length 95 cm Barrel length 39 cm
Weight	3·5 kg
Effective range	400 m
Operation	Gas
Muzzle velocity	870 m/sec
Sight	Front—blade with protecting ears Rear—aperture
Magazine	30 round detachable box type
Cyclic rate	600 rpm

The SIG530 was designed in conjunction with the Italian firm of Beretta. Originally intended to be a scaled-down version of the SIG510, it was soon found that the delayed blowback system was unacceptable for the chamber pressures involved when using the 5·56 mm cartridge. Consequently, after some discussion between the two companies, a gas-operated system using the same roller locking action as the SIG510 was agreed. A useful feature of this system is that, due to the tolerances of the roller lock, different powered cartridges may be fired without the need of a regulator.

The weapon is capable of firing rifle grenades as standard. A folding skeleton stock version is also available. Both versions may be fitted with a bayonet and bipod.

Not yet in service: small-scale trials and sales only.

SIG530

SG540 rifle

Manufacturer: **Schweizerische Industrie-Gesellschaft (Switzerland)**

Calibre	5·56 mm
Dimensions	Length with fixed stock 95 cm Length with folding stock 71·4 cm Length of barrel 49 cm
Weight	3·5 kg
Effective range	400 m
Operation	Gas
Muzzle velocity	980 m/sec
Sight (normal)	Front—protected post Rear—aperture
Magazine	20 or 30 round box type
Cyclic rate	650–800 rpm

SG542 rifle

Manufacturer: **Schweizerische Industrie-Gesellschaft (Switzerland)**

Calibre	7·62 mm
Dimensions	Length with fixed stock 100 cm Length with folding stock 75 cm Length of barrel 49·5 cm
Weight	3·9 kg
Effective range	400 m
Operation	Gas
Muzzle velocity	820 m/sec
Sight (normal)	Front—protected post Rear—aperture
Magazine	30 round box type
Cyclic rate	650–800 rpm

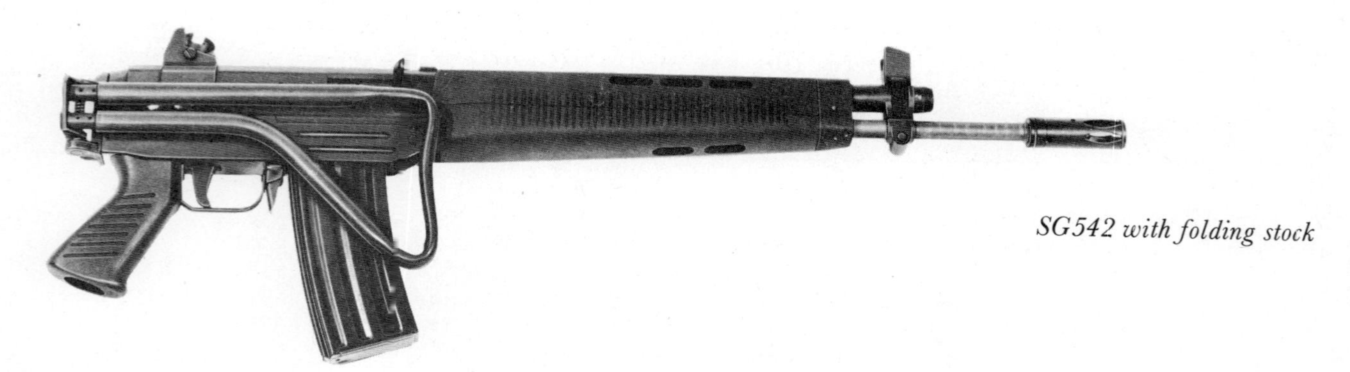

SG542 with folding stock

SG542 with bipod and telescopic sight

The SG540 and the SG542 are dealt with together because their configuration and mechanisms are the same, although their weights and calibres (5·56 mm and 7·62 mm respectively) are different.

The SG540 and SG542 are gas-operated rifles firing from a rotating locked bolt. The gas valve has three settings: 0 for grenade launching, 1 for normal firing and 2 for use when the weapon is badly soiled. The sights for these two rifles are similar to those of the G3, the foresight being of the protected post variety and the rear of a rotating aperture type. An optional night sight set at 400 m on the SG540, and 600 m on the SG542, is available. The trigger is of the pressure-point type, often found in composition rifles. The trigger pressure increases just before firing giving better performance on single-round shooting. The selector lever, situated above the pistol grip on the left side, has three settings: safe, semi-, and full automatic. However, an optional burst control, firing 3 rounds, can be fitted if required. An externally released bolt stop holds the working parts open after the last round is fired. No tools are needed for field stripping.

Both weapons have plastic stocks, pistol-grips and trigger guards except on the tubular folding stock version where metal is used. The muzzle is equipped with a 22 mm flash suppressor which doubles as a grenade launcher and boss for the tubular-type bayonet.

Not yet in service.

SKS carbine

Manufacturer: **State factories (USSR)**

Calibre	7·62 mm
Dimensions	Length 102·1 cm Barrel length 52·1 cm
Weight	3·5 kg
Effective range	450 m
Operation	Gas
Muzzle velocity	735 m/sec
Sight	Front—hooded post Rear—tangent
Magazine	10 round non-detachable box

First designed and produced during the closing stages of World War II, the SKS was the first Soviet weapon to use the now standard 7·62 mm intermediate cartridge.

The action of the weapon is basically a scaled-down copy of the obsolete 14·5 mm PTRS anti-tank rifle. The action is locked by the bolt being tilted into lugs in the receiver by the bolt carrier. The gas system uses a piston with a piston-rod to unlock the action and force it to the rear for the first 20 mm, thereafter inertia takes over combined with the return-spring to complete the loading cycle. The SKS is loaded using either a 10 round charger (called 'stripper clip' in the USA) or individual rounds. The magazine is non-detachable, but the magazine release catch, when actuated, allows the magazine to swing downwards, thus allowing rounds to be spilled out for unloading purposes. Besides this rather unusual feature, the weapon also has a permanently attached folding bayonet which, when not required, lies in a recess in the forestock below the barrel.

Although no longer in first-line service with the Soviet Army, the weapon was produced in vast numbers, and has appeared in slightly modified form in all communist countries. For instance, the Yugoslav version features an integral grenade launcher on the muzzle, and is designated M59. The Chinese Type 56 SKS series rifle features a longer barrel.

In service with all Warsaw Pact and communist Chinese forces.

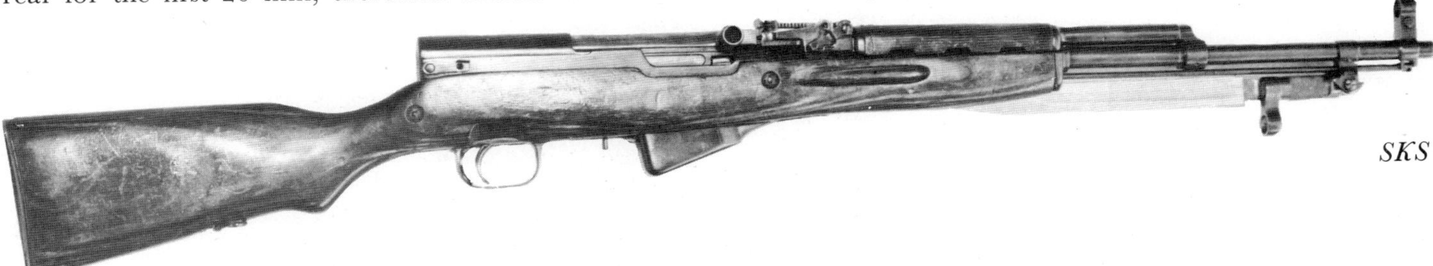

SKS

Kalashnikov AK47 and AKM rifles

Manufacturer: **State factories (USSR)**

Calibre	7·62 (× 39 mm)
Dimensions	Length 86·8 cm (AKM—87·6 cm) Barrel length 41·4 cm
Weight	4·3 kg (AKM—3.1 kg)
Effective range	400 m
Operation	Gas
Muzzle velocity	710 m/sec (AKM—715 m/sec)
Sight	Front—protected post Rear—tangent
Magazine	30 round detachable box type
Cyclic rate	600 rpm

AK47 (Polish model)

AK47 with folding stock

AKM

AKM with folding stock

AKM with stock folded

Although, at the end of World War II the Russians had begun introducing the SKS rifle, using the new 7·62 × 39 mm M43 intermediate cartridge, the need was felt for one weapon to replace both the venerable sub machine guns (PPSH41 and PPS43) and the variety of rifles then still in service, using the old M1908 rimmed case. As over 30 million have been produced to date in many countries, albeit with variations, the AK47 seems to meet the requirement.

First produced within 4 years of the cessation of hostilities, this gas-operated weapon uses a rotating bolt, engaging locking shoulders in the receiver, to lock the action. The bolt carrier and piston rod are attached as one piece. A blank firing device and a bayonet may be fitted. Night sights may also be fitted. An old-fashioned, but nevertheless useful, feature is the stowing of a cleaning rod below the barrel. A folding stock version is also available. A hold-open device and a flash eliminator are not fitted as standard, which is unusual for a weapon of this type.

The AK47 is now being replaced by the AKM. Merely a lightened and modified version, the AKM uses a stamped-steel receiver, a ribbed receiver cover, and a cyclic rate reducer is incorporated in the trigger mechanism. The bayonet, which is not interchangeable with the AK47, can, together with the scabbard, be used as a wirecutter. It is also made with a folding stock. Hungary produces a sub machine gun version of the AKM.

Standard in all Warsaw bloc countries and China (Type 56), the Kalashnikov is also produced in Yugoslavia (M64) and Finland (M60 and M62), and it may be encountered in most communist-supported irregular forces.

In service with most communist and some other forces.

SVD Dragunov sniper rifle

Manufacturer: **State factories (USSR)**

Calibre	7·62 cm (M1908)
Dimensions	Length 122·4 cm Barrel length 61 cm
Weight	4·4 kg
Effective range	900 m
Operation	Gas
Muzzle velocity	830 m/sec
Sight	Front—protected post Rear—tangent
Magazine	10 round detachable box type
Cyclic rate	Semi-automatic

The Dragunov is a semi-automatic sniping rifle and, like the French FRF1, was designed for that purpose.

Using the basic and well-proven Kalashnikov action, the weapon has been strengthened to handle the old M1908 7·62 mm rimmed cartridge. The trigger mechanism has been modified to give a more positive pull-off. Issued with the PS01 telescopic sight, the rifle has a cheek-piece attached to the rather unusual skeleton stock with pistol-grip. Ordinary iron tangent sights are also fitted.

The Dragunov is now replacing the M1891/30 bolt-action rifles, although large numbers of these will still be found in use by satellite countries.

In service with the Soviet and other Warsaw Pact forces.

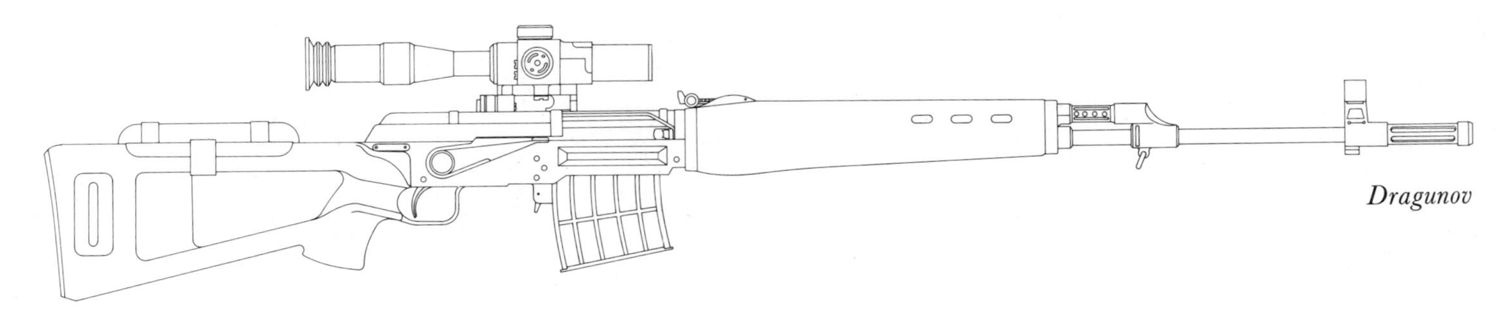

Dragunov

Moisin-Nagant rifle

Manufacturer: **State factories (USSR)**

Calibre	7·62 mm (Russian rimmed and M1908 (Spitzer))
Dimensions	Length 101·6 cm (132 cm with bayonet extended) Barrel length 52 cm
Weight	4·1 kg
Effective range	600 m
Operation	Bolt
Muzzle velocity	775 m/sec
Sight	Front—hooded post Rear—tangent
Magazine	5 round detachable box type

(Statistics are for the M1944 rifle)

First adopted by the Russian Army in 1891, the Moisin-Nagant rifle was a combination of a Russian and Belgian

Moisin-Nagant M1944 carbine

design. The weapon is robust but features an unnecessarily complicated bolt, and an awkward safety-catch which requires the cocking-piece to be pulled rearwards and twisted to apply. Produced in enormous numbers, some six variants appeared before production ceased in the late 1940s. The main adaptations were in the reduction of length, different sling attachments, and improvements to the iron sights, which, on the early models, did not do justice to the accuracy potential of the rifle. However, when fitted with telescopic sights, the Moisin-Nagant matches up to its other bolt-action contemporaries. The final model was the M1944 carbine which was fitted with a folding bayonet, as opposed to the socket type which all previous models had.

Although now obsolete in the Soviet Army, the Moisin-Nagant is still used by Warsaw Pact countries' second-line troops, and was also produced in China as the Type 53 rifle.

In service with some Warsaw Pact second-line forces.

Type 53 rifle

Manufacturer: **State factories (People's Republic of China)**

See the Moisin-Nagant.

In service with some communist Chinese forces.

HAKIM rifle

Manufacturer: **Ordnance factory (United Arab Republic)**

Calibre	7·92 mm

See the AG 42.

In service with the Egyptian forces.

RASHID rifle

Manufacturer: **Ordnance factory (United Arab Republic)**

Calibre	7·62 mm M43
Dimensions	Length 101·6 cm
Weight	3·9 kg
Effective range	450 m
Operation	Gas
Muzzle velocity	735 m/sec
Sight	Front—hooded post Rear—tangent leaf
Magazine	10 round detachable box type
Cyclic rate	Semi-automatic

The 7·62 mm Rashid semi-automatic rifle is the result of combining the 7·92 mm Hakim rifle and the Soviet 7·62 mm Simonov (SKS) carbine which the UAR received from the USSR in 1954. Made at the same factory as the Hakim rifle, the Rashid has a slightly altered action in that a bolt-handle is provided whereas the bolt of the Hakim is retracted by pulling back the receiver cover. Features of the SKS incorporated in this rifle were reduced weight and length, the folding knife bayonet and the three gas-relief holes on either side of the stock. However, a very limited number of these rifles was produced before the UAR adopted the AK47 as the standard infantry small arm.

In service with the Egyptian forces.

Lee Enfield no 4 Mark I rifle

Manufacturer: **Royal Small Arms Factory and others in the United Kingdom and overseas**

Calibre	·303 in and later, 7·62 mm (NATO)
Dimensions	Length 112·7 cm Barrel length 64 cm
Weight	4·1 kg
Effective range	500 m
Operation	Bolt
Muzzle velocity	745 m/sec
Sight	Front—blade with protecting ears Rear—vertical leaf with aperture battle sight or L type
Magazine	5 or 10 round detachable type

The first Lee turnbolt system rifle was introduced into the British Army in 1888 and was only replaced some time after the Korean War.

The bolt-locking system differs from its Mauser counterpart in that the action is locked at the rear of the receiver beside the charger-guide as opposed to the Mauser breech-lock.

During its 60-odd years service with the British and Commonwealth forces, the weapon underwent many minor modifications including a post-World War II conversion from its original ·303 in calibre to 7·62 mm (NATO). Many millions were manufactured and may still be found in use all over the world, particularly in African countries. Large reserves are also still held by Commonwealth and other nations. Although now replaced by the FN SLR the no 4 version of the rifle, first introduced in 1941, is still used for training purposes, especially by cadets. Designated L42A1, the rifle's modern sniper version is fitted with a cheekpiece and no 32 telescopic sight and converted to fire the 7·62 mm (NATO) cartridge. This is still the official British sniper weapon although the FN rifles are all capable of taking a telescopic sight.

Although not as strong an action as the Mauser, the Lee action is considerably faster; this, combined with the 10 round charger-loaded magazine, makes the weapon capable of a high rate of accurate fire when used by well-trained infantrymen. This type of action is also considerably easier to produce and is consequently cheaper to manufacture than most of its counterparts.

Obsolescent, but in service with many forces, and as a sniper rifle in the United Kingdom forces.

Lee Enfield no 4 Mark 1

Lee Enfield L42A1 sniper rifle

Browning automatic rifle

Manufacturer: **Colt Industries, Marlin–Rockwell Corporation, and Olin–Mathieson Corporation (Winchester—Western Division) (United States)**

Calibre	·30–06 and 7·62 mm (NATO)
Dimensions	Length 121·4 cm (M1918A2) Barrel length 61 cm
Weight	8·6 kg
Effective range	800 m
Operation	Gas
Muzzle velocity	855 m/sec
Sight	Front—blade Rear—leaf with aperture
Magazine	20 round detachable box type
Cyclic rate	500–600 rpm (fast) 300–400 rpm (slow)

Originally designed in 1917 by John Browning, the BAR met a need for a relatively light automatic squad support weapon. A gas-operated action, the original 1918 model did not feature the bipod which was fitted in 1937, thus becoming the model 1918A1. Both weapons were

BAR M1918A2

capable of select fire.

Used throughout World War II and Korea, the BAR was modified with different sights and a butt monopod, and the bipod was moved to attach just behind the muzzle. Instead of being fitted with a select fire lever the rifle, designated Model 1918A2, became fully automatic, but with the choice of two rates of fire. Single shot can be fired, however, by rapid tapping of the trigger when the rifle is set on the slow rate. In 1922, a version for use by light armoured cavalry was issued in small numbers, the main modification being the addition of a heavier finned barrel.

A short-barrelled version of the BAR was also produced by Colt. Called the Monitor, it was sold mainly to police and other law-enforcement agencies. The final military version was the T34 which was made in 7·62 mm (NATO), but it saw little service.

Fitted with a variable gas-port and locked by a hinged tilting bolt, the BAR utilised a great deal of machining time and was correspondingly expensive to produce. Nevertheless, it lasted well, for the weapon remained in service with the regular US armed forces for over 35 years.

In service with the United States National Guard and most South American forces.

M1 Garand rifle

Manufacturer: **Springfield Armory, Winchester Repeating Arms Company and others. Also made under licence in Italy (United States)**

Calibre	·30–06
Dimensions	Length 110·7 cm
	Barrel length 61 cm
Weight	4·3 kg
Effective range	550 m
Operation	Gas
Muzzle velocity	855 m/sec
Sight	Front—blade with protecting ears
	Rear—aperture
Magazine	None. Uses 8 round *en bloc* clip
Cyclic rate	Semi-automatic

Designed to meet US Army requirements for a semi-automatic rifle during the 1920s, the Garand was adopted in 1932, and entered service in 1936 as the M1 rifle.

The action is locked by a twisting bolt engaging in lugs set in the receiver behind the breech. The bolt is cammed into and out of this position by a one-piece piston-operating rod which taps gas from a point approximately 2·5 cm from the muzzle.

The 8 round *en bloc* clip, when loaded, stays within the rifle. Single cartridges may not therefore be loaded once a clip has been inserted. The clip is ejected when the last round is fired, the action remaining open ready for the insertion of another loaded clip.

The M1 may be fitted with a grenade launcher, and a bayonet is available. Over $4\frac{1}{2}$ million were produced in the USA, where the weapon is still in service with some units of the National Guard. Produced under licence by Breda and Beretta in Italy, the Garand was supplied to the Italian Army. The basic Garand design is still used by the Italians in their 7·62 mm (NATO) Beretta M59. Denmark and Indonesia were also supplied with Italian-produced Garands and the weapon was sold in large numbers as surplus, and may be encountered in many less well-developed countries and, particularly, in South America.

In service with the United States National Guard and with the South American, Danish and Indonesian forces.

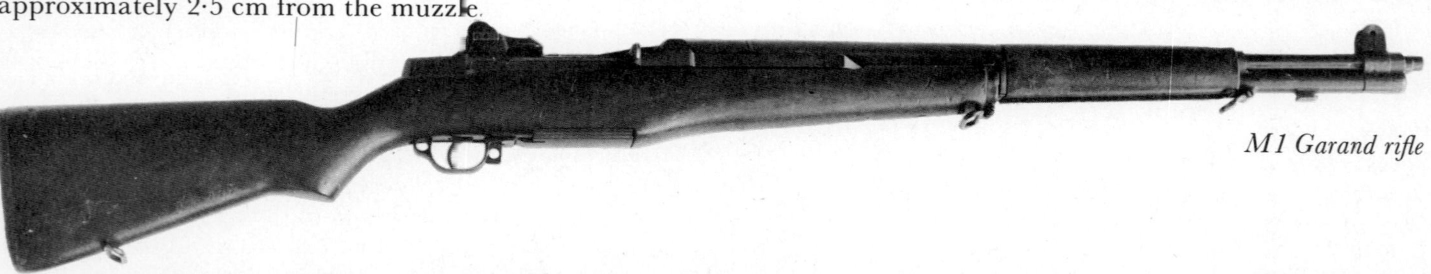

M1 Garand rifle

M1 carbine (and variants)

Manufacturer: **Winchester Repeating Arms Company, General Motors Corporation (Inland Manufacturing Division) and others (United States)**

Calibre	·30 in
Dimensions	Length 90·4 cm Barrel length 45·7 cm
Weight	2·5 kg
Effective range	300 m
Operation	Gas
Muzzle velocity	600 m/sec
Sight	Front—blade with protecting ears Rear—aperture on ramp, battle
Magazine	15 or 30 round detachable box type
Cyclic rate	750 rpm

Originally designed and produced by Winchester to meet the United States Government's requirements for a light carbine, over 6 million of the M1 and its variants were produced by some nine other companies, including General Motors, which supplied some 2·6 million of the total number.

The return system uses gas tapped into a chamber below the barrel. This in turn causes a tappet-type piston to strike the operating rod, driving it some 8 mm to the rear. Inertia, combined with the return spring, then takes over to allow the normal reloading cycle to take place. The turning bolt is almost a scaled-down copy of that used in the M1 Garand rifle.

M1

M1A1

M2

The M1 carbine was produced in four variants:

M1: the standard model.

M1A1: mechanically the same, but fitted with a folding stock and pistol-grip for use by airborne troops. A belt-mounted holster was available with this model as it was thought almost light enough to be used as a pistol.

M2: this version had a selector-switch mounted on the left of the receiver to facilitate full automatic fire.

M3: same as M2, but capable of taking telescopic sights or the infra-red 'Snooper Scope'.

All models could be fitted with a grenade launcher or bayonet and with either 15 or 30 round magazines.

The M1 carbine saw service with the United States forces in Vietnam, and stocks of the weapon are still held in the United States. Large numbers have been sold and are still in use and the weapon may be encountered in almost every small country.

In service with the Chilean, Indonesian, Japanese, Mexican and Taiwanese forces and the United States National Guard.

M14 and M14E2 rifles

Manufacturer: **Springfield Armory, Harrington and Richardson Arms Company and Olin–Matheson Chemical Corporation (Winchester—Western Division) (United States)**

Calibre	7·62 mm (NATO)
Dimensions	Length 112 cm Barrel length 56 cm
Weight	3·9 kg
Effective range	550 m
Operation	Gas
Muzzle velocity	855 m/sec
Sight	Front—blade with protecting ears Rear—aperture
Magazine	20 round detachable box type
Cyclic rate	750 rpm

Built around the basic Garand action, the M14 (or T44 as it was named in its experimental form) was a contender in the NATO trials of the early 1950s to find a suitable United States rifle to fire the then newly standardised 7·62 mm(NATO) round. Finally attaining more favourable results in United States trials than its European competitors, the rifle was standardised as the M14, and adopted by the United States forces in June 1957.

Using gas tapped from a point approximately 20 cm from the muzzle (as opposed to the 2·5 cm of the Garand) the operating rod and bolt function in the same way as the Garand. This feature, combined with a 20 round detachable box magazine and a flash-hider are the main differences between the two rifles. All models are capable of automatic or semi-automatic fire, but the change levers are usually locked to provide semi-automatic and so preventing wastage of ammunition.

The rifle comes in two versions, the standard M14 and the M14E2. The latter is the squad/section automatic weapon and differs only by the addition of a compensator, rubber recoil pad, pistol and fore-end grips and a bipod. A workshop-fitted winter trigger is also available for both versions.

Now no longer in production, the M14 is capable of

M14

M14E2

firing grenades and of taking a bayonet. Two types of folding stock are available and, in addition, a sniper version, fitted with a Leatherwood Redfield telescopic sight. Although being phased out of the United States Army, this weapon may still be found in large numbers in the States and, possibly, in South America.

In service with the United States forces.

M16 rifle

Manufacturer: **Colt Industries (United States)**

Calibre	5·56 mm
Dimensions	Length 98 cm Barrel length 50·7 cm
Weight	2·9 kg
Effective range	400 m
Operation	Gas
Muzzle velocity	990 m/sec
Sight	Front—post with protecting ears Rear—aperture
Magazine	20 and 30 round box type
Cyclic rate	650–850 rpm

Development of the M16 started in the late 1950s at the instigation of the United States Army Infantry Board. A small test order for the rifle, then known as the AR15 and based on a design submitted by Armalite Inc, was placed (see AR18). In 1962, the USAF ordered 8500 rifles and the US Army took 1000 for evaluation in Vietnam. Further orders followed, whereupon Colt took over the manufacture. By 1969 the USA had accepted the M16 as the standard military rifle. Over 2½ million have been produced to date.

The M16 is a selective fire gas-operated rifle using a gas return system that eliminates the need for a piston and regulator. Gas is tapped from the barrel via a vent about 13 cm from the muzzle and returns through a tube to the bolt carrier. Here it expands into a chamber, forcing the carrier rearwards but momentarily leaving the bolt in its forward locked position. The bolt has a small lug riding in a cam channel on the carrier. As the carrier moves back, the bolt is rotated and unlocks. Subsequent rearward movement of the carrier withdraws the bolt. Some attention has been given to recoil energy which is very low (about 4·5 ft/lb), and the straight line construction channels the recoil directly to the firer's shoulder. A later version, the M16A1, has a chromium-plated chamber and barrel. It has also been produced in a carbine version. Other features are an optional burst control and an optional plunger-type bolt assist.

Standard features include a dust-cover which opens automatically on firing, charging, or on bolt release. There is a bolt-stop which holds the bolt open after the last round is fired, and a trigger guard which hinges down for winter firing. The fixed carrier handle is tapped for mounting a telescopic sight and a removable light-weight bipod. Trials were carried out with disposable magazines in Vietnam, but little came of the idea.

Grenade launching with the M16, in common with the majority of modern combat rifles, is simplified by the

M16A1

M16 with telescopic sight

incorporation of a launcher/flash suppressor at the muzzle. Energa and all the current United States military rifle grenades (see grenades section) can be launched without attachments. It is also possible to launch standard US hand grenades with the appropriate adapter. In addition, a 40 mm independent grenade launcher can be fitted under the forestock (see grenade launchers).

A training kit which converts the M16 to fire ·22 LR ammunition, for use in indoor and other restricted ranges, has been made available by the Military Armarmant Corporation.

In service with the United States, British, Malaysian, South Vietnamese, Australian, South Korean and Taiwanese forces.

Colt Commando rifle

Manufacturer: **Colt Industries (United States)**

Calibre	5·56 mm
Dimensions	Length 80 cm (stock folded 71 cm) Barrel length 25·4 cm
Weight	2·9 kg
Effective range	200 m
Operation	Gas
Muzzle velocity	880 m/sec
Sight	Front—post with protecting ears Rear—aperture battle
Magazine	20 round detachable box type
Cyclic rate	700–800 rpm

Due to the large amount of close-quarter fighting encountered by the US troops in Vietnam, the need arose for a really short weapon using the 5·56 mm round. The result was the Colt Commando which, in effect, is a shortened version of the M16.

Using the same receiver, the Colt Commando is fitted with a shorter barrel to which a longer flash eliminator is added. There is no provision for a bayonet or grenade launcher. The distinguishing feature of the weapon is the telescopic stock, which, when pushed in, gives a total length of 71 cm as opposed to the 97 cm of the M16. Accuracy, due to the barrel length being halved, is down by some 20%.

In service with the United States Special Forces.

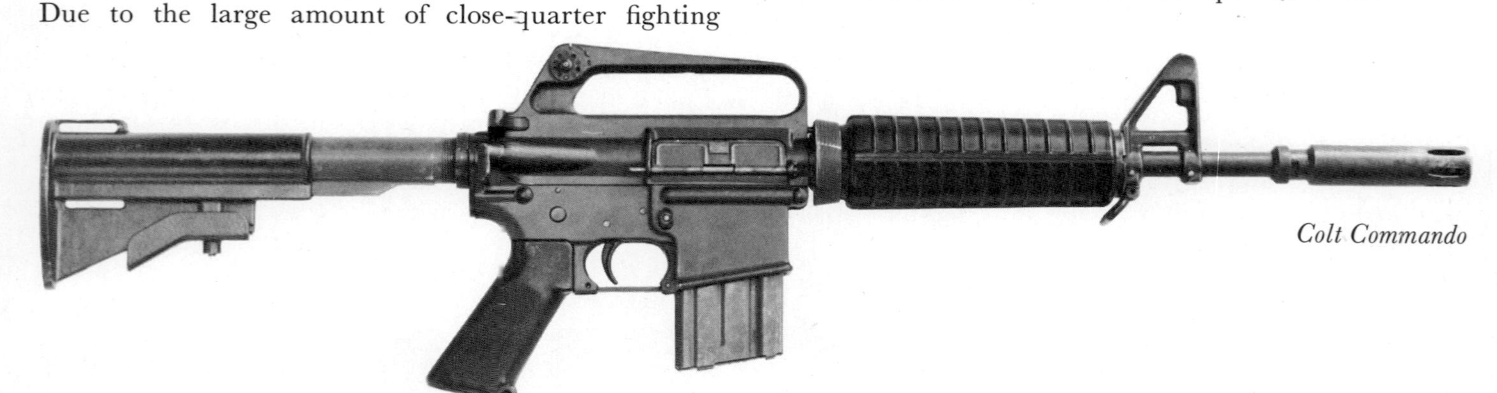

Colt Commando

M1903A4 sniper rifle

Manufacturer: **Springfield Arsenal (United States)**

Calibre	·30-06
Dimensions	Length 110 cm Barrel length 61 cm
Weight	5 kg
Effective range	900 m
Operation	Bolt
Muzzle velocity	850 m/sec
Sight	Telescopic
Magazine	5 round non-detachable integral type

The Model 03 Springfield first appeared in 1903 as the standard United States rifle. Adopting a shorter cartridge in 1906, this rifle continued as standard until replacement by the M1 Garand began in 1936. Remaining in service throughout World War II mainly with the US Marine Corps, the weapon was phased out shortly after.

Using a Mauser-type action, the weapon features an extra locking lug, situated behind the extractor, to handle the high stresses involved when using this very powerful cartridge.

When the need for a sniping version arose during World War II, the 03 was simply adapted by removing the iron sights and mounting an M73B1 (Weaver 330C) telescopic sight. It was then designated M1903A4.

Still in use by United States forces, the only change has been the adoption of the lighter M84 telescopic sight.

In service with the United States forces.

Remington model 700 sniper rifle

Manufacturer: **Remington Arms Company Incorporated (United States)**

Calibre	7·62 mm (NATO)
Dimensions	Length 105·5 cm Barrel length 56 cm
Weight	3·1 kg
Effective range	820 m
Operation	Bolt
Muzzle velocity	850 m/sec
Sight	Telescopic
Magazine	5 round detachable integral type

This Mauser action weapon is a militarised version of the commercial Remington model 700 sporting rifle, and has been adapted only by changing the high-quality civilian finish to the dull finish required for military use.

The telescopic sight is a Redfield variable power (3–9 ×).

In service with the United States Marine Corps.

Remington Model 700

Remington Model 700 with Starlightscope (Star–Tron Mark 303A)

Armalite AR18 rifle

Manufacturer: **Armalite Incorporated (United States) and Howa Industries (Japan)**

Calibre	5·56 mm
Dimensions	Length 96·5 cm (stock folded 73 cm) Barrel length 47·6 cm
Weight	3 kg
Effective range	450 m
Operation	Gas
Muzzle velocity	990 m/sec
Sight	Front—protected post Rear—aperture
Magazine	20 round detachable box type
Cyclic rate	750 rpm

AR18

One of the latest weapons offered by the Armalite Company, the AR18 was designed with cheaper production as one of its main features. Thus it utilises steel stampings, instead of the alloy forgings of the M16, to enable licensed production in countries not equipped with modern plant and machinery.

Gas-operated, the rifle uses a piston-operating rod as opposed to the Ljungman direct-gas system of the M16. The bolt carrier, having unlocked the rotating bolt, is returned by two springs, the guides of which pass through the carrier. The weapon has a folding stock as standard, and a light bipod may be fitted. Grenades may be fired from the built-in launcher and provision is made for a bayonet. A telescopic sight is available, and may be fitted to the standard weapon. Like the M16, the AR18 uses a straight line stock configuration which is useful for instant aiming during automatic fire.

Although the rifle has yet to sell in large numbers, it has been extensively tested by the US Army, though not adopted as yet. Police and civilian hunting models are available, and production of the military weapon has started at the Howa Industries plant in Japan.

Not yet in service.

M59/66 rifle

Manufacturer: **State factories (Yugoslavia)**

Calibre	7·62 mm
Weight	4·2 kg

The M59/66 rifle is a modification of the M59, the Yugoslav copy of the Soviet SKS, and has replaced it as the standard Yugoslav army rifle. The modifications consist of a permanent fixture of a spigot-type grenade launcher and grenade launcher sight, the latter being hinged behind the normal foresight and an increase in the length of the folding knife bayonet by 6 cm. It can be used as a normal rifle when the grenade launcher sight is folded down on the top of the barrel. See the SKS for further details.

In service with the Yugoslav forces.

M54 sniper rifle

Manufacturer: **State factories (Czechoslovakia)**

Calibre	7·62 mm
Dimensions	Length 114·8 cm Barrel length 73·2 cm
Weight	4·1 kg (loaded)
Effective range	800 m
Operation	Bolt
Muzzle velocity	795 m/sec
Sight	Rear—telescopic (× 2½) Front—open adjustable
Magazine	5-round, hinged-box type
Cyclic rate	10 rpm

The M54 sniper rifle was developed by the Czechs from the Soviet M1891/30 Moisin Nagant sniper rifle. Although using the same butt and firing mechanism (including magazine) and the same 7·62 × 54R round, the resemblance ends there. The M54 has been considerably reduced in size and weight, but at a cost of a reduced maximum range from 1300 m to only 1000 m. It is, however, claimed to be just as effective at the battle range of 800 m, in spite of being provided with a less powerful telescopic sight. In appearance the main differences between the M54 and the M1891/30 lie in the smaller size of the M54's telescopic sight and the absence of the forward wooden stock and cleaning rod, leaving the M54 with a clean sporting-rifle-type barrel. No bayonet is provided for this rifle, which is likely to be replaced shortly by the Soviet SVD sniper rifle.

In service with the Czechoslovak forces.

M54 sniper rifle in use

Machine Guns

Prior to World War I, the machine gun was not readily thought of as an infantry close support weapon, but was considered more as a light artillery piece. However, the British, German and American armies were gradually replacing the wheeled mounts of their water-cooled guns with tripods for use by infantry and the Americans had experimented with the Lewis gun, despite an initial rejection, after it was put into series production in Belgium and later produced in Britain and the USA. The Madsen LMG, which the Danes had been producing since 1904, was becoming popular with many smaller nations and remained in service until after World War II.

During World War I, the British made extensive use of the Lewis gun, but the Americans, for some still unknown reason, were issued mostly with the awkward and unreliable French Chauchat. Their native-designed Browning Automatic Rifle (BAR) appeared only for the 3 or 4 months preceding the Armistice in November 1918. All these weapons were air-cooled and could not give sustained fire due to the inability to change the barrel. The Germans, however, preferred to adapt their proven 08 Maxim water-cooled gun into a light machine gun by adding a buttstock, pistol-grip and bipod, thus making the weapon (MG 08–15) capable of being used by one man, so long as the belt was contained in the box which could be attached to the side of the gun.

Shortly after the end of World War I, the French, greatly impressed with the American BAR, went on to design their BAR-based Chatellerault which they adopted in 1924. The main difference between the two was that the magazine of the Chatellerault was top- as opposed to bottom-mounted, and the weapon could be stripped more easily by hingeing the buttstock. The British and Americans retained their proven Lewis guns, and the Americans their BAR as well.

These three countries also maintained production of their heavier weapons, the Hotchkiss, Vickers and Browning 1917 respectively. The Germans, however, forbidden the use of water-cooled machine guns by the articles of the Treaty of Versailles, converted their earlier Dreyse water-cooled guns to air-cooled for use by the infantry.

At that time, military opinion held that sustained fire could only be maintained by the use of a water-cooling jacket, and so the League of Nations concluded that the Germans were then effectively denied a sustained fire capacity. To circumvent this, the Germans proceeded, not only to make the gun air-cooled, but also to modify it so that the barrel could be rapidly detached and changed, thereby eliminating the need for water-cooling. Known as the MG13, the gun remained in service as standard until 1935.

During the 1920s, the Czech firm of ZB at BRNO were working on a design of a light machine gun with a detachable barrel. Introduced as the ZB26, in 7·92 mm, the weapon later went on to be produced with modifications by the British from 1938 in ·303 in and was known as the Bren. Although a variety of mounts were available for the gun during the course of World War II, it never replaced the Vickers gun in the sustained fire role. It is worthy of note that the British adopted the Czech design in preference to their own Vickers-Berthier which, along with the Danish Madsen, underwent extensive trials in 1932. This decision was one of the first breaks in the then somewhat nationalistic and traditionalist military thinking in Britain. The Americans, meanwhile, had developed their air-cooled Browning M1919 tank gun into an infantry model on a tripod (later superseded by the light M2 tripod) to become the M1919A4. This model remained standard until well after the Korean War. A LMG version, known as the M1919A6, was fitted with a buttstock, pistol-grip and bipod but, due to its lack of attachable belt container, remained as a 2 man operated weapon. The BAR was also retained until well after Korea.

During this period most large countries with their own arms plants were also turning out LMGs, many of them based on weapons already proven in service with other armies.

Gas operation was becoming popular for the LMG and, although belt and clip feed were still prevalent, the value of a relatively dirt-free and durable box magazine was being realised. The drum or pan magazine, and particularly that of the Lewis, caused stoppages if even slightly bent.

Refining on the idea of the MG13, the Germans began series production of their MG34 in 1936. What might be classed as the first true general purpose machine gun (GPMG), the MG34 was made available with a wide variety of mounts ranging from a buffer-mounted tripod which could be fitted with telescopic sights to AA or heavy pillbox mounts. Although belt-fed, the gun could easily be carried and fired by one man by inserting a 50 round belt into a round basket drum which was then attached to the feed-tray. By removing the top cover and fitting an adaptor, the 75 round saddle drum (originally produced for use with the MG15 aircraft gun) could be utilised. This spring-loaded magazine raised the rate of fire and, used in conjunction with a large ring sight, made the weapon well suited for anti-aircraft use. With the addition of an armoured barrel-jacket and removal of the select fire mechanism, the gun became the standard tank co-axial machine gun. Although not renowned for its reliability under adverse conditions due to the close machining tolerances, it did set the precedent for this type of multi-purpose weapon.

During World War II, the MG34 was superseded by the MG42. Cheaper to produce due to the wide use of stampings, the MG42 was lighter and had a higher rate of fire than its predecessor. The gun could be used with almost as wide a variety of mounts and was considerably more reliable.

Among the numerous designs to come out of Germany during the course of the war was the FG42. The Luftwaffe, ever aware of the specialist role of their paratroops, first gave them the MP38 SMG before the war. (This weapon was originally issued to armoured troops as well and went on to be used by men of all arms.) Later, as the need was felt for a lighter support weapon than the MG34, the FG42 appeared. Again made primarily from stampings, this gas-operated weapon featured a hitherto unique fire selection device. When firing single shots, the weapon fired from a closed bolt for greater accuracy and from an open bolt on automatic to give greater cooling capacity. This system has since been used on several post-war weapons, although the wartime US Johnson MG also featured this device. Only approximately 5000 FG42s were manufactured, but the weapon was popular and is reported to have been reliable and accurate.

At the end of World War II, most countries continued to use their wartime weapons, precedent being put on rebuilding the economies rather than re-equipping the armies. However, as the formation of NATO and other defensive alliances to meet the threats took place, so the need to update the member nations' armies became urgent.

NATO, having finally decided to standardise on the 7·62 × 51 mm round, then proceeded to have various countries tender designs for weapons to take this cartridge.

The Belgians, admirably aware that a gun designed using the best features of well-proven weapons can often be preferable to something entirely new, proceeded to produce the MAG GPMG. Copying the feed mechanism of the MG42 and the bolt of the BAR, the MAG, though expensive to manufacture, has been supplied in modified form to over 20 countries. The gun may be used on a bipod or tripod fitted with a telescopic or infra-red night sight. Mounts are also available for fitting on to soft-skinned or armoured vehicles and single or dual mounts are fitted to helicopters on pods or brackets.

The Germans, content that their MG42 has withstood the test of time, continue to use the weapon in 7·62 mm with some modifications. The gun is also manufactured under licence in Italy, where it is sometimes fitted with a heavier bolt to reduce the rate of fire. Yugoslavia still produces the weapon in its original 7·92 mm calibre as the SÁRAC.

The Americans, like the British before the war, were prepared to concede to proven designs in preference to native ones and so the 7·62 mm US M60 machine gun, like the MAG, used the MG42 feed mechanism and the bolt of the FG42.

In the Warsaw Pact countries, the 7·62 mm M43 cartridge was designated the official calibre, and the adoption of this intermediate cartridge led to a series of LMGs, the main designs being produced by the Soviet and Czech arsenals. The Czechs, particularly, produced some interesting weapons, the most revolutionary being the Vz52 series. Not only capable of taking either belt or magazine feed without the addition or subtraction of any parts, the weapon cocked by withdrawing the pistol-grip assembly in much the same way as the British BESA tank gun.

The earlier Soviet RP46 and RPD LMGs (merely developments of the old Degtyarev action) were later replaced by the RPK, which was basically a LMG version of the prolific Kalashnikov rifle, and the two weapons shared a fair degree of parts interchangeability.

The Soviet Union, although a great believer in the intermediate cartridge, has retained its old M1908 7·62 mm rimmed cartridge for use in their PK GPMG. Again using the Kalashnikov action, the PK may be fitted with a heavier barrel for use in tanks and in the sustained fire role.

Today, some countries, in addition to the LMG or GPMG, produce a squad automatic rifle version (SAR) of their assault rifle. Fitted with a bipod and heavier barrel, the SAR serves as an extra section support weapon. The SAR version of the Italian BM59 or the Belgian FAL are examples of this.

Since the American introduction of the 5·56 mm cartridge for use not only in their assault rifle but even in SMG and LMG form, the larger European arms firms have all begun producing and marketing similar light weapons in the same calibre. As the controversy over the merits of this cartridge and the search for a new NATO standard calibre continue, these weapons appear to have sold to minor nations in small numbers only.

Ironically, the old practice of using an interchangeable cartridge for the rifle and LMG would probably prove to be unrealistic in a future European conflict as the LMG should theoretically be able to provide covering, or supporting, fire against troops and soft skinned vehicles at ranges in excess of 500 m–600 m, and this is something which the 5·56 mm round is not able to do. Thus, should NATO decide to adopt the 5·56 mm or a similar cartridge (some countries are experimenting with even smaller rounds) then a full calibre MG will have to be maintained and this will create a logistic problem.

Not only the question of interchangeability of ammunition, but also that of parts, provides a good argument in favour of the Italian and Belgian SAR idea. In America, Eugene Stoner, designer of the M16 Armalite rifle, has designed a system whereby a wide variety of weapons may be assembled using the same bolt and receiver. A novel idea, the system has failed to sell as yet (the first model being built some 8 years ago), although NWM de Kruithoorn in the Netherlands are now producing it under licence.

Until NATO decides on its new standard calibre, future LMG design will hang in the balance. In Russia, however, it is thought that an early change of calibre from 7·62 mm is unlikely as the Warsaw Pact countries have only recently completed almost overall standardisation.

James Dowdall

L7 series GPMG, with the Canadian dial sight, mounted on a tripod

MAG (GPMG) general purpose machine gun

Manufacturer: **Fabrique Nationale Herstal (Belgium)**

Calibre	7·62 mm (NATO) and 6·5 mm (Sweden)
Dimensions	Length 125 cm Barrel length 54 cm
Weight	10·8 kg
Effective range	800 m on bipod 1400 m on tripod
Operation	Gas
Type of fire	Automatic
Muzzle velocity	850 m/sec
Sight	Front—folding blade or protected post Rear—aperture battle and leaf with notch
Feed system	Disintegrating link belt
Cyclic rate	700–1000 rpm
Barrel change	Yes

The MAG (or the GPMG L7 series in UK) was developed using the best points of well-proven weapons. The piston and bolt are derived from the Browning automatic rifle. The basic tipping bolt has been changed to lock on the bottom of the receiver instead of the top, as on the BAR. The feed mechanism is almost a pure copy of that used on the German MG42 of World War II, which could be classed as an earlier counterpart of the MAG due to the wide adaptability of both guns.

A belt-fed gun, the MAG may be used as a light or medium machine gun. A variable gas regulator allows a choice of cyclic-fire rate of 700–1000 rpm. The barrel, with a chrome-plated and stellite-lined bore, is quick-detachable, and a heavy-duty version may be used in the sustained-fire role. Provision for a firing solenoid is made for use in armoured vehicles or aircraft. A 50 round belt-box may be attached to the side and various pouches to catch the disintegrating link belt, and empty cases may be fitted. The gun may be fired if the quick-detachable stock is removed, although the fitting of a back-plate is advised to prevent entry of dirt.

A very popular weapon, the MAG in its various forms has been sold to over 20 countries in 7·62 mm (NATO), although Sweden opted for the 6·5 mm Swedish round.

In service with the Argentinian, Belgian, Dutch, Indian, Israeli, South African, Swedish (6·5 mm), United Kingdom and certain other Commonwealth and South American forces.

MAG GPMG on a tripod.

MAG GPMG

C1 medium machine gun

Calibre	7·62 mm

See the ·30 Browning.

In service with the Canadian forces.

Types 53 and 57 medium machine guns

Manufacturer: **State factories (People's Republic of China)**

See the SG43 and SGM.

In service with the communist Chinese forces.

Types 56 and 56-1 light machine guns

Manufacturer: **State factories (People's Republic of China)**

See the DP and DPM range of machine guns.

In service with the communist Chinese forces.

Type 56 LMG

ZB26/30 light machine gun

Manufacturer: **State factories (Czechoslovakia)**

Calibre	7·92 mm, 7·65 mm, 7·0 mm, ·303 in, ·30 in
Dimensions	Length 116·5 cm Barrel length 67 cm
Weight	9·6 kg
Effective range	900 m
Operation	Gas
Type of fire	Select
Muzzle velocity	760 m/sec (in 7·92 mm)
Sight	Front—blade Rear—drum aperture
Feed system	20 round detachable box magazine
Cyclic rate	500 rpm
Barrel change	Yes

Although no longer in front line service in any major army, the ZB26, ZB30 and derivatives were produced by, or sold to, so many nations in such numbers and calibres that the weapon will certainly be encountered for some years to come. Originally designed in 1924 by Vaclav Holek, the gun was slightly modified to be-

ZB 30 LMG

come ZB30. Both models have been manufactured in China, the ZB 30 in Iran and Rumania, and in Yugoslavia as the Model 30J. The ZB is the forerunner of the British Bren gun, and was produced in 7·92 mm (standard), 7·65 mm, 7·0 mm, ·303 in and ·30 in. Spain produced the weapon in 7·62 mm (NATO) with belt feed called the FAO.

The action is locked using a simple tilting bolt engaging in recesses in the top of the receiver. The barrel is heavily finned for cooling purposes and is quickly detachable using a rotating-barrel locking-nut. The gun may be used on a tripod, or with the standard bipod which is adjustable for height. A hinged butt-plate, when not in use, lies along the top of the stock. Although normally used with a 20 round magazine, locally produced extended magazines have been encountered. An expensive drum-type rear sight is fitted. Due to the large amount of machining required to produce the weapon, and particularly the long receiver/piston housing and finned barrel, the gun was not cheap. Nevertheless, it functions very reliably and is renowned for its accuracy.

In service with reserve and irregular forces worldwide.

Vz52 and Vz52/57 light machine guns

Manufacturer: **Ceskoslovenská Zbrojovká (Czechoslovakia)**

Calibre	Vz52—7·62 mm × 45 mm (M52 Czech) Vz52/57—7·62 mm (M43)
Dimensions	Length 104 cm Barrel length 54·5 cm
Weight	9 kg
Effective range	800 m
Operation	Gas
Type of fire	Select
Muzzle velocity	745 m/sec (M52)
Sight	Front—blade with removable hood Rear—U-notch
Feed system	25 round box magazine or 100 round belt
Cyclic rate	900–1000 rpm

Although outwardly resembling a normal LMG, the Czech Vz52 and Vz 52/57 differ in many respects from other more conventional types. The locking system of this gas-operated gun is on the same tilting bolt system as its forerunner the ZB26, which, with modifications, became the Bren gun. However, this gun is unusual in that a box magazine or a belt may be used without the addition of any extra parts. By merely closing the belt-feed cover and opening the top cover, a box magazine may be fitted, and vice versa. The cocking-handle is dispensed with, and the action is retarded by pulling the pistol-grip/trigger mechanism to the rear. The type of fire is selected by pulling the top part of the trigger for single shots and the lower part for fully automatic, in the same way as the German MG34.

The barrel, which is fitted with a variable gas cylinder similar to the Bren, may be removed by rotating the top-feed cover to the right and pulling the barrel forward.

The original Vz52 was produced in 7·62 mm × 45 mm (M52 Czech) cartridge. However, the gun was later changed to accept the Soviet 7·62 mm (M43), thus becoming the Vz52/57. The Vz52 is now obsolete.

In service with the Czechoslovak forces (Vz52/57).

Vz 52 LMG

Vz59 general purpose machine gun

Manufacturer: **State factories (Czechoslovakia)**

Calibre	7·62 mm M1908 and 7·62 mm (NATO)
Dimensions	Length 121 cm (Vz 59), 111 cm (Vz 59L)
	Barrel length 69 cm (Vz 59), 59 cm (Vz 59L)
Weight	19 kg (Vz 59 with tripod), 8·6 kg (Vz 59L)
Effective range	1000 m
Operation	Gas
Type of fire	Automatic
Muzzle velocity	830 m/sec
Sight	Front—blade with hood Rear—leaf
Feed system	50 or 250 round link belt
Cyclic rate	700–800 rpm
Barrel change	Yes

The general purpose Vz 59 machine gun is now the standard machine gun of the Czech Army and, like the Soviet PK, uses the old M1908 7·62/54 mm rimmed cartridge. An export version in 7·62 mm (NATO), the Vz 59N has been purchased by a few small nations.

The gun is capable of several variations. When mounted on its tripod (which can be opened up to elevate the gun for anti-aircraft use), it is known as the Vz 59. When designated Vz 59L, the gun is fitted either with a light barrel and detachable tripod as a section automatic rifle, or with a heavier and longer barrel and tripod as a light machine gun. The solenoid-fired version for tank use is the Vz 59T.

The weapon utilises the same sliding-trigger cocking mechanism and quick-change barrel of its forerunner, the Vz 52. However, the old dual-feed belt and box magazine have been replaced with belt feed only, from a 250 round belt or a 50 round container which can be mounted on the gun. The swinging wedge lock is very similar to that used in the Vz 58 assault rifle. Gas flow may be adjusted using the two-position type of regulator. On the 7·62 mm (NATO) version, a four-position regulator is fitted, giving a rate of fire exceeding 1000 rpm for anti-aircraft use when used in the number 4 position. A hinged butt-plate is standard and, apart from the normal sights, infra-red sights or a ×4 telescopic sight may be attached to any version.

In service with the Czechoslovak forces.

Vz 59 GPMG.

Madsen light machine gun

Manufacturer: **Dansk Rekyriffel Syndikat AS Madsen (later known as Dansk Industri Syndikat AS Madsen) (Denmark)**

Calibre	·303 in, ·30–06, 7·92 mm, 7 mm, 6·5 mm
Dimensions	Length 116·5 cm
	Barrel length 47·7 mm
Weight	10 kg
Effective range	900 m
Operation	Recoil
Type of fire	Select
Muzzle velocity	900 m/sec
Sight	Front—blade Rear—tangent
Feed system	30 round detachable-box magazine
Cyclic rate	400 rpm
Barrel change	Yes

(Statistics are for Model 1950 (·30–06))

Although no longer in use by any major army, the Madsen LMG was produced in such a variety of models and calibres that it may still be encountered in use with some irregular troops and some South American police forces. Introduced in the early 1900s the Madsen was the first machine gun to use a box magazine.

The long-recoil action is basically an automated Peabody-Martini hinged block-type, controlled by a guide-stud on the breech block engaging in lugs on a switch-plate attached to the receiver wall. A separate feed-arm, operated by an actuating-block, pushes the cartridge out of the magazine opening into the chamber. A powerful independent extractor-cum-ejector is used to extract the cartridge from the chamber with enough force to eject it from the bottom of the receiver.

The Madsen was produced in a dozen different calibres and sold to 34 countries. Belt-fed aircraft versions were also produced and a water-cooled version was sold to Chile. Basically designed to fire rimless ammunition, the Madsen did not function too well with ·303 in, 8 mm, 6·5 mm (Dutch) or the Russian 7·62 mm cartridges. Expensive to manufacture and requiring quality ammunition, the Madsen has, nevertheless, seen extensive service in large and small wars for nearly 70 years.

Obsolescent, but still in service.

Madsen LMG (Thai Navy version)

Madsen Saetter light machine gun

Manufacturer: **Dansk Industri Syndikat AS Madsen (Denmark)**

Calibre	7·62 mm (NATO) or any calibre from 6·5 mm to 8 mm
Dimensions	Length 116·5 cm Barrel length 56 cm
Weight	15·3 kg
Effective range	800 m
Operation	Gas
Type of fire	Automatic
Muzzle velocity	850 m/sec
Sight	Front—barleycorn Rear—tangent
Feed system	50 round link belt
Cyclic rate	650–1000 rpm
Barrel change	Yes

This gas-operated belt-fed gun is the latest weapon produced by the Madsen Company. Two versions of the gun are available, an infantry and a tank model. Both are

Madsen Saetter LMG

Madsen Saetter LMG on a tripod.

Madsen Saetter LMG—manufacturer's drawing.

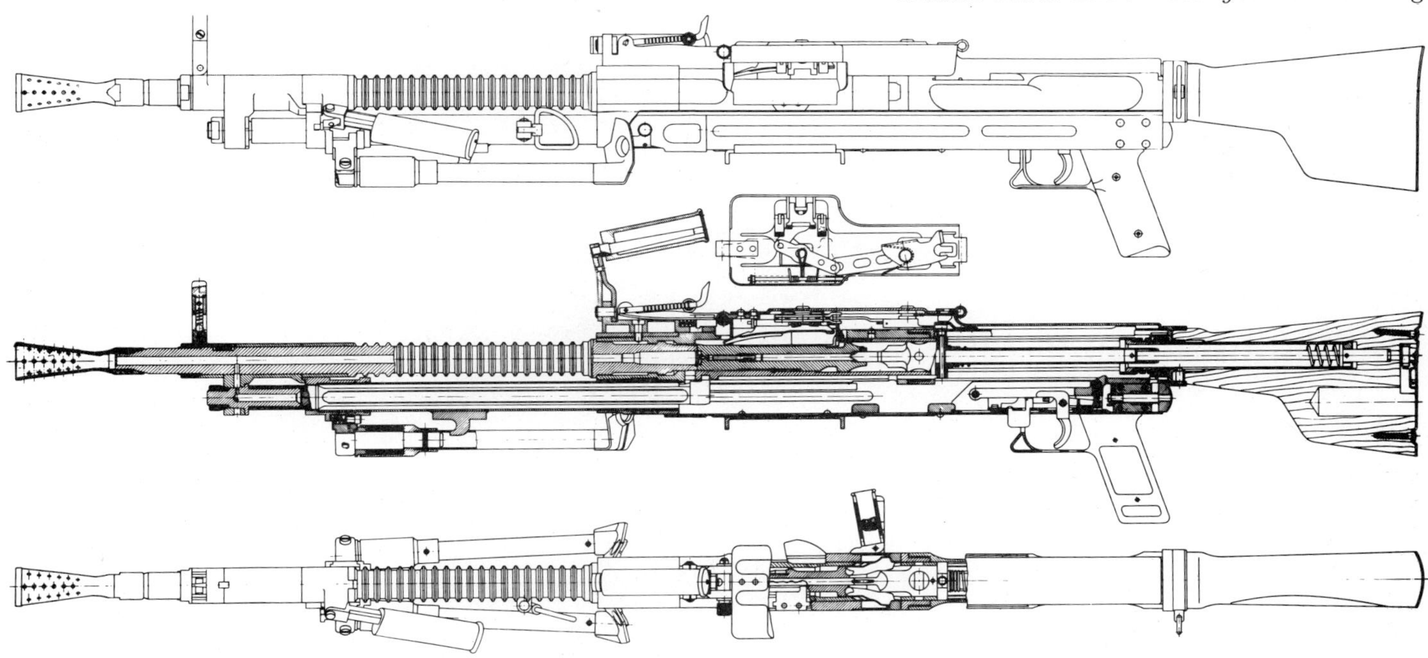

available in calibres ranging from 6·5 mm to 8 mm. Using simplified means of manufacture, consisting generally of simple turning, punching and precision-casting operations, the gun may be easily produced abroad without the sophisticated equipment normally needed. However, only Indonesia has so far taken advantage of this and adopted the gun, as well as manufacturing it. The rate of fire may be adjusted to any speed between 650 and 1000 rpm, and the gun is fed from 50 round non-disintegrating link belts which may be contained in a box attached to the side of the receiver. The feed system is a copy of that used in the MG42. The action is locked using wedges attached to the rear of the bolt which projects through slots on either side of the carrier to engage recesses in the receiver. A light tripod may be used for sustained fire.

The Madsen Saetter tank machine gun uses the same action, without the butt. It is worthy of note that this model has been produced with an air gap between the gas-cylinder and piston, thus cutting down carbon build-up and also the amount of operating gas which filters back into the tank. A ·50 calibre version was produced in prototype form only.

In service with the Indonesian forces.

M1924/29 light machine gun

Manufacturer: **Manufacture d'Armes de Chantellerault (France)**

Calibre	7·5 mm
Dimensions	Length 118 cm Barrel length 50 cm
Weight	9·2 kg
Effective range	800 m
Operation	Gas
Type of fire	Select
Muzzle velocity	823 m/sec
Sight	Front—blade Rear—tangent
Feed system	25 round box magazine
Cyclic rate	550 rpm
Barrel change	No

The first models of this weapon appeared in 1924 as a replacement for the Chauchat. Using a newly designed 7·5 mm rimless cartridge, the gun was designed M1924 Chatellerault. However, the new round was found to be ballistically unstable and a shorter 7·5 mm round was produced. Modified to this cartridge, the gun was then adopted as the M1924/29. The action of this weapon is almost a direct copy of that used in the Browning automatic rifle, with its bolt tipping on a pin into recesses in the receiver top. However, unlike the BAR, the M1924/29 is fed from the top, and features two triggers, the forward one for single shots and the rear for fully automatic. The rate of fire is checked by an actuator in the buttstock. A butt monopod may be fitted and a folding butt-plate shoulder rest is a standard fitting.

A version for use in armoured vehicles and fixed defences appeared in 1931. This model used the same action, but was fed from a horizontal box magazine or a side-mounted 150 round drum. Although now obsolete in the French Army, the M1924/29 may be found in many of the former French colonies or mandates, and a number have been sold to Middle Eastern countries, although these are probably now being replaced by Soviet weapons.

In service with former French mandates and some Middle Eastern forces.

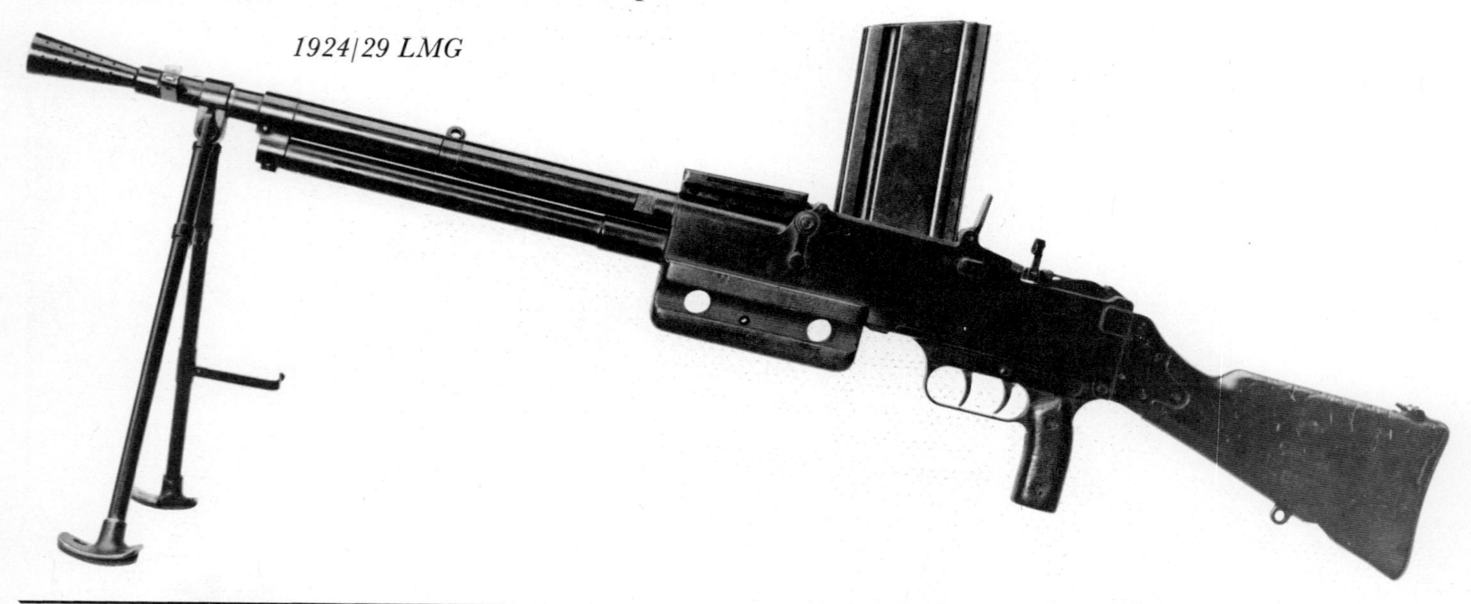

1924/29 LMG

MAS (or AAT) 52 general purpose machine gun

Manufacturer: **Manufacture d'Armes de Saint Etienne (France)**

Calibre	7·5 mm and 7·62 mm (NATO)
Dimensions	Length 114 cm (butt extended) or 98 cm (butt retracted)
Weight	11·3 kg heavy barrel 9·8 kg (light barrel)
Effective range	800 m
Operation	Delayed blowback
Type of fire	Automatic
Muzzle velocity	820 m/sec (7·5 mm)
Sight	Front—barleycorn Rear—tangent with leaf U-notch
Feed system	50 round non-disintegrating link belt
Cyclic rate	650–700 rpm

Designed to meet French needs for a general purpose machine gun, the MAS52 has replaced the M1924/29. The feed mechanism of the MAS52 is straightforward and is virtually a copy of the German MG42. However, the delayed blowback action, although not uncommon, uses a novel system of bolt delay. Between the head and the body of the two-piece bolt is a locking lever engaging a shoulder in the receiver at one end and the heavy rear bolt section at the other end. On firing, the bolt head bearing against the locking lever must overcome the resistance presented by the locking lever bearing against the shoulder in the receiver and the heavy bolt body. By the time this resistance has been overcome, the bullet has left the muzzle. The chamber of the gun is fluted also due to the lack of slow initial extraction. It is interesting to note that, at the time of adoption, the prevalence of empty case distortion was thought to be advantageous to French forces (who were then involved in several conflicts and police actions) because distortion would prevent the cases being reloaded by their opponents.

The weapon features a retractable shoulder stock and an easily detachable barrel. A heavy barrel is used in the sustained fire role. Apart from the bipod or tripod, a butt monopod may be fitted, and a variety of mountings is available. A version for use in armoured vehicles with a heavy barrel is also produced.

In service with the French forces.

MAS (AAT) 52 GPMG

MAS (AAT) 52 GPMG on a tripod

MG34 general purpose machine gun

Manufacturer: **Mauser Werke AG (Germany) and others**

Calibre	7·92 mm
Dimensions	Length 122 cm Barrel length 62 cm
Weight	12 kg
Effective range	800 m
Operation	Recoil, gas-boosted
Type of fire	Select on standard model
Muzzle velocity	800 m/sec
Sight	Front—folding blade Rear—leaf with V-notch
Feed system	50 round non-disintegrating link belt or 75 round saddle drum
Cyclic rate	800–900 rpm
Barrel change	Yes

Although no longer in use by any major power, the MG34, due to wide post-war distribution, may still be encountered in use by small armies or in the hands of irregular forces or guerillas.

The MG34 was the first true general purpose machine gun. Supplied to the pre-war German Army with a multitude of mounts and accessories, the gun was mounted on vehicles, used as a coaxial tank gun, and heavy support MG on a tripod with telescopic sights, or as the basic infantry section LMG. Fitted with a 75 round saddle-drum magazine (originally designed for the MG15 aircraft gun) which stepped up the rate of fire even higher, the weapon was particularly useful in the anti-aircraft role. The MG34 (predecessor to the MG42) is recoil-operated incorporating a muzzle-attached recoil-booster, using gas trapped at the muzzle to rebound on the end face of the barrel to give it additional rearward thrust. The interrupted screw-locked bolt is locked to the barrel by roller studs on the bolt-head engaging in cam slots in the receiver to rotate it through 90°. The barrel can be changed by swinging the unlatched receiver through 180° and withdrawing the barrel to the rear. (An asbestos glove was originally issued with the gun for carrying out this procedure.) The pawl-type feed action is operated by a stud on the rear bolt section engaging in a hollow feed arm pivoting at the rear of the feed cover.

The standard model is fitted with a rocking trigger. Single shots are obtained when the top half of the trigger is pulled. Pressure on the lower trigger, or a two-finger trigger pull, gives full automatic fire. Later versions included models for use in armoured vehicles with heavy barrel jackets. Shorter barrel models had slight feed and recoil-booster modifications and were fully automatic only. The 50 round non-disintegrating link belts may be joined together or carried in a drum attached to the feed tray. The bipod, which is adjustable for height, may be attached to the front or the rear of the barrel jacket. This weapon is machined to very close tolerences and is consequently less reliable under adverse conditions than its successor the MG42.

In service, but obsolete.

MG34 GPMG

MG42 light machine gun

Manufacturer: **Mauser Werke AG (Germany) and others**

Calibre	7·92 mm
Dimensions	Length 123 cm Barrel length 56·6 cm
Weight	11·6 kg
Effective range	800 m (bipod)
Operation	Recoil, gas-boosted
Type of fire	Automatic
Muzzle velocity	820 m/sec
Sight	Front—folding blade Rear—tangent with V-notch
Feed system	50 round non-disintegrating link belt
Cyclic rate	1100–1200 rpm

Shortly after the start of World War II, the German Army expressed a need for a gun to replace the expensive MG34 which had proved unreliable under adverse conditions. The design of the MG42 marked a complete change in contemporary automatic weapon production. Utilizing a maximum of steel stampings the weapon had a

MG1, 2 and 3 (MG42/59 commercial) light machine guns

Manufacturer: **Rheinmetall GmbH (Germany) and under licence in Italy**

Calibre	7·62 mm (NATO)
Dimensions	Length 122·5 cm Barrel length 56·6 cm
Weight	11·6 kg
Effective range	800 m (bipod)
Operation	Recoil
Type of fire	Automatic
Muzzle velocity	820 m/sec
Sight	Front—folding blade Rear—tangent with V- notch
Feed system	50 round non-disintegrating link belt
Cyclic rate	1200–1300 rpm with light bolt 700–900 rpm with Italian heavy bolt

(Statistics are for the MG3)

MG42 LMG.

MG42 LMG on a tripod.

then unique locking system.

With the bolt in the forward position, two locking rollers, situated in the front portion of the two-piece bolt, are cammed into engagement with recesses in the barrel extension by the wedge-shaped firing-pin carrier contained in the rear half of the bolt. On firing, the rollers hold the bolt in place until the barrel has recoiled a distance of 8 mm, whence inertia takes over to unlock and allow the normal reloading cycle to take place. A recoil booster muzzle attachment, using gas trapped at the muzzle to push on the barrel face assisting it rearwards, also doubles as a flash hider. Due to the high cyclic rate (1200 rpm), the barrel was made quickly detachable by placing the rear end in a yoke which, when the release lever was pushed forward, would swing the barrel out to the right of the gun and allow it to be withdrawn. A stud on the top of the rear bolt section operates a curved feed arm, pivoting at the rear of the feed cover, to shuttle the feed across and back. By the end of World War II, nearly one million had been produced since its introduction in 1942.

Some five years after the end of World War II, when the newly formed Bundeswehr was being equipped, production of the MG42 began again. Altered to take the 7·62 mm (NATO) round, and redesignated MG1, this model differed by having only very minor modifications to the bolt and feed mechanism. Some original MG42s were also converted to 7·62 mm (NATO) and designated

MG2. The final version is the MG3, the main difference being that the feed has been adapted to accept not only the standard DM1 non-disintegrating link belt, but also the DM6 and US M13 non-disintegrating link belts. The ejection port has been enlarged and the barrels have chrome-plated bores.

When used with the bipod, a drum containing a 50 round belt, or box with 100 rounds, may be mounted on the side of the receiver. A tripod is available for use in the sustained fire role. A folding sight (for use against aircraft) is fitted as standard in front of the rear sight. Produced under licence in Italy for the Italian Army, the gun has been modified by the introduction of a heavier bolt and buffer spring which reduce the rate of fire down to approximately 700–900 rpm. Yugoslavia still produces the gun in its original calibre of 7·92 mm, and calls it the SARAC.

In service (as MG3) with the West German, Austrian, Chilean, Danish, Spanish, Iranian, Italian, Norwegian, Pakistani and Portuguese forces.

MG42 LMG in the sustained fire role

HK21 light machine gun

Manufacturer: **Heckler and Koch GmbH (Germany)**

Calibre	7·62 mm (NATO). Also 7·62 mm × 39 mm and 5·56 mm
Dimensions	Length 102 cm Barrel length 45 cm
Weight	7·3 kg
Effective range	800 m
Operation	Delayed blowback
Type of fire	Select
Muzzle velocity	800 m/sec
Sight	Front—hooded post Rear—drum aperture
Feed system	Non-disintegrating link belt, 80 round drum or 20 round G3 box magazine
Cyclic rate	850 rpm
Barrel change	Yes

The HK21 is another from the Heckler and Koch family of roller-locked delayed blowback weapons and

HK21 7·62 mm LMG

HK13 5·56 mm LMG

HK11 7·62 mm (NATO) LMG

is virtually a LMG version of the G3.

Firing from an open bolt on full automatic and single shots from a closed bolt, the gun is capable of taking either a belt feed or, by changing the feed mechanism, an 80 round drum or the standard 20 round G3 box magazine. The bipod, which is adjustable for height, may be fitted at the front or the rear of the barrel casing. Barrel changing is fast and simple, the barrel being withdrawn to the rear. It is worthy of note that the HK21 shares some 48% interchangeability of parts with the G3, including the telescopic and infra-red sights. A wide variety of mountings is available for the weapon. The HK21 may be converted to take the 5·56 mm cartridge by changing the barrel, bolt and feed mechanism. These three components are also available to convert the gun to 7·62 mm × 39 mm (copy of the Soviet M43).

Although not yet sold in large numbers, the gun, nevertheless, represents an interesting design in terms of the interchangeability of calibres. The models HK11 (7·62 mm (NATO)), HK12 (7·62 mm × 39 mm) and HK13 (5·56 mm) are almost identical to the HK21 except that provision is made for magazine feed only, either by dual drum or box magazine. These weapons do not feature the interchangeability of the HK21 system. A belt-fed version of the HK13 (5·56 mm) is produced and is designated the HK23.

In service with the Portuguese forces.

HK23 5·56 mm belt-fed LMG

IMG-K light machine gun

Manufacturer: **State factories (German Democratic Republic)**

See the RPK.

In service with the DDR forces.

BM59 light machine gun

Manufacturer: **Pietro Beretta (Italy)**

See the BM 59 rifle.

In service with the Italian forces.

BM59 LMG

Model 70/223 light machine gun

Manufacturer: **Pietro Beretta (Italy)**

Weight	4·1 kg

See the 70/223 rifle. Not yet in service.

Model 70/223 LMG derived from the Beretta 70/223 rifle

M62 general purpose machine gun

Manufacturer: **Nittoku Kogyo Kyokai (Japan)**

*Calibre*fizzfi	7·62 mm (NATO)—full or reduced power
Dimensions	Length 120·5 cm Barrel length 60 cm
Weight	10·7 kg
Effective range	800 m
Operation	Gas
Type of fire	Automatic
Muzzle velocity	850 m/sec
Sight	Front—hooded blade Rear—aperture leaf
Feed	US M13 disintegrating link belt
Cyclic rate	650 rpm
Barrel change	Yes

The Model 62 is the standard machine gun of the Japanese Ground Defence Force and, like the Model 64 rifle is capable of firing a reduced power 7·62 mm (NATO) cartridge. Belt-fed, the gun uses the US M13 metallic link disintegrating belt. The gas return system is unusual in that it employs an independent gas piston which is returned by its own spring. The action is locked using a standard tilting-bolt system. A delay between locking and firing is normally apparent with this type of action, however, the Model 62 locks and fires simultaneously.

The gun may be used on the US buffer-mounted M2 tripod in the support role, and the finned barrel is quickly detachable and features an excellent flash suppressor. The weapon is well made and better than normal accuracy is obtained due to an efficient buffer system and very heavy bolt carrier.

In service with the Japanese forces.

RM2 light machine gun

Manufacturer: **Productos Mendoza SA (Mexico)**

Calibre	30·06 in
Dimensions	Length 110 cm Barrel length 61 cm
Weight	6·4 kg
Effective range	800 m
Operation	Gas
Type of fire	Select
Muzzle velocity	840 m/sec
Sight	Front—hooded barleycorn Rear—aperture
Feed system	20 round detachable-box magazine
Cyclic rate	600 rpm
Barrel change	No

The exceptionally light Mendoza RM2 is basically an improved version of the earlier Model 45, and is now standard issue in Mexico.

The action is locked using a turning-bolt system and still retains the classic Mendoza feature of a firing-pin which, in the event of breakage, is reversible. The working parts may all be drawn to the rear by hingeing the butt and trigger mechanism downwards in the same way as the Type D BAR, although the barrel is non-detachable. This factor combined with the light weight could almost class the RM2 as an automatic rifle.

In service with the Mexican forces.

RM2 LMG

SB 30 light machine gun

Manufacturer: **State factories (Rumania) and in Iran**

See the ZB26/30.

In service with the Rumanian and Iranian reserve forces.

M51 light machine gun

Manufacturer: **Schweizerische Industrie-Gesellschaft (Switzerland)**

Calibre	7·5 mm
Dimensions	Length 127 cm Barrel length 56 cm
Weight	16 kg
Effective range	800 m
Operation	Recoil
Type of fire	Automatic
Muzzle velocity	750 m/sec
Sights	Front—folding blade Rear—tangent
Feed system	50 or 250 round link belt
Cyclic rate	1000 rpm
Barrel change	Yes

The standard machine gun of the Swiss Army, the M51 was developed at the Swiss Government arms plant at Berne and is produced by SIG. Based on the German wartime MG42, the M51 uses a majority of heavily milled parts as opposed to the wide use of stampings inherent in the MG42. This use of both heavy and expensive parts adds almost 4·6 kg to the basic weight of its predecessor, thus losing many of the advantages inherent in the lighter gun, such as its cost-effectiveness and ease of manufacture.

The M51 is operated using the same recoil action as the MG42, but substitutes the earlier locking device for a system using flaps to lock the bolt, as opposed to the roller-locking of the MG42 bolt. The quick-detachable barrel is changed in the same way as the MG42. A tripod mount is available which may be fitted with an optical sight. A 50 round belt may be carried in a drum attached to the left-hand side of the feed-tray. The feed system is also almost a direct copy of that used in the MG42.

Although still in wide use in the Swiss Army, it is thought that this gun may shortly be replaced by the SIG 710–3.

In service with the Swiss forces.

SIG 710-1 general purpose machine gun

Manufacturer: **Schweizerische Industrie-Gesellschaft (Switzerland)**

Calibre	6·3 mm, 7·92 mm, 7·62 mm (NATO)	*Type of fire*	Automatic
Dimensions	Length 116 cm Barrel length 50 cm	*Muzzle velocity*	790 m/sec
		Sight	Front—folding barleycorn Rear—tangent with V notch
Weight	11·3 kg	*Feed system*	Link belt
Effective range	800 m	*Cyclic rate*	750–1400 rpm
Operation	Delayed blowback	*Barrel change*	Yes

SIG 710-2 general purpose machine gun

Manufacturer: **Schweizerische Industrie-Gesellschaft (Switzerland)**

Calibre	6·5 mm, 7·92 mm, 7·62 mm (NATO)	*Type of fire*	Automatic
Dimensions	Length 119 cm Barrel length 55 cm	*Muzzle velocity*	790 m/sec
		Sight	Front—blade with ears Rear—tangent with V notch
Weight	10·9 kg	*Feed system*	Link belt
Effective range	800 m	*Cyclic rate*	750–1400 rpm
Operation	Delayed blowback	*Barrel change*	Yes

SIG 710-3 general purpose machine gun

Manufacturer: **Schweizerische Industrie-Gesellschaft (Switzerland)**

Calibre	7·62 mm (NATO)	*Muzzle velocity*	790 m/sec
Dimensions	Length 114·6 cm Barrel length 56 cm	*Sight*	Front—blade with ears Rear—tangent
Weight	9·65 kg	*Feed system*	Link and disintegrating link belt
Effective range	800 m		
Operation	Delayed blowback	*Cyclic rate*	800–950 rpm
Type of fire	Automatic	*Barrel change*	Yes

SIG 710-1 GPMG

SIG 710-2 GPMG

SIG 710-3 GPMG

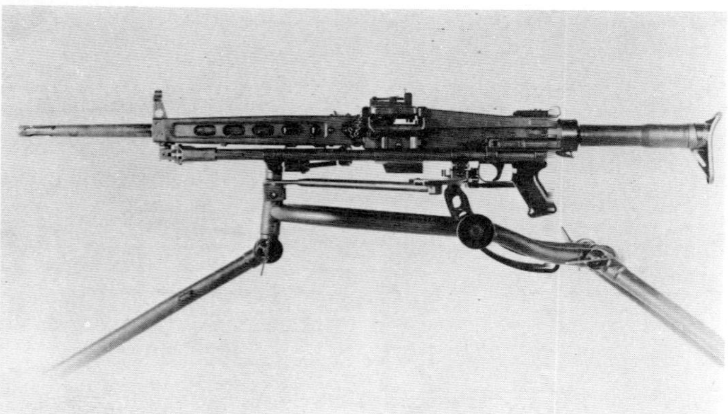

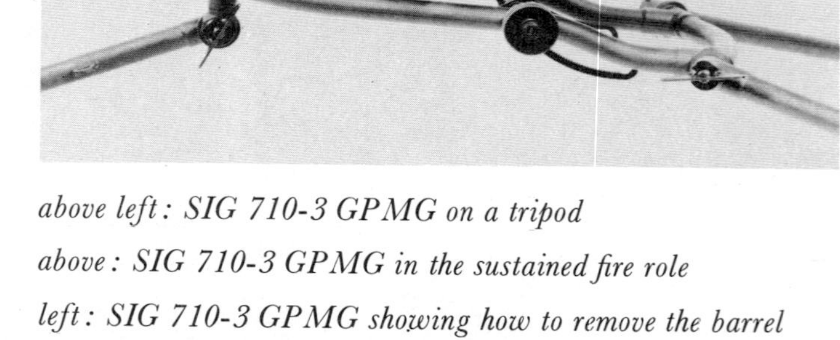

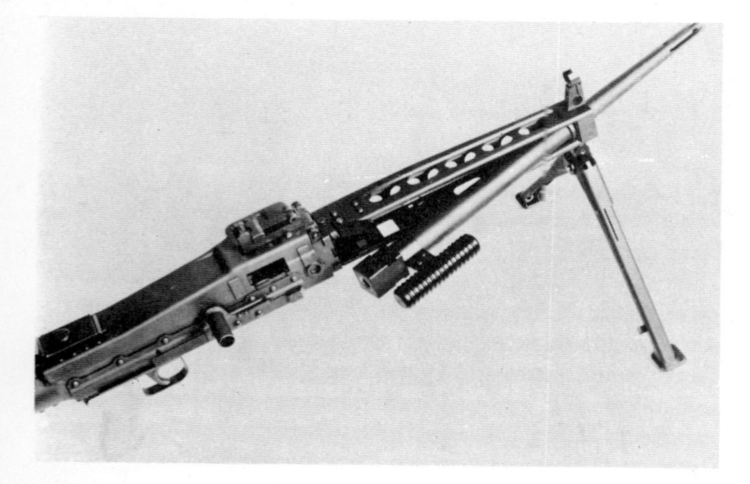

above left: SIG 710-3 GPMG on a tripod

above: SIG 710-3 GPMG in the sustained fire role

left: SIG 710-3 GPMG showing how to remove the barrel

The SIG 710 series of general purpose machine guns are offered in three versions. The 710-1 and 710-2 are available in 6·5 mm, 7·92 mm and 7·62 mm (NATO). The 710-3 is so far only available in 7·62 mm (NATO). Using the same delayed blowback roller-locked action as the Stg 57, the 710 series has a feed system very similar to that of the MG42 and uses a link belt with a choice of lengths, or a 50 round belt capable of being carried in a drum attached to the feed tray.

The 710-1 is similar both internally and externally to the German MG42V which was being developed at the close of World War II.

The 710-2 differs mainly in its lack of barrel jacket. The carrying handle is used to change the barrel by turning the handle down and removing the barrel forwards.

The 710-3 is somewhat lighter than the earlier versions due to a wider use of stampings. The barrel jacket extends only half the length of the barrel which is removed using the attached handle to pull the barrel to the right and thence rearwards. Disintegrating link belt may also be used with the 710-3. As well as the standard bipods, a wide variety of tripods and accessories is available, including telescopic sights and blank-firing barrels.

In service with the Swiss forces.

RP46 light machine gun

Manufacturer: **State factories (USSR)**

Calibre	7·62 mm M1908	*Type of fire*	Automatic
Dimensions	Length 128 cm Barrel length 61 cm	*Muzzle velocity*	840 m/sec
Weight	13 kg	*Sight*	Front—protected post Rear—tangent
Effective range	800 m	*Feed system*	250 round belt or 47 round pan
Operation	Gas	*Cyclic rate*	600 rpm

DP and DPM light machine guns

Manufacturer: **State factories (USSR)**

Calibre	7·62 mm M1908	*Type of fire*	Automatic
Dimensions	Length 127 cm Barrel length 60 cm	*Muzzle velocity*	840 m/sec
Weight	9 kg	*Sight*	Front—protected post Rear—tangent
Effective range	800 m	*Feed system*	47 round pan
Operation	Gas	*Cyclic rate*	600 rpm

RPD light machine gun

Manufacturer: **State factories (USSR)**

Calibre	7·2 mm	*Type of fire*	Automatic
Dimensions	Length 103 cm Barrel length 52 cm	*Muzzle velocity*	840 m/sec
Weight	7 kg	*Sight*	Front—protected post Rear—tangent
Effective range	800 m	*Feed system*	100 round belt
Operation	Gas	*Cyclic rate*	650–750 rpm

DPM LMG (Chinese version)

RP46 LMG

RPD LMG

The DP first appeared in 1926, and was later developed to give many different configurations of the basic weapon.

A gas-operated weapon, the action is locked using flaps cammed by the firing pin into recesses in the receiver. A weak feature of the early system was the return spring. Coiled around the piston, it weakened and distorted easily due to barrel heat. The DP used a 47 round pan-type magazine. A version known as DT was also produced using a variable-length stock, a 60 round magazine, a pistol-grip and a non-detachable barrel.

During World War II both versions were modified by placing the return spring in a cylindrical container behind the action. The addition of a pistol-grip and a stronger bipod completed the modification and the weapons were then known as the DPM and, as a tank version, the DTM. Using the same action the RP46 is a basic variant of the DP and was designed as a company support weapon. The weapon is belt-fed and a carrying handle has been added, but not to the heavier duty barrel which, like that of the DP and DPM, is detachable. The DP 47 round magazine may also be used alternatively by removing the belt-feed device, to make the gun more versatile.

The final version in the Degtyarev range is the RPD. Firing the 7·62 mm M43 intermediate cartridge, the weapon uses the same scaled-down type of gas and bolt-locking system as the DP series and the RP46. A purely belt-fed gun, the belt was contained in a drum which was attached below the gun. This allowed for easier carriage and use by one man if necessary. A variant is the RPDM which uses a longer piston.

Although now obsolete in the Soviet Army, all these weapons are still to be found in use in Warsaw Pact and in North Korean (Type 62 LMG) forces. The communist Chinese have also produced exact copies of these weapons (Types 56 and 56–1 LMG).

In service with the Warsaw Pact, Chinese and North Korean forces.

Type 62 light machine gun

Manufacturer: **State factories (USSR)**

See the DP and DPM range of machine guns.

In service with the North Korean forces.

RPK light machine gun

Manufacturer: **State factories (USSR)**

Calibre	7·62 mm M43
Dimensions	Length 103 cm Barrel length 61 cm
Weight	5 kg
Effective range	800 m
Operation	Gas
Type of fire	Select
Muzzle velocity	735 m/sec
Sight	Front—protected post Rear—tangent
Feed system	30 or 40 round box magazines, or 75 round drum magazine
Cyclic rate	600 rpm

This gas-operated LMG is a development of the AKM assault rifle and has replaced the old RPD as the section support weapon.

The weapon differs from the AKM in several respects. A longer and heavier barrel with a folding bipod is fitted, though there is no provision for the fitting of a bayonet. The barrel is not detachable. The weapon may feed from a 40 round box magazine a 75 round drum magazine or the standard AK 47 or AKM 30 round magazine. Any of these magazines may be used with any Kalashnikov weapon. All parts are interchangeable with the AKM except the forearm, buttstock, rearsight and the modified receiver. Some RPKs are capable of mounting an infra-red sighting device. The weapon is also available in Yugoslavia (M65A and B) and in East Germany (IMG-K).

In service with the Soviet forces.

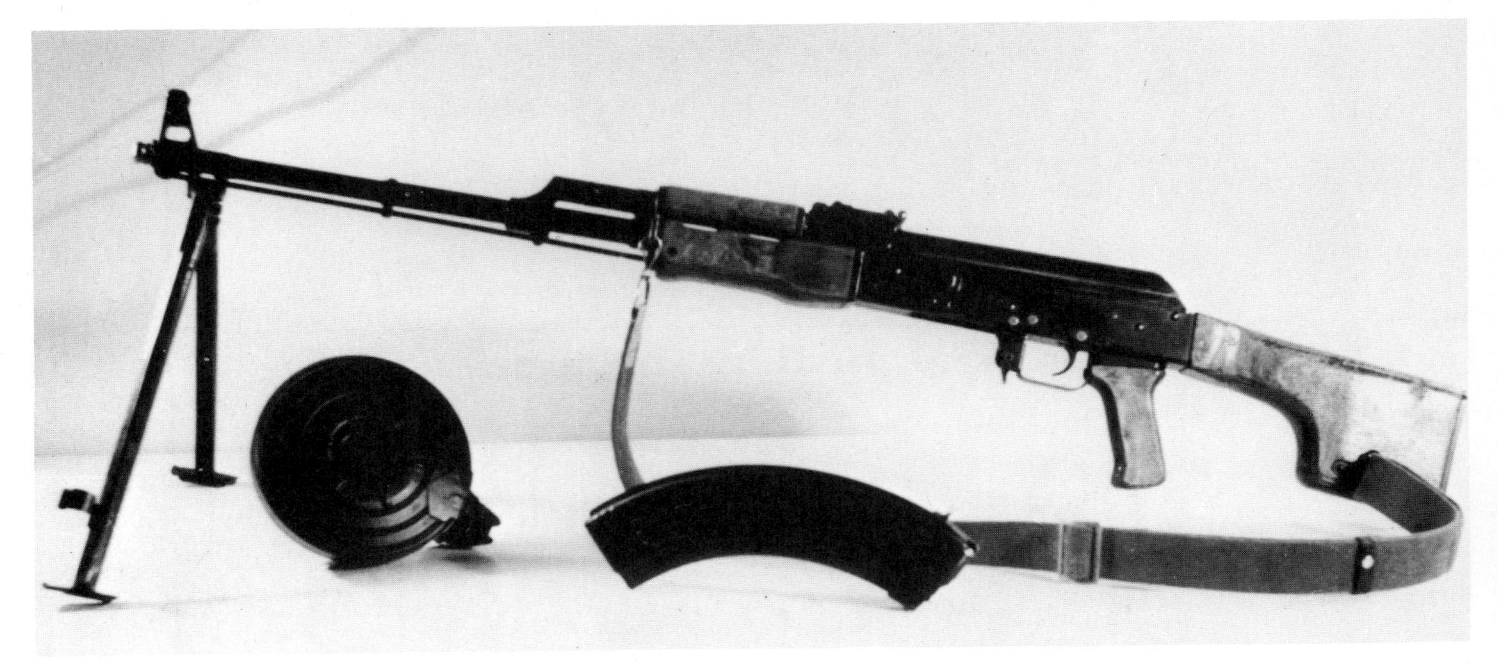

RPK LMG (showing drum and box type magazines)

PK general purpose machine gun

Manufacturer: **State factories (USSR)**

Calibre	7·62 mm M1908
Dimensions	Length 116 cm Barrel length 65·5 cm
Weight	8·9 kg
Effective range	1000 m
Operation	Gas
Type of fire	Automatic
Muzzle velocity	825 m/sec
Sight	Front—post with ears Rear—tangent
Feed system	50, 200 or 250 round link belt
Cyclic rate	650 rpm
Barrel change	Yes

The PK is the latest machine gun in use with the Warsaw Pact countries. A general purpose machine gun, the weapon may be used in three roles. The LMG version known as the PK is used with the adjustable bipod and fed from a choice of 50, 200 or 250 round square belt boxes. The 50 round box may be attached to the bottom of the gun in the same way as the RPD. When used as a heavy machine gun the weapon is designated PKS and uses a tripod. An extension for the tripod is available making the gun suitable for use in the AA role. Equipped with a solenoid firing device, the gun becomes the PKT for use in armoured vehicles. A gas regulator and carrying handle is fitted to the quick-detachable barrel and a bar-type flash suppressor has replaced the earlier cone-type flash hider.

Being a Kalashnikov design, the action is locked using the familiar turning bolt system. The feed mechanism is operated by two cams on either side of the one-piece piston/bolt carrier which cause the vertically mounted feed-lever to pivot inwards on recoil and outwards on counter-recoil. The round is extracted from the belt by a cartridge-gripper mounted on the carrier. When the carrier is driven rearward, the round is forced on to the feed tips by a depressor working in conjunction with the feed-cam. The PK uses a light skeleton stock and some models are fitted with brackets for infra-red sights.

In service with the Warsaw Pact forces.

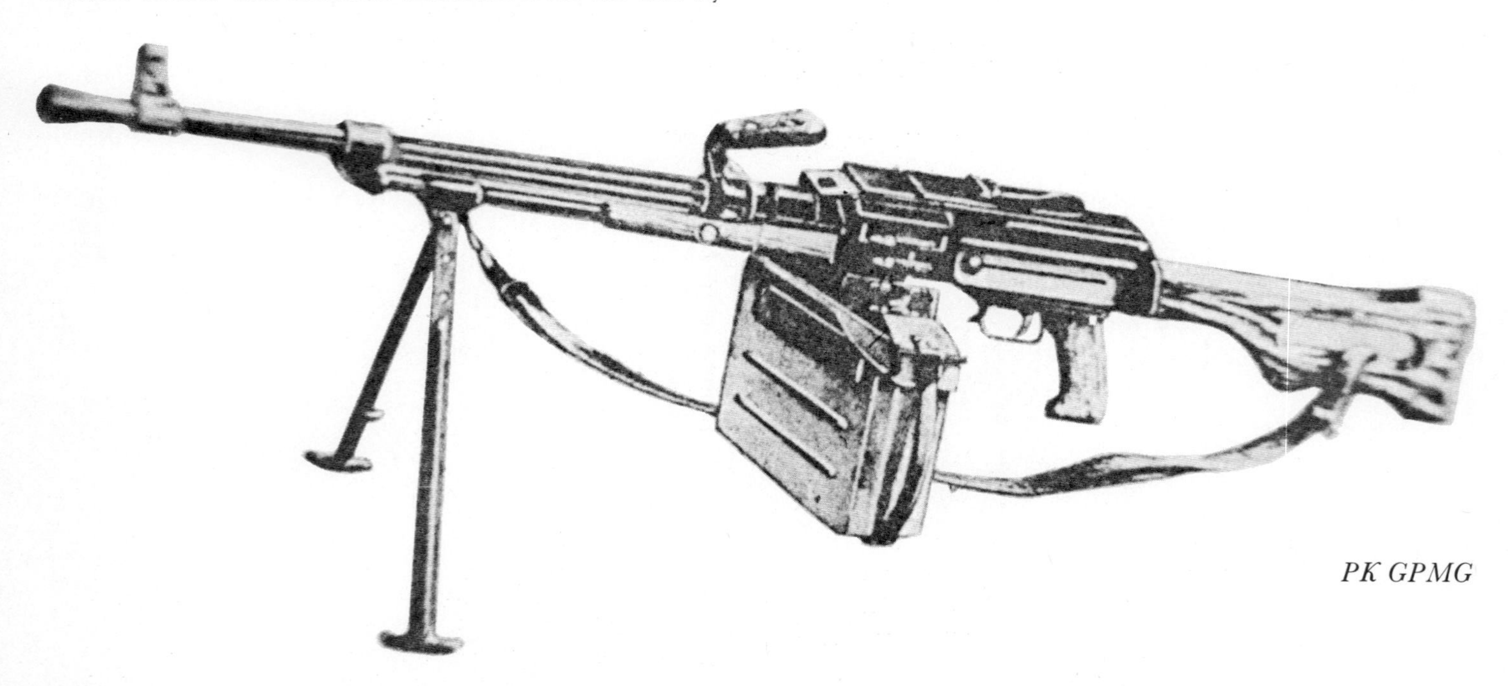

PK GPMG

Goryonov SG34 and SGM medium machine guns

Manufacturer: **State factories (USSR)**

Calibre	7·62 mm M1908
Dimensions	Length 112 cm Barrel length 71·5 cm
Weight	13·5 kg
Effective range	1500 m
Operation	Gas
Type of fire	Automatic
Muzzle velocity	745 m/sec
Sight	Front—blade Rear—leaf suitable for two differently powered loads
Feed system	250 round link belt
Cyclic rate	600–700 rpm
Barrel change	Yes

The Goryonov series of medium machine guns is used by almost all of the European and Asian communist countries, and has been manufactured in China and Hungary. The Soviet-produced weapon comes in two basic versions, the SG43 and SGM. Slightly modified versions of both models have been produced, though these differ only in minor details, such as the addition of dust covers and different barrel locks. The main recognisable features are the smooth barrel with the cocking handle mounted between the spade grips, containing oiling brushes, of the SG43, as opposed to the splined barrel and right-side mounted cocking handle of the later SGM. Both versions may be used on a Sidorenko-Malinovsky tripod, or on a wheeled mount with an optically mounted shield. The SGM was modified for use with the older Sokolov-type wheeled mount which was used with the now obsolete Maxim water-cooled machine guns. This version is known as the SGMB. Both wheeled mounts may be upturned and used as anti-aircraft mounts. Vehicle mounts are also available, and a solenoid-fired version of the gun, known as the SGMT, was produced for use in armoured vehicles. All models have a quick-detachable barrel which has a chrome-lined bore and is fitted with a carrying handle. The action is locked using a tilting bolt which is unusual in that it recesses into the right-hand side of the receiver. The cartridge-gripper is held by a cartridge feed slide which, in turn, is attached to the bolt. As the bolt is withdrawn, the gripper extracts the cartridge from the belt and, having cleared the feed tray, is forced downwards by the cartridge-depressor to be fed into the chamber by the forward motion of the bolt. It is interesting to note that the cartridge feed slide may be quickly removed without stripping the weapon, and many of these guns captured in Vietnam were found to be totally inoperable due to this vital component having been jettisoned by the Viet Cong.

Goryonov SG34 MMG in the anti-aircraft role

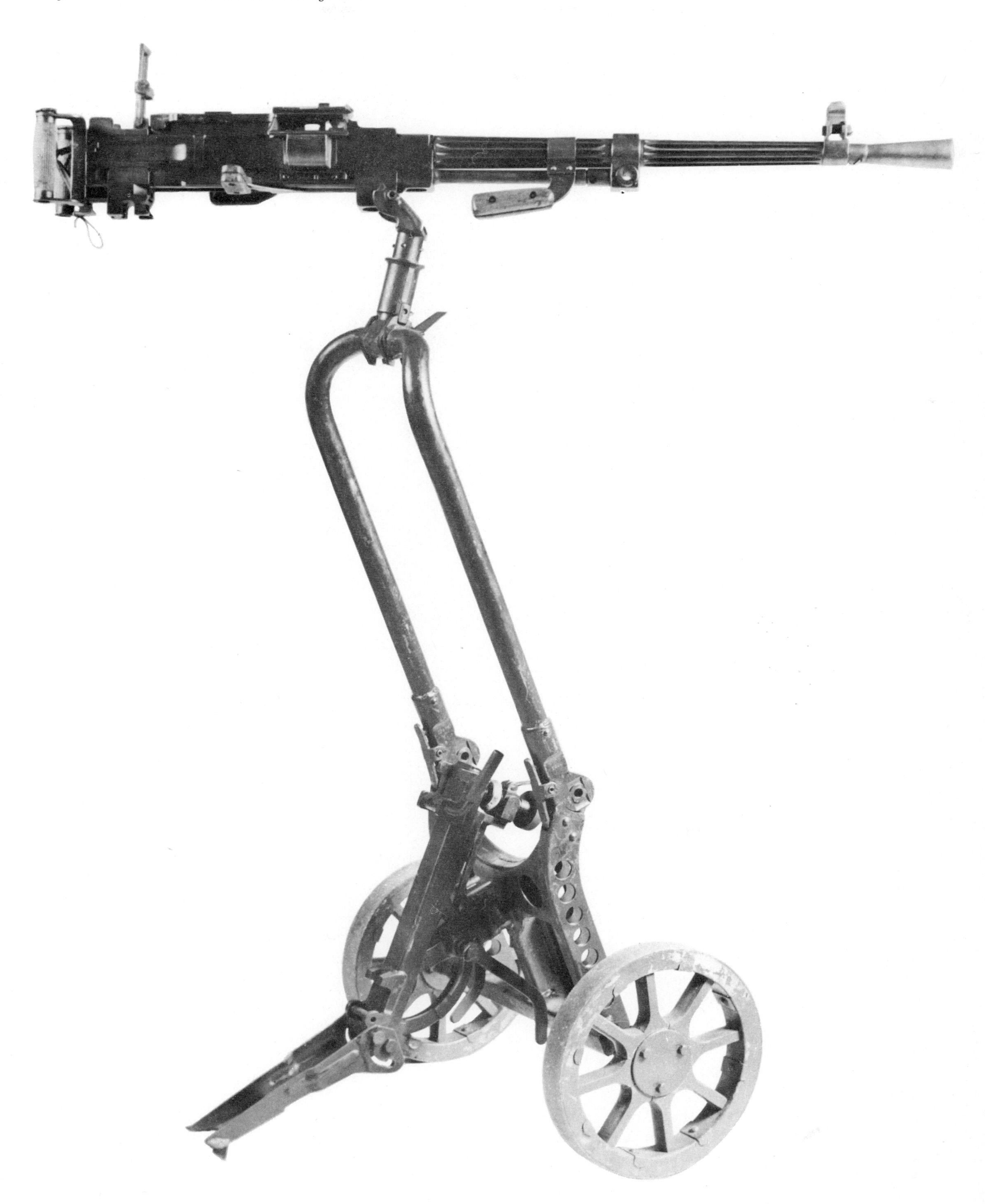

Goryonov SG34 MMG

The Goryonov weapons are being replaced by the PK general purpose machine gun. The communist Chinese version of the SG43 is known as the Type 53 heavy machine gun and the SGMB as the Type 57 heavy machine gun. The Czechoslovak and Polish maufactured versions of the SG43 are stamped Vz43 and Wz43 respectively. A version produced in Hungary uses the same action, but is fitted with a pistol-grip trigger mechanism and RPD-type buttstock and bipod. The Hungarian gun is used as a general purpose machine gun in the same way as the PK. When firing the Type L or LPS light bullets, the range figures on the right-hand side of the leaf-sight should be used and the left-hand side figures with the yellow-tipped heavy bullets.

In service with all the Warsaw Pact forces.

Bren light machine gun

Manufacturer: **Royal Small Arms Factory (United Kingdom) and Inglis & Company (Canada)**

Calibre	·303 in. Also 7·62 mm (NATO) and 7·92 mm
Dimensions	Length 108 cm Barrel length 56 cm
Weight	8·7 kg
Effective range	640 m
Operation	Gas
Type of fire	Select
Muzzle velocity	730 m/sec
Sight	Front—blade with ears Rear—leaf with aperture
Feed system	30 round box magazine, or 50 and 100 round pan type
Cyclic rate	480 rpm
Barrel change	Yes

(Statistics are for the Mk. 3)

The Bren was adopted by the British in August 1938 and, in modified form, is still in service today.

Produced under licence from the firm of ZB, or Brno in Czechoslovakia, the Bren is a modified version of their ZB 26. The gun is gas-operated and the bolt is locked into a recess in the top of the receiver by a cam on the piston/slide assembly. The quick-detachable barrel incorporates a gas regulator with four different ports and a carrying handle. Early versions were fitted with drum-type rear sights, but the conventional leaf type was adopted for the first modified model. A folding bipod is fitted, the early models of which were adjustable for height. A 30 round curved box magazine is normally used, although 50 and 100 round pan-type magazines can be fitted in conjunction with a special feed-piece. Designed mostly for use with vehicle mounted guns, the pan type were unpopular due to awkwardness and saw little service.

A large number of Bren guns were produced by Inglis in Canada, including a model chambered for 7·92 mm and supplied to nationalist China. When Britain adopted the 7·62 mm (NATO) cartridge, Mk3 Brens were converted to this calibre and named L4A1. Succeeding models in this series incoporated only minor modifications, including chrome-plating of the barrel bore. The weapon uses a 30 round straight box magazine but may also be used with the standard 20 round SLR magazine. Both weapons may be encountered in a wide variety of small armies, particularly those supplied by the United Kingdom. The L4 series Brens are in restricted front-line service in the British forces and also in use in reserve forces elsewhere. It is renowned still for its accuracy and reliability.

In service with some regular and reserve United Kingdom forces, some Commonwealth reserve forces and a number of small foreign forces.

Bren LMG

L4A1 light machine gun

Manufacturer: **Royal Small Arms Factory (United Kingdom)**

See the Bren.

In service with some United Kingdom and Commonwealth forces.

Bren L4A3 LMG

L7 Series general purpose machine gun

Manufacturer: **Royal Small Arms Factory (United Kingdom)**

See the MAG.

In service with the United Kingdom and certain Commonwealth forces.

L7A2 GPMG.

L7A1 GPMG on a tripod.

L7 series GPMG—co-axial version.

L7 series GPMG for helicopter mounting

Vickers Mk 1 medium machine gun

Manufacturer: **Vickers-Armstrong Limited, Royal Ordnance factories (United Kingdom) and Colt's PTFA (United States)**

Calibre	·303 in, and ·30 in (as made by Colt and designated USMG Model 1915)
Dimensions	Length 109 cm Barrel length 72 cm
Weight	15 kg (without water), 18 kg (with water), 40·6 kg (with tripod and water)
Effective range	2000 m
Operation	Recoil with gas assistance from muzzle-booster
Type of fire	Automatic
Muzzle velocity	740 m/sec
Sight	Front—hooded blade Rear—leaf with aperture
Feed system	250 round canvas belt
Cyclic rate	450–550 rpm
Barrel change	Yes

Vickers MMG

Although obsolete in the British Army since about 1968, the Vickers medium machine gun may still be found in use in former British territories and is likely to remain in service with many smaller countries having arms agreements with the United Kingdom. First introduced into the British Army in 1912, this reliable and robust weapon has been used by all Commonwealth nations and has been sold abroad in various calibres.

The Vickers uses an inverted Maxim-type toggle-locking system. Recoil-operated, the gun uses a booster, fastened over the muzzle, which rebounds some of the gas on to a cup attached to the end of the barrel. This device merely aids the recoil action in driving the barrel rearwards. The gun is water-cooled and capable, therefore, of very heavy sustained fire. History recalls the gun having been fired continuously for periods of 8 hours, or more, stopping only to replace worn out barrels or locks. The Vickers gun has been produced with both smooth and corrugated barrel water-jackets. A condenser is fitted to hide and to recoup the steam. A brass-studded 250 round canvas belt is one of the main causes of malfunctions, being prone to expansion or contraction due to climatic conditions. This causes the rounds to slip out of place in the belt. A heavy (22·6 kg) tripod is used with the gun, which is fitted with a calibrated traverse ring and elevating wheel. When used with the specially designed ·303 in Mk 7z or Mk 8z (single base nitro-cellulose loaded) bullet, nearly 900 m may be added to the standard range of the weapon which is in excess of 2000 m. Barrels used with the standard Mk 7 cartridges should never be used with the Mk 7z or 8z cartridges for overhead fire due to the erratic wear pattern.

Head-space adjustment is vitally important on this type of action. Excess space will cause ruptured or bulged cases and insufficient space will prevent the lock from going forward completely thereby preventing firing. Adjustment is made by the addition or subtraction of shims placed behind the adjustment nut on the lock connecting rod. The action is returned using a fusee spring which is also adjustable. Although several adjustments are necessary to make the Vickers function correctly, when these are carried out regularly, the gun is highly efficient, though heavy, and expensive to produce.

A number of Vickers guns were manufactured by Colt in the United States during World War I. Adopted as the United States machine gun model 1915, they were in ·30 calibre. These guns were later sold to Britain during World War II for use by the Home Guard. The Vickers was also sold abroad in several calibres, particularly 7·65 mm. It sold particularly well in South America.

In service, but obsolescent.

·30 Browning medium machine gun

Manufacturer: **General Motors (A C Spark Plug Division) and others (United States)**

Calibre	·30 in
Dimensions	Length 104 cm Barrel length 61 cm
Weight	14 kg
Effective range	900 m
Operation	Recoil
Type of fire	Automatic
Muzzle velocity	850 m/sec
Sight	Front—blade Rear—leaf
Feed system	250 round fabric belt or disintegrating link belt
Cyclic range	400–500 rpm
Barrel change	Yes

(Statistics are for the M1919A4)

Although the basic design of this gun dates from 1910, the weapon was first adopted as the M1917 the same year. Recoil-operated, the action is locked by a breech locking-piece which is cammed up into slots in the rear of the bolt to lock the bolt, barrel, barrel extension and lock frame in the battery position. As the action travels rearwards on firing, the breech locking-piece is cammed out of engagement by the lock frame. Actuated by the rear of the barrel extension, an accelerator pivots on its pin to assist in driving the bolt to the rear. This accelerated action provides the vital primary extraction needed in this type of action, thus eliminating the need for lubricated cases or a fluted chamber. A pivoting extractor-lever, attached to the side of the bolt and actuated by a feed cam in the receiver wall, withdraws a fresh cartridge from the belt on recoil and feeds it down into the 'T' slot on the bolt-face. A feed-lever, pivoting on the top cover and engaging in a cross-over cam groove on the bolt, operates the conventional belt-feed slide with sprung pawls.

Early versions were water-cooled, but these have been obsolete for some years and are unlikely to be found in service except in the smaller developing countries, or with irregulars. However, the prolific air-cooled models are still in wide use today as secondary armament in armoured vehicles or in infantry use on a wide variety of tripods. The most common version is the M1919A4 which is usually mounted on the light M2 tripod or on light reconnaissance vehicles. Some versions were fitted with a butt, bipod, carrying handle and lighter barrels, and these were designated M1919A6. Lightened and electrically-fired versions were available for use in aircraft and may be found fitted with spade grips for ground use. Some M1919A4s were converted to 7·62 mm (NATO) for the United States Navy. This version is now standard in the Canadian Army as the C1 7·62 mm machine gun.

Although replaced by the M60 in the United States Army, the weapon remains in second-line use.

In service with the Argentinian, Danish, Dominican, Dutch, French, Greek, Israeli, Italian, Japanese, Norwegian, Spanish, Turkish, United Kingdom and some irregular forces.

Browning 1919A4 MMG

M60 general purpose machine gun

Manufacturer: **Bridge Tool and Manufacturing Company and General Motors (Inland Manufacturing Division) (United States)**

Calibre	7·62 mm (NATO)
Dimensions	Length 111 cm
	Barrel length 65 cm
Weight	10·4 kg
Effective range	900 m
Operation	Gas
Type of fire	Automatic
Muzzle velocity	850 m/sec
Sight	Front—blade
	Rear—leaf
Feed system	Disintegrating link belt
Cyclic rate	600 rpm
Barrel change	Yes

The M60 is the standard general purpose machine gun of the United States Army. A wide variety of mountings is also available for use on soft-skinned or armoured vehicles and helicopters.

A gas-operated weapon, the M60 belt-feed system is basically a copy of that used in the German MG42 and the action, which is locked using a turning bolt, is that of the German World War II FG42. The sprung firing-pin aids the main spring to complete the bolt-locking rotation. The quick-detachable barrel has a stellite-lined bore and flash suppressor. The earlier M60s were not fitted with a carrying handle, consequently a hot barrel had to be changed using the bipod (which is fitted with

M60 GPMG

M60 GPMG on a tripod

perforated heat shields), or with an asbestos glove issued with the gun. The gas cylinders of these early models were also attached to the barrel. The barrel of the latest version, the M60E1, is now fitted with a carrying handle and the gas-cylinder and bipod are mounted on the gun.

The weapon is manufactured using as many stampings or fabrications as possible. The M60 is the first standard United States machine gun to be fitted with a quick-detachable barrel. (The World War II Johnson LMG barrel was quick-detachable, but the weapon was adopted in small numbers only by the United States Marine Corps and some United States Army units.) The M60 has been in service since the early 1960s and saw extensive service in Vietnam. It has virtually replaced the Browning ·30 calibre machine gun.

In service with the United States, Australian, South Vietnamese and some other United States-equipped forces.

SARAC light machine gun

Manufacturer: **State factories (Yugoslavia)**

See the MG 42.

In service with the Yugoslav forces.

M65A and M65B light machine guns

Manufacturer: **State factories (Yugoslavia)**

See the RPK.

In service with the Yugoslav forces.

30 J light machine gun

Manufacturer: **State factories (Yugoslavia)**

See the ZB 26/30.

In service with some reserve forces in Yugoslavia.

Type 54 heavy machine gun

Manufacturer: **State factories (People's Republic of China)**

See the DSLK 38/46.

In service with the communist Chinese forces.

Vz 43 heavy machine gun

Manufacturer: **State factories (Czechoslovakia)**

See the SG43 and SGM.

In service with the Czechoslovak forces.

Kulomet ZB-60 heavy machine gun

Manufacturer: **Ceskoslovenska 'Zbrojovka' (Czechoslovakia)**

Calibre	15 mm
Dimensions	Length 205 cm Barrel length 109 cm
Weight	159 kg (with tripod)
Effective range	2400 m
Operation	Gas
Muzzle velocity	905 m/sec
Sight	Front—blade Rear—aperture
Feed system	40 round metallic link belt
Cyclic rate	430 rpm

In general design the ZB-60 is a larger version of the well-known ZB Vz53 which saw service in large numbers in the British Army as the Besa. The action of the two guns is very similar as is the general outline, particularly the robust square-sectioned receiver. The gun was issued in infantry form on a wheeled tripod with detachable wheels and folding front legs which tuck under the front of the tripod when on the move. The gun is intended for infantry fire support and it has only a limited use against aircraft, mainly due to its slow rate of fire and restricted mount. There is a wide range of ammunition available, including an armour-piercing round for which a penetration of 190 mm at 500 m is claimed.

In service with some Middle Eastern forces.

M621 heavy machine gun

Manufacturer: **Groupement Industriel des Armements Terrestres (France)**

Calibre	20 mm
Dimensions	Length 220 cm
Weight	45 kg
Effective range	2000 m
Operation	Gas
Muzzle velocity	1030 m/sec
Sight	As required
Feed system	250 round metal link belt
Cyclic rate	300–740 rpm

A recent design, the M621 is an attractive proposition for infantry use due to its light weight. It offers a wide

M60 GPMG

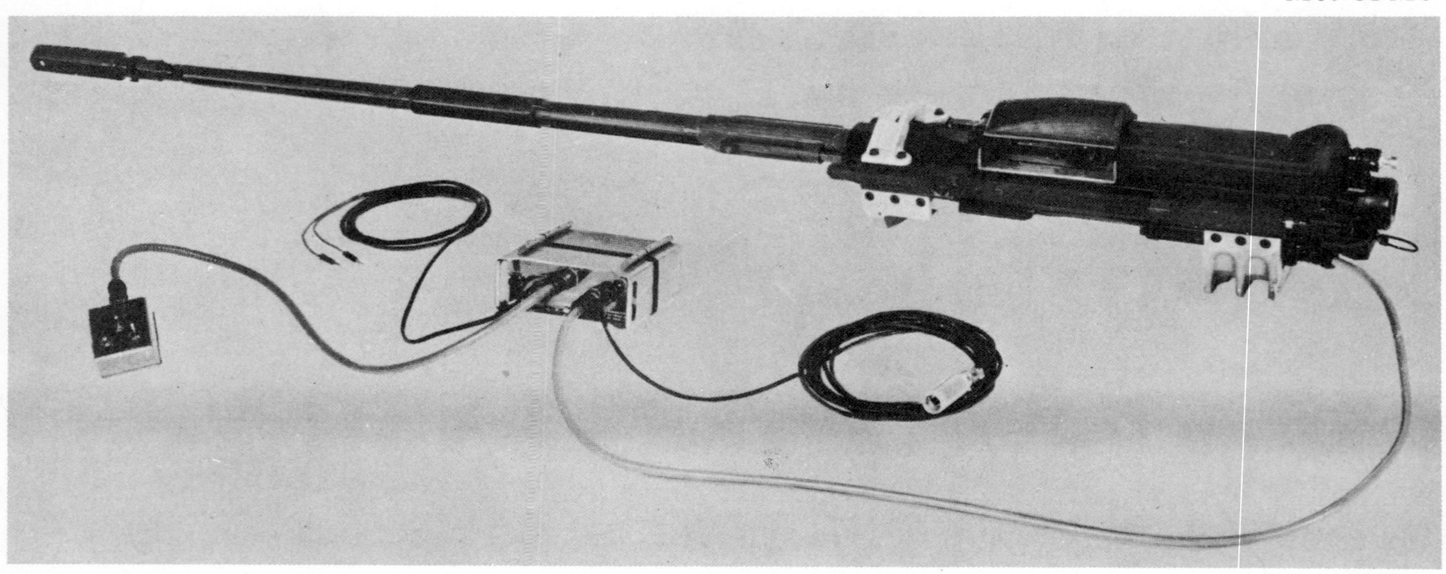

M621 HMG helicopter-mounted

range of rates of fire by using electric ignition, although this can be dispensed with and a more conventional percussion method fitted if it is desired to use other types of ammunition. Much thought has gone into reducing weight in all features of the gun and it is only 7 kg heavier than the ·50 in Browning, yet it is far more powerful and lethal.

The infantry version can be carried on, and fired from, a light vehicle, towed behind a truck, or mounted in a light carrier and armoured vehicle. The recoil is kept low by using the technique of firing the round as the barrel runs forward, and the electric ignition allows great flexibility in the type of fire used. The range of ammunition is based on the standard NATO round, adapted for the electric primer, and there is a number of different mountings which allow the gun to be carried in aircraft as well as ground vehicles.

In service with the French forces.

M693 (modèle F1) heavy machine gun

Manufacturer: **Groupement Industriel des Armements Terrestres (France)**

Calibre	20 mm
Dimensions	Length 269·5 cm Barrel length 206·5 cm
Weight	70·5 kg
Effective range	2000 m
Operation	Gas and blowback
Muzzle velocity	1050 m/sec
Sight	As required
Feed system	250 round metal link belt
Cyclic rate	740 rpm

The M693 has obvious family links with the 621, but the two are not entirely similar. This gun is a little heavier and possibly more robust as a result. It is built of very few parts and the assembly consists of only three main sub-assemblies. The bolt is locked to the breech block slide assembly, which carries the barrel at its forward end. Locking is achieved by two swinging flaps, not unlike the Degtyarev principle, and these are unlocked by two short-stroke pistons. The remaining rearward motion is largely powered by blowback and there is a strong buffer spring to arrest the bolt. As is becoming normal practice with modern 20 mm guns, the round is fired on counter-recoil before the barrel runs out, but on this gun it is a percussion mechanism, albeit with electric control.

A twin-sprocket feed mechanism allows a dual-feed arrangement with a rapid change from one type of ammunition to the other and the belts are of a special type which permits them to turn through a large angle without jamming in the feed slides.

This gun is intended for mounting on infantry vehicles, and is believed not to have been tried on a ground mounting.

In service with the French forces.

MK 20 Rh202 heavy machine gun

Manufacturer: **Rheinmetall GmbH (Germany)**

Calibre	20 mm
Dimensions	Length 261 cm Barrel length 184 cm
Weight	122·2 kg
Effective range	2000 m
Operation	Gas
Muzzle velocity	1050 m/sec
Sight	As required
Feed system	Two or three way belt-feed using disintegrating metal link belt.
Cyclic rate	600–1000 rpm

The MK Rh202 is an impressive modern rapid-fire gun, intended for use as an AA weapon to give protection against low-flying aircraft and helicopters and as a ground weapon on infantry carriers and light armoured vehicles. Much effort has gone into producing a gun with a short inboard length so that it may be mounted in small turrets, and this has been achieved with some success despite the fact that the mechanism operates with a reciprocating bolt.

The gun displays a number of unusual features. Recoil is reduced by firing the round as the barrel is returning to battery and the ingenious feed mechanism allows two different types of ammunition to be instantly available at the breech by the changing of a lever. The three-way mechanism permits a container of ammunition to be ready above the feed system with, if required, a third type of round. Finally, if needed, the gun will fire alternately from each belt, thus providing a mixture of projectiles from belts containing one type each. A recent configuration of the gun offered is the Hs669N from AS Konsberg Vapenfabrik in Norway.

The armour-piercing ammunition is claimed to defeat 320 mm of armour plate at 1000m, which is very good for a 20 mm round. There is the usual range of ammunition available, including HE.

In service with the West German forces and on trial in other countries.

MK 20 Rh202 HMG

Wz43 heavy machine gun

Manufacturer: **State factories (Poland)**

See the SG34 and SGM.

In service with the Polish forces.

DShK 38/46 heavy machine gun

Manufacturer: **State factories (USSR)**

Calibre	12·7 mm × 108 mm
Dimensions	Length 158·5 cm Barrel length 107 mm
Weight	35·5 kg
Effective range	2000 m 1000 m (anti-aircraft)
Operation	Gas
Type of fire	Automatic
Muzzle velocity	860 m/sec
Sight	Front—post with ears Rear—leaf
Feed system	250 round link belt
Cyclic rate	540–600 rpm
Barrel change	Yes

The DShK 38/46 is the standard heavy machine gun of most European and Asian communist countries. The weapon may be mounted either on a vehicle, or on a wheeled mount which may be converted for use in the anti-aircraft role by removing the wheels and unfolding the legs. A special anti-aircraft ring sight is available for use in this configuration.

The action of the weapon is of the Degtyarev type which is locked, using flaps cammed by the carrier, into recesses in the receiver. The feed mechanism of the DShK 38/46 is of the normal shuttle type, and may be adapted to left- or right-hand feed. The barrel is detachable and is fitted with a unique muzzle brake. A quadruple-mounted version of the gun is produced by

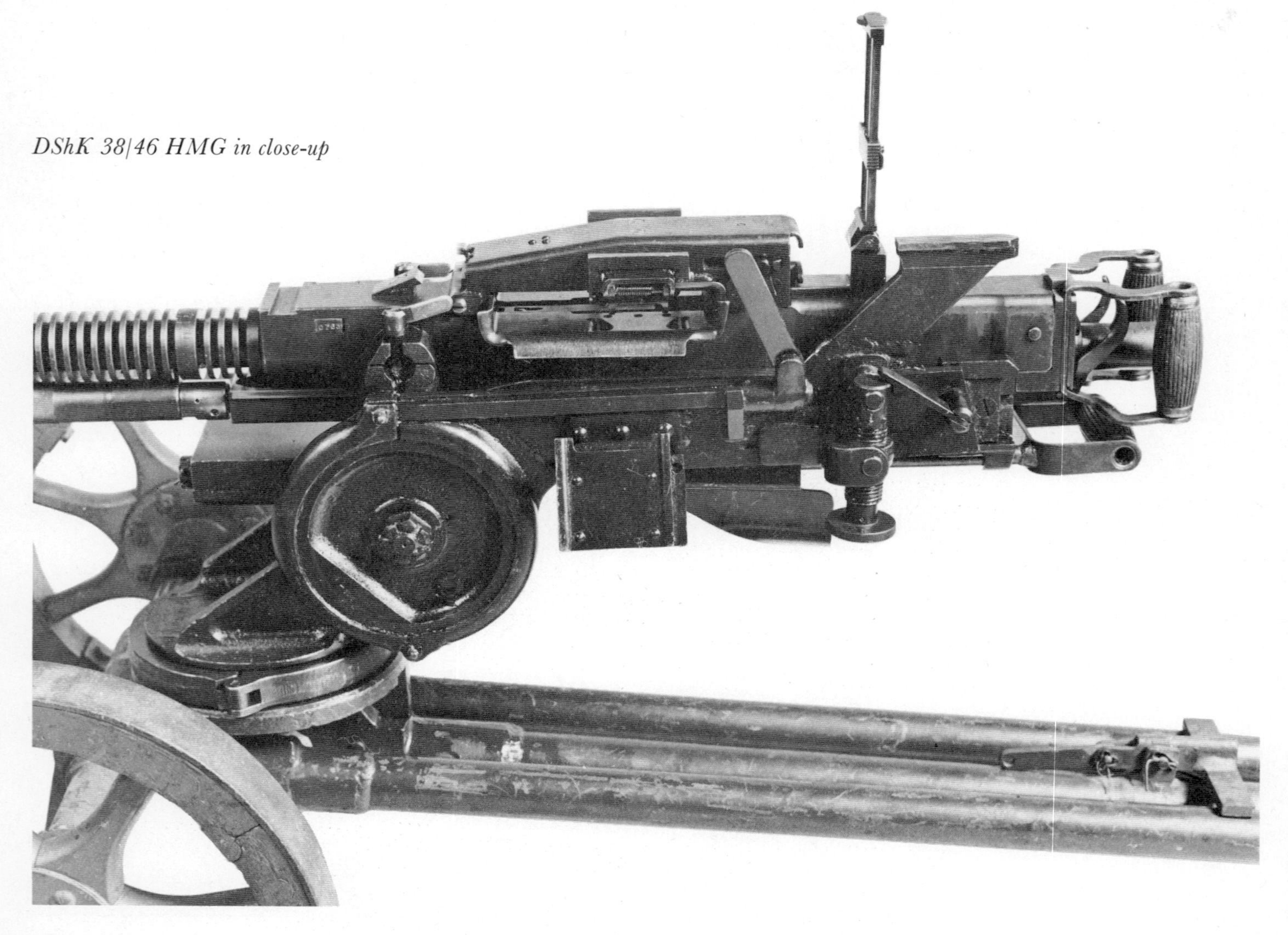

DShK 38/46 HMG in close-up

the Czechs as a light, wheeled anti-aircraft weapon against targets travelling at up to 930 kph.

The communist Chinese version DShK 38/46 is known as the type 54 heavy machine gun.

In service with the Soviet, other Warsaw Pact and most other communist forces.

DShK 38/46 HMG

KPV heavy machine gun

Manufacturer: **State factories (USSR)**

Calibre	14·5 cm
Dimensions	Length 200 cm Barrel length 135 cm
Weight	48·9 kg
Effective range	1100 m
Operation	Recoil
Muzzle velocity	990 m/sec
Feed system	100 round metal link belt
Cyclic rate	600 rpm

This is a modern automatic weapon well suited to both ground and anti-aircraft use. It was designed in the mid-1950s to use the ammunition developed for the anti-tank rifles of World War II, and this gives it a formidable punch when attacking armour. The gun is unusual among Soviet machine guns in that it locks the bolt by turning it and engaging lugs on the bolt-head with the sides of the breech. The recoil operation is also a departure from the normal gas one but has obviously been designed to allow a rapid and easy barrel-change.

The KPV has been made in large numbers and is well distributed among the Warsaw Pact armies. In its AA form it is paired or quadrupled and is then known as the ZPU–2 or ZUP–4. The lighter version is the ZPU–2 which was encountered in quantity in Vietnam, where it claimed a substantial number of US aircraft of all types. Against aircraft the effective range is almost doubled to 2000 m, which makes it especially formidable. The more usual manner of use now is to mount the gun, either singly or in pairs, on Soviet armoured personnel carriers for use as light anti-armour guns.

In service with the Soviet and many other Warsaw Pact forces.

Browning M2 heavy machine gun

Manufacturer: **Colt Industries, Marlin–Rockwell Corporation, Springfield Arsenal and others (United States)**

Calibre	·50 in
Dimensions	Length 164·3 cm (M2 144·7 cm) Barrel length 114·3 cm (M2 91·4 cm)
Weight	38·2 kg (M2 29·9 kg)
Effective range	1400 m
Operation	Recoil
Muzzle velocity	890 m/sec (M2 884 m/sec)
Sight	Front—blade Rear—open U or aperture
Feed system	100 round metallic link belt
Cyclic rate	400–500 rpm

This gun is a scaled-up version of the ·30 model Browning. It was originally developed in the last days of World War I as an anti-aircraft weapon for front line trenches. The first issues were made in 1921 and resembled the ·30 gun in almost every particular, including the water-cooled barrel. Shortly afterwards a lighter and handier air-cooled version appeared and this is the M2. The barrel for the M2 proved to be too light and a heavy barrel was introduced, hence the HB in the designation. This was a much more robust barrel and it is the most common one found today.

Some models of the M2HB have had their rate of fire accelerated to as high as 700 rpm, but at this speed the barrel soon heats up and has to be changed, but for AA work this can be accepted. The most frequent use of the gun in recent years has been as the armament on soft-skinned light vehicles or armoured personnel carriers. In this role it provides a valuable back-up to the ·30 guns which are usually carried on the same vehicles.

The armour penetration of the bullet is low by modern standards, but it is extremely damaging against wheeled transport and light fortifications. Against troops in the open, it is less effective due to its low rate of fire, and it is usually kept in reserve when these targets appear. As an AA weapon it is effective when used in pairs or fours to increase the practical rate of fire, and the heavy bullet is very damaging to light aircraft and helicopters.

The Browning is still widely used in the US Army and in many other armies, notably those in the centre and south of the American continent, but off-shore sales have spread it to all corners of the Western world in one form or the other.

In service with United States and many Western forces.

Browning M2 HMG

Mortars

The mortar is a weapon in which the main recoil force is transmitted directly to the ground through a base plate attached to the rear of the barrel. It is this lack of a recoil system which distinguishes a mortar from all other guns and howitzers which fire explosive shell. It is no new invention. Mortars have been in service since the earliest guns—the first recorded instance of their use being in the Siege of Constantinople in 1451, when one or two large guns were upturned and used to throw stone balls in a high trajectory on to the decks of ships. After that date, mortars continued as an artillery, or ship-board, piece of ordnance and they were all large and heavy.

Infantry had no use for these early mortars, and indeed they had hardly any need of them since the guns were always close to them supplementing the fire of the muskets with round shot and grape. The arrival of the modern rifled guns with their long range brought a change to the intimate close support provided by the smooth-bore gunner, and in World War I the infantry hardly saw its supporting artillery at all. It was this war which saw the re-introduction of the mortar to the battlefield, its operators being mainly infantrymen. When the opposing forces were dug in within a few hundred yards of each other, a weapon was needed which would throw projectiles, and preferably big projectiles, into the enemy trenches. For this the mortar was ideal and in no time a number of curious—and dangerous—equipments were being made to throw containers of high-explosive across no-man's-land. The high trajectory of these mortars meant that their projectiles fell in an almost vertical straight line and if the range had been correctly estimated no trench was proof against them. But they were still heavy and clumsy, and the rate of fire was pitifully slow.

Sir Wilfred Stokes, who was the managing director of a firm of manufacturers of agricultural machinery, changed all this in 1915. He produced the prototype of what has become the standard infantry mortar throughout the world. The Stokes mortar was a simple tube of good quality steel mounted on a flat steel base-plate and supported at the muzzle end by a bipod which was adjustable in elevation and azimuth by means of screws. At the breech was a fixed firing pin, while the propellant was contained in a cartridge in the tail of the bomb. To fire the mortar the bomb was dropped down the barrel tail first. By this means a very high rate of fire could be achieved since the only delay between rounds was the time needed for the bomb to fall down the barrel and for the loader to put another in at the muzzle. All but a very few mortars use the Stokes principle today.

After World War I the use of Stokes-type mortars spread rapidly and, by 1939, all the first-line armies had one or more types of mortar in service. World War II gave a great impetus to their use and manufacture since they provided a useful source of close support fire for infantry, and the control and handling of them passed into the hands of infantry battalions, except for the large versions which remained artillery pieces in all armies.

All light and medium mortars can be manpacked and so can be taken nearly everywhere a man can move. They are reasonably cheap to make and to maintain. The rate of fire can be very high for short periods, as many as 20 rounds per minute being achievable: a platoon of 81 mm mortars can put down a heavier weight of metal on the target than can a battery of field guns—though only for a short time. Concealment of a mortar is generally easy, and the control of the fire is straightforward and does not require complicated survey techniques as with a gun. By being sited inside the infantry battalion area, the response to fire requests is rapid and the high angle fire allows targets behind cover to be engaged.

The disadvantages are less apparent, but exist all the same. The range of most mortars is short for present day engagements, and efforts to increase the range generally end by making the mortar larger and heavier and more like a howitzer. Until recently, accuracy was poor because there had to be 'windage' around the bomb when it was in the barrel to allow it to drop down quickly on to the firing pin. This 'windage' also allowed the propellant gas to escape round the bomb on firing and gave rise to varying ballistics and a spread of shot on the target. However, such loose-fitting bombs were not unduly expensive to make and so the inaccuracy could be compensated to some extent by firing more of them. This situation has now partially changed. Modern mortars still use a loose-fitting bomb—but with a plastic driving band which expands on firing to fit the bore so that accuracy is now very good. Although the mortar is reasonably cheap, the ammunition nowadays is not. Modern bombs are made to very fine tolerances and so are expensive. Moreover, they are heavy and awkward to carry and, although three men can carry a medium mortar on their backs, they may have to be followed by a long line of other men carrying the ammunition. Helicopters, however, are reducing the need for manpacking on the modern battlefield.

Mortars are generally classified in three sizes, light, medium and heavy. Light mortars appeared in the 1920s to provide intimate support to the infantry platoon and company and to provide a greater range and effectiveness than could the various rifle-mounted grenade launchers which came into service in World War I. Most of these light mortars survive, though their use is declining as other weapons replace them. The simplest light mortar was, and still is, the British 2 in. This is a piece of straight tube with a minimal base plate and a simple trigger mechanism, as the bomb is not fired by the Stokes principle. There is no sight and aiming is by eye and judgement. The range is about 500 m and the consistency good. At the other end of the scale is the 60 mm family developed from a French design. Some of these weigh almost 18 kg and have a maximum range of 1500 m. Not only are they too heavy for a platoon, but the maximum range is too great for a platoon's needs and is generally wasted. More than 1000 m range requires some sort of fire controller to correct the fall of shot, and this is absent in the 60 mm field. Most of these complicated light mortars have now fallen into disuse, though some remain in the armies of the emergent nations. The 2 in is retained in the British and Commonwealth armies for smoke and illumination purposes.

Medium mortars are generally battalion weapons and their calibre varies between 70 mm and 90 mm. In general, 80–82 mm covers the majority of all medium mortar calibres around the world. The Western nations tend towards 81 mm, and the Soviet Bloc 82 mm. It has been said that this extra 1 mm gives the Soviets the advantage in that they can fire Western bombs whereas the reverse is not possible. Just how much this matters is very questionable. All these medium mortars have roughly similar characteristics and performances. The maximum range is about 4000 m, the weight of the bomb is about 4·5 kg–5·4 kg, the total weight of the mortar is about 45 kg and it breaks down into three manpack loads. In most armies there is a platoon of six to the battalion and in mechanised battalions the mortars are carried in personnel carriers with open tops so that the mortar can be fired from the vehicle without it having to be dismounted. These mechanised mortars are very formidable since their mobility is only limited by their vehicle and the crew can fire from what is virtually a prepared position within seconds of halting. The lethality of the modern bomb is good and the casing breaks up into a large number of fragments when it explodes. The smoke rounds carry a useful load of smoke composition and the illuminating types can usually provide a light source of up to half a million candle power which will burn for half a minute.

The modern medium mortar probably offers the best compromise between weight, bulk and effectiveness for all of the mortar family and it is no accident that there is a great similarity in their sizes. Heavy mortars, on the other hand, are less popular and except for special purposes they are not so attractive as the medium. A heavy mortar is generally taken to be one that is over 100 mm in calibre. The most usual calibre is 120 mm and there are several different makes of this size. Britain used to have a 4·2 in (roughly 107 mm) mortar and the United States still has. These heavy mortars are too big and heavy for the infantry, except in rare instances, and they are the responsibility of the artillery or other specialists. Most armies which employ them man them with heavy mortar companies and deploy them as short range artillery in support of infantry, or use them for special purposes such as laying heavy concentrations of chemicals or smoke. One notable exception to this rule is the Israeli Army which employs mortars of up to 160 mm in the infantry close support role.

JOHN WEEKS

M48 medium mortar

Manufacturer: **State factories (Czechoslovakia)**

Calibre	82 mm
Barrel length	135 cm
Baseplate dimensions	63 cm diameter
Weight in firing position	60 kg
Carriage weight	60 kg
Range	4000 m
Rate of fire	8–10 rpm
Operation	Automatic
Sight	Optical
Ammunition	HE (3·3 kg)
Crew	3

The Czech 82 mm mortar M48 is another mortar developed with guerrilla warfare in mind. It breaks down easily into three man-pack loads and incorporates the novel feature of a tiny fixed baseplate which allows the normal circular baseplate to be dispensed with on hard ground. The carrying handle on the muzzle cover aids transportation, especially when the mortar has to be moved, hot, in action. The elevating and traversing mechanism and sights, employed for ease of manipulation, are larger than those of most other mortars of this size.

In service with Czechoslovak and various South-East Asian and Middle East forces.

M31 light mortar

Manufacturer: **State factories (People's Republic of China)**

See the M2 and M1935.

In service with the communist Chinese and North Vietnamese forces and the Vietcong.

Type 63 light mortar

Manufacturer: **State factories (People's Republic of China)**

Calibre	60 mm
Barrel length	61 cm
Bipod length	56 cm
Baseplate dimensions	25·4 cm diameter
Weight in firing position	12·3 kg
Range	1530 m
Rate of fire	15–20 rpm
Operation	Automatic
Sight	Optical
Ammunition	HE
Crew	2

The type 63 communist Chinese 60 mm mortar was developed from the French Stokes-Brandt mortar of the same calibre, which was used by the nationalist Chinese. With the emphasis on portability in guerrilla warfare, however, the type 63 is lighter, smaller all round and has one recoil cylinder only, and yet its rate of fire and range are the same as those of the French mortar. The entire weapon folds together for carriage, the baseplate and bipod beneath the barrel, and can be easily transported in rough country by its carrying handle by one man, while the second crewman carries the ammunition.

In service with the communist Chinese, North Vietnamese, Viet Cong, Pathet Lao and Albanian forces.

60 mm (Type 63) mortar

Type 53 medium mortar

Manufacturer: **State factories (People's Republic of China)**

See the Soviet M1937 (new type) mortar.

Type 55 heavy mortar

Manufacturer: **State factories (People's Republic of China)**

See the Soviet M1943 mortar.

M1935 light mortar

Manufacturer: **Stokes-Brandt (France)**

See the M2, and M31 (People's Republic of China).

In service.

60 mm commando mortar

Manufacturer: **Hotchkiss-Brandt (France)**

Calibre	60 mm
Barrel length	65 cm
Overall length	68 cm (automatic), 86·1 cm (manual)
Weight in firing position	7·7 kg (automatic), 10 kg (manual)
Range	1050 m (charge 2)
Rate of fire	Variable
Operation	Manual or automatic
Sight	White line
Ammunition	Mk61 HE (with V9 fuse) coloured HE, Mk61 smoke, Mk 63 illuminating and practice
Crew	1

This mortar has been designed for either automatic or manual fire and is simple to operate.

In both automatic and controlled fire configurations the weapon is equipped with a carrying sling and muzzle cover. In the automatic mode the tube is equipped with a breech baseplate incorporating a fixed firing pin. In the controlled mode a reduced-sized rectangular baseplate is fixed into the breech block and the weapon is fired by pulling a lanyard. Sighting is by means of the white line on the barrel.

In service with some ex-French colonial forces.

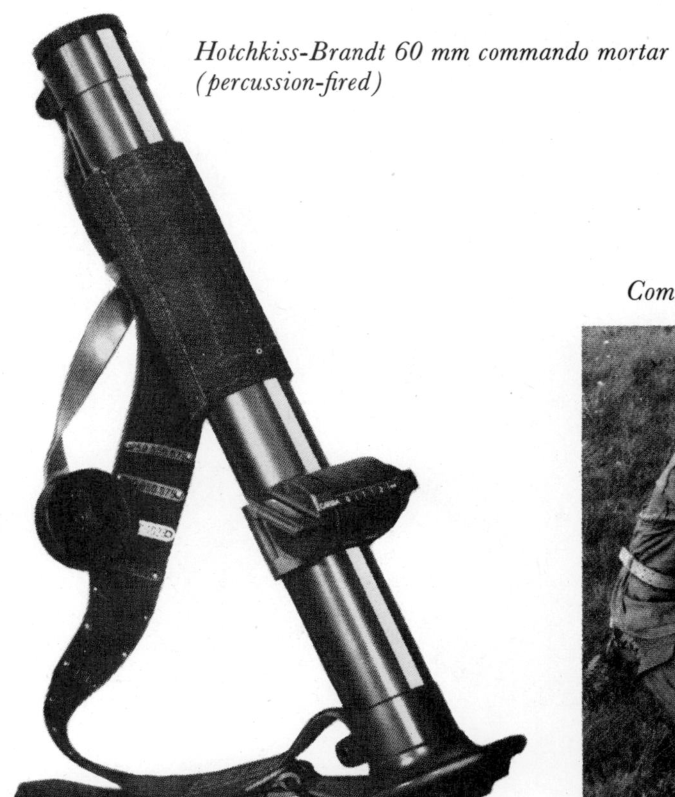

Hotchkiss-Brandt 60 mm commando mortar (percussion-fired)

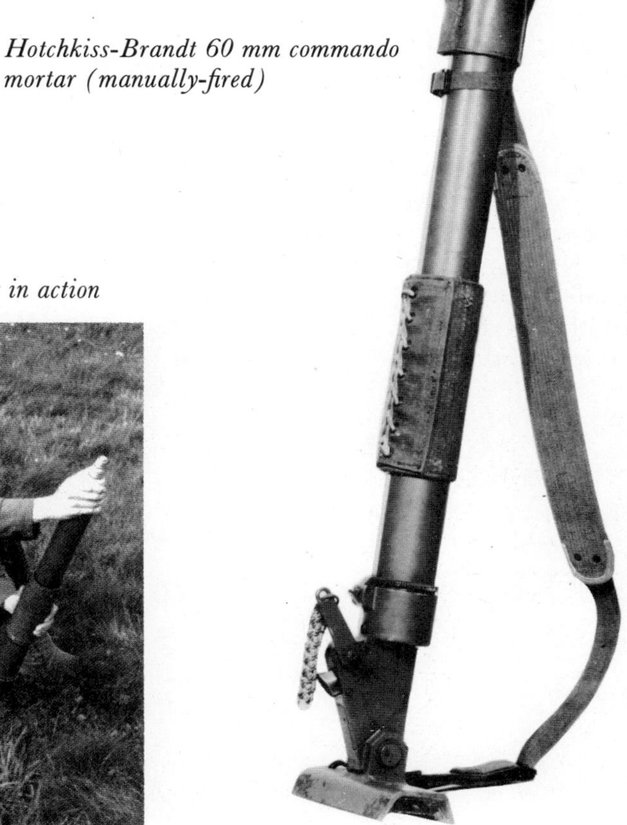

Hotchkiss-Brandt 60 mm commando mortar (manually-fired)

Commando mortar in action

MO-60-63 light mortar

Manufacturer: **Hotchkiss-Brandt (France)**

Calibre 60 mm
Barrel length 72·4 cm (with breech)
Weight 3·8 kg
Bipod weight 5 kg
Baseplate weight 6 kg
Weight in firing position 14·8 kg
Range 2000 m
Rate of fire 25 rpm
Operation Automatic
Sight Cross-levelling collimator
Ammunition Mk 61 HE (with V9 fuse), coloured HE, Mk 61 smoke, Mk 63 illuminating, practice, and old Brandt and United States 60 mm bombs
Crew 3

The MO-60-63 is a conventionally designed mortar. It can be manpacked by one man quite easily, though more usually by two. One man carries the baseplate and the second the barrel and bipod. The sight unit is of the cross-levelling type which does not have to be removed for firing, and the baseplate permits 360 degree firing. This mortar will fire United States 60 mm bombs, old Brandt bombs, and the newer Mk 61 and Mk 63 range of bombs which are mentioned above with 60 mm commando mortar.

In service with the French and West German forces.

Hotchkiss-Brandt 60 mm mortar

MO-81-61C medium mortar

Manufacturer: **Hotchkiss-Brandt (France)**

Calibre 81 mm
Barrel length 115 cm
Barrel weight 12·4 kg
Bipod weight 12·2 kg
Baseplate weight 14·8 kg
Weight in firing position 39·4 kg
Range 4100 m
Rate of fire Variable
Operation Automatic
Sight Cross-level collimator
Ammunition M57D (with V19Pa fuse)
M57D coloured HE
M57D smoke
Mk 62 illuminating
M570 practice
Crew 3

MO-81-61 medium mortar

Manufacturer: **Hotchkiss-Brandt (France)**

Calibre 81 mm
Barrel length 145 cm
Barrel weight 14·5 kg
Bipod weight 12·2 kg
Baseplate weight 14·8 kg
Weight in firing position 41·5 kg

Hotchkiss-Brandt 81 mm mortar (long barrel)

Range	4100 m
Rate of fire	Variable
Operation	Automatic
Sight	Cross-level collimator
Ammunition	Mk 61 (with V19P fuse) Mk 61 coloured HE Mk 61 smoke Mk 68 illuminating (3·5 kg) Mk 61 practice
Crew	3

This 81 mm mortar has two barrel lengths, the short designated MO-81-61C and the long MO-81-61L. The weight of both versions is sufficiently low for them to be man-packed in three loads, or carried as a single load by a mule. The short-barrelled version fires the M57D range of ammunition (3·3 kg), consisting of HE, coloured explosive smoke and practice rounds, and the Mk 62 illuminating round (3·1 kg).

The Mk 61 range of ammunition (4·3 kg) is designed for the long-barrel mortar and consists of bombs similar to those of the M57D range. However, both mortars can fire both types of ammunition, taking range table conditions into account.

In service with the French and Yugoslav forces.

MO-120-60 (light) heavy mortar

Manufacturer: **Hotchkiss-Brandt (France)**

Calibre	120 mm
Barrel length	163·2 cm
Barrel weight	34 kg
Bipod weight	24 kg
Baseplate weight	36 kg
Weight in firing position	94 kg
Range	5500 m
Rate of fire	8–15 rpm
Operation	Automatic
Ammunition	PEPA (charge 4), M44 HE, PEPA/LP, coloured HE, Mk 62 illuminating, phosphorous smoke and practice
Crew	3

The MO-120-60 is the lightest of a range of 120 mm mortars manufactured by Hotchkiss-Brandt. Its total weight of 94 kg permits it to be broken down into a three-man load. It is a conventionally designed weapon with most refinements eliminated in order to reduce as much weight as possible. In addition the barrel weight of 34 kg indicates that it is thin-walled and the maximum charge – 4 – suggests that the barrel structure imposes limitation on range.

Nevertheless, a wide choice of ammunition is available for this weapon. The M44 HE bomb is the primary round; others include coloured HE, smoke, illuminating and training. In addition a range of secondary propelled rounds can be fired which helps compensate for the loss of range. The bombs weigh between 13·8 kg and 13 kg.

Hotchkiss-Brandt 120 mm (MO-120-60) mortar.

In service with the French and Argentinian forces.

MO-120-M65 heavy mortar

Manufacturer: **Hotchkiss-Brandt (France)**

Calibre	120 mm
Barrel length	164 cm with breech
Barrel weight	44 kg with breech
Bipod weight	24 kg
Baseplate weight	26 kg
Weight in firing position	104 kg
Carriage weight	40 kg
Range	9000 m
Rate of fire	8–12 rpm
Operation	Automatic or controlled
Ammunition	PEPA/LP HE (finned with additional propulsion) (13·4 kg), M44 HE (13 kg), practice, smoke and marking, and Mk 62 20 illuminating (13·6 kg)
Crew	2 or 3

The MO-120-M 65 is an attempt to combine some of the lightness of the MO-120-M 60 with the fire power of the MO-120-AM 50. Normal transportation is achieved by putting the weapon on a light trailer which can be towed by a vehicle or pulled by two men. However, due to the relatively light weight, it is possible to manpack the weapon in three roughly equal loads, using special harness.

This is a smooth-bored weapon fired from a tripod and baseplate and capable of either automatic of controlled operation. In addition, the breech is equipped with a safety device to prevent accidental percussion when, for example, the weapon is being unloaded. The weapon is capable of firing any 120 mm ammunition, including the PEPA/LP (projectile empermé à propulsion additionelle/longue portée) HE round with additional propulsion.

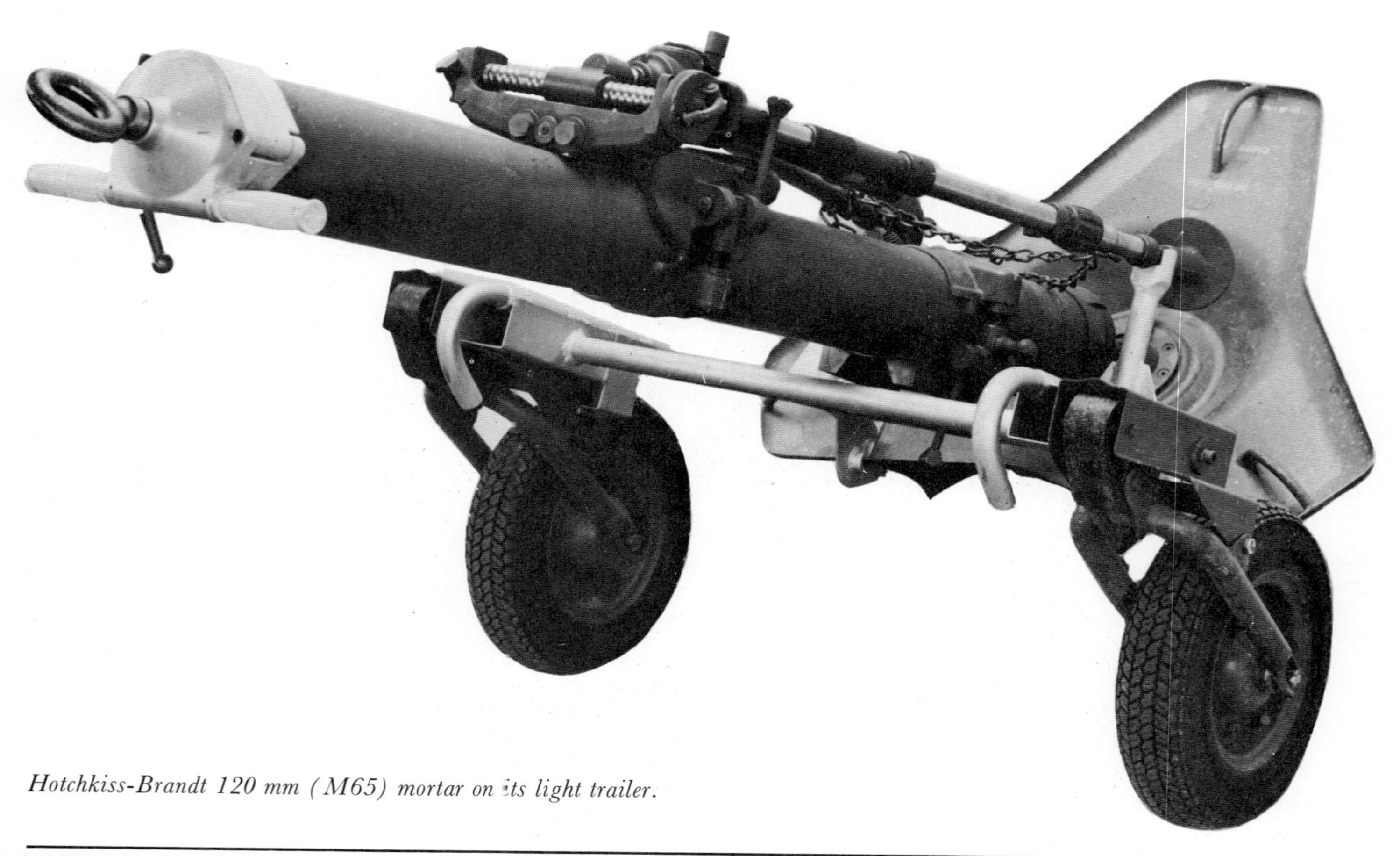

Hotchkiss-Brandt 120 mm (M65) mortar on its light trailer.

MO-120-AM50 heavy mortar

Manufacturer: **Hotchkiss-Brandt (France)**

Calibre	120 mm
Barrel length	174·6 cm with breech
Barrel weight	76 kg with towing ring
Baseplate weight	80 kg
Weight in firing position	402 kg or 242 kg (without undercarriage)
Carriage weight	86 kg
Range	9000 m
Rate of fire	8–12 rpm
Operation	Automatic or controlled
Ammunition	PEPA/LPHP (finned with additional propulsion) (13·4 kg), M 44 HE (13 kg), practice, smoke and marking, Mk 62 smoke (13 kg) and Mk 62 ED illuminating (13·6 kg)

Hotchkiss-Brandt 120 mm (AM50) mortar on its light trailer.

This weapon is a smooth-bore mortar capable of both automatic and controlled fire. Although a bipod is provided for greater stability in sustained fire, it is mounted on a pair of road wheels from which it can also be fired. In a travelling position a screw-on ring mount is attached to the muzzle end of the tube, and the whole unit is towed by a suitable vehicle. The road wheels are equipped with a special locking device to stop the weapon moving when it is fired without its bipod.

The AM50 fires the same range of ammunition as the other Hotchkiss-Brandt 120 mm mortars.

In service with the French forces.

MO-120-RT-61 heavy rifled mortar

Manufacturer: **Hotchkiss-Brandt (France)**

Calibre	120 mm
Barrel length	280 cm with breech
Barrel weight	114 kg
Baseplate weight	194 kg
Weight in firing position	582 kg
Carriage weight	257 kg
Range	13 000 m
Rate of fire	6–10 rpm
Operation	Automatic or controlled
Ammunition	PRPA (rifled with additional propulsion) HE (18·7 kg), PR 14 HE (18·7 kg), Preclair illuminating (15·7 kg and 1·5 m cp)
Crew	3

Hotchkiss-Brandt 120 mm (MO-120-RT-61) rifle mortar in action.

The Hotchkiss-Brandt 120 mm rifled mortar is among the largest mortars available today. It is mounted and towed on a specially designed pair of road wheels from which it is also fired. Stabilisation is achieved by the baseplate, which is effective both on hard and marshy ground. The manufacturers claim that the weapon can be bought into action in 1½ min and out again in 2 min.

This weapon is capable of either automatic or controlled fire and has its own range of ammunition. The PR 14 HE bomb is comparable in its effect to the standard 105 mm artillery shell. The bomb weighs 18·7 kg and has a maximum range of 8350 m. In addition, the PRPA (Projectile rayé à propulsion additionelle), which also weighs 18·7 kg, has a maximum range of 13 000 m due to the incorporation of a rocket motor which is initiated during flight. Firing of conventional ammunition requires the use of range conversion tables since the other Hotchkiss-Brandt bombs are calibrated for different barrel lengths. The barrel of this mortar is rifled from breech to muzzle with 40 grooves with a uniform twist of 10·5 degrees. The screw-on breech piece has a spherical ball butt flattened on one side and which is locked into a socket in the base plate. The firing mechanism is completely watertight and can be used submerged.

In service, and on trial with the French forces.

52 mm mortar

Manufacturer: **Israel Military Industries**

Calibre	52 mm
Barrel length	49 cm
Baseplate weight	1·3 kg
Weight in firing position	7·9 kg
Range	130 m–420 m
Rate of fire	20–35 rpm
Operation	Manual
Sight	White line for alignment
Ammunition	HE (10 kg) Smoke (9·2 kg) Illuminating (8 kg)
Ammunition packing	Wooden box of 18 rounds in 9 fibre containers grouped in packs of 3 with carrying slings
Crew	1

This is a small hand mortar used by Israeli infantry for close support. It is a smooth-bore, muzzle-loaded weapon operated by one man. The weapon is equipped with a fixed handle, instead of a wrap-around hand guard, and is fired manually by turning a knob which tensions a spring and then releases it causing a pin to strike the base of the round.

Three types of ammunition are available. A HE round, propelled by a base ignition cartridge containing 4 gm of ballistite powder and carrying a main charge of 150 gm of TNT. The smoke round contains 400 gm of composition which ignites after a delay of 7·5 sec, and emits dense smoke for about 100 sec. The para-illuminating round burns at 100,000 cp for at least 30 sec. The parachute opens after an 8 sec delay at a height of 100 m and a range of 350 m.

In service with the Israeli forces.

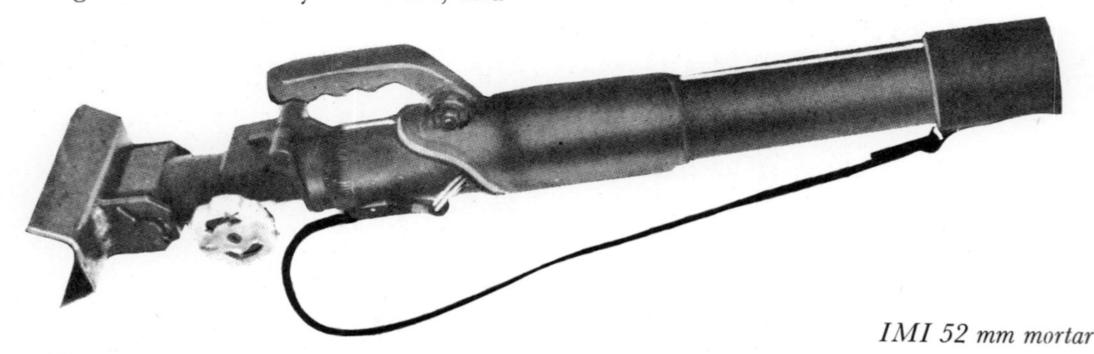

IMI 52 mm mortar

ECIA 60-C commando mortar

Manufacturer: **Esperanza y Cia SA (Spain)**

Calibre	60·7 mm
Barrel length	65 cm
Baseplate	Fixed
Weight in firing position	5 kg
Range	1070 m
Rate of fire	30 rpm
Operation	Automatic
Sight	Clip-on circular level with direct ranging
Ammunition	HE (1·4 kg) Smoke (1·43 kg) Illuminating (1·43 kg) Practice (1·43 kg)
Ammunition packing	25 rounds in individual containers packed into a wooden box
Crew	1

The 60 mm ECIA commando mortar is a small-bore hand mortar made from a special alloy. Its extremely light weight enables it to be carried and operated by one man, and it is intended for issue to infantry sub-units.

The fixed baseplate is not quite hemispherical, but is designed to enable the weapon to be fired from almost any position. The firing pin is screwed in through the baseplate to the tube and can be replaced as necessary. Unlike many hand mortars this one is equipped with a clip-on sight which consists of a circular level and direct ranging device. When not in use the sight is stowed in a box on the carrying sling. The sling is attached to the baseplate and a muzzle cap and the hand-protector sleeve are fitted to it.

Various types of ammunition are available: a fragmenting HE bomb with a damage radius of 50 m; smoke, illuminating, exercise and training bombs are available; also, possibly, a white phosphorus round. Twenty-five rounds are packed in individual containers with their auxiliary charges in a robust, waterproof, wooden box.

In service with the Spanish forces.

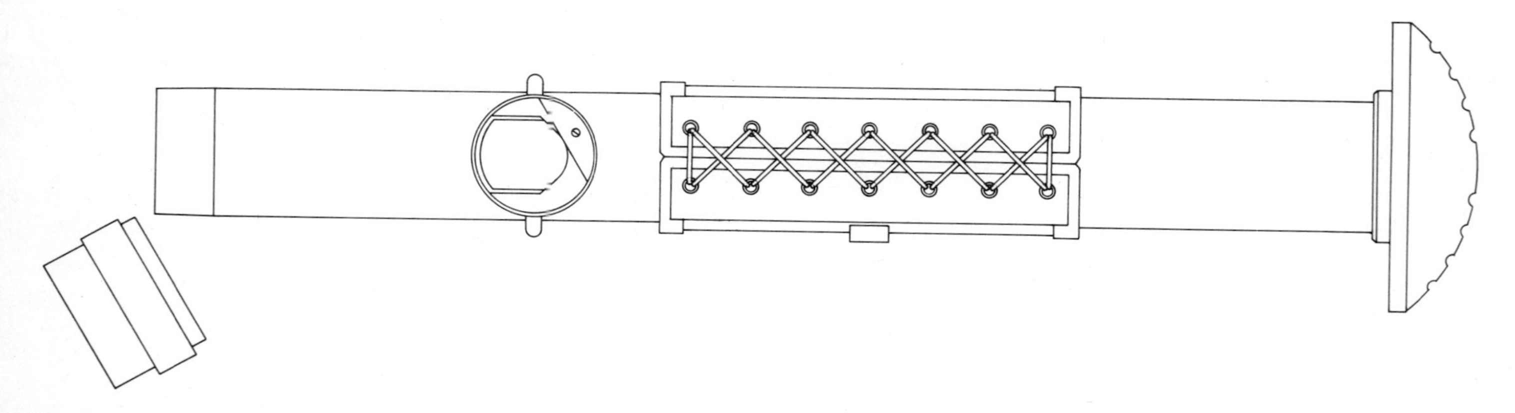

ECIA 60-C (commando) mortar

ECIA 60-L light mortar

Manufacturer: **Esperanza y Cia SA (Spain)**

Calibre	60·7 mm
Barrel length	65 cm
Weight in firing position	11·5 kg
Range	2100 m (at charge H)
Rate of fire	30 rpm
Operation	Automatic or manual
Sight	Optical self-levelling
Ammunition	HE (1·43 kg)
	HE (2·27 kg)
	Smoke (1·43 kg)
Ammunition packing	25 rounds in individual containers packed into a wooden box
Crew	2

The ECIA 60-L is a smooth-bore light mortar capable of manual or automatic fire. The entire weapon and its accessories weigh some 15 kg, and can be manpacked by one man.

Like the ECIA 60 mm commando mortar, the 60-L has a light barrel of special alloy with a very fine interior finish. The breech-block firing mechanism and mounting ball are fixed to the base of the breech block. The firing mechanism can be cocked for manual fire or locked for automatic. The rectangular baseplate is designed to bed firmly and distribute the recoil evenly over the surface. An adjustable socket joint for the ball mount enables the mortar to be traversed through 360 degrees without re-bedding the baseplate.

The folding tripod mount is made from high-strength alloy specially chosen for its low weight. A buffer joint connects the mount to the barrel collar so that the recoil does not displace the mount which has the elevation adjustment gear and a limited azimuth adjustment. An alloy barrel collar with an interior bronze lining slides quite freely on the barrel, thus giving the mount additional stability after firing.

The sight unit has pendular characteristics which cause it to swing automatically into an aiming position.

Two HE rounds are available for this mortar. The standard HE round is the same as that of the 60-L, while the other is a larger bomb containing 0·53 kg of TNT, but with a smaller range. Smoke, illuminating, practice and other rounds are available, but the manufacturer gives little information on them. Packaging of ammunition is the same as that of the 60-L.

In service with the Spanish forces.

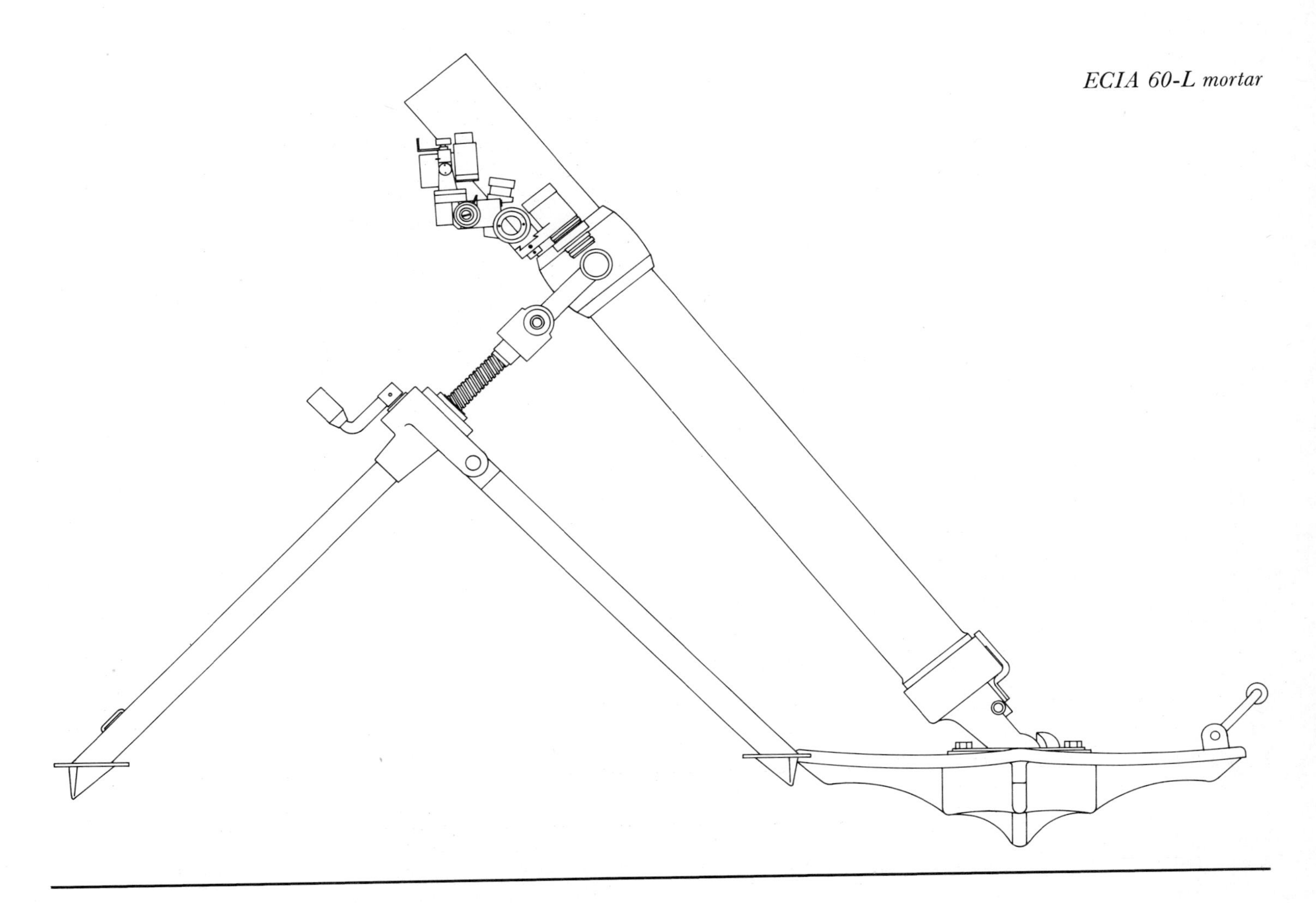

ECIA 60-L mortar

ECIA 81-L medium mortar

Manufacturer: **Esperanza y Cia SA (Spain)**

Calibre	81·35 mm
Barrel length	100 cm
Weight in firing position	43 kg
Range	4570 m
Rate of fire	15 rpm
Operation	Automatic or manual
Sight	Optical self-levelling
Ammunition	HE (4·1 kg) HE light (3·4 kg) Smoke (4·3 kg)
Ammunition packing	9 individual containers packed in a wooden box
Crew	3–4

The ECIA 81-L medium mortar follows the general pattern of the rest of the ECIA family. It has a smooth-bore barrel made from a special alloy, and the hexagonal baseplate allows a 360 degree traverse without being moved. The mortar can be manpacked by three men.

There are two HE rounds, one slightly lighter and with a reduced effect, a smoke bomb and a practice bomb.

In service with the Spanish forces.

ECIA 81-L mortar

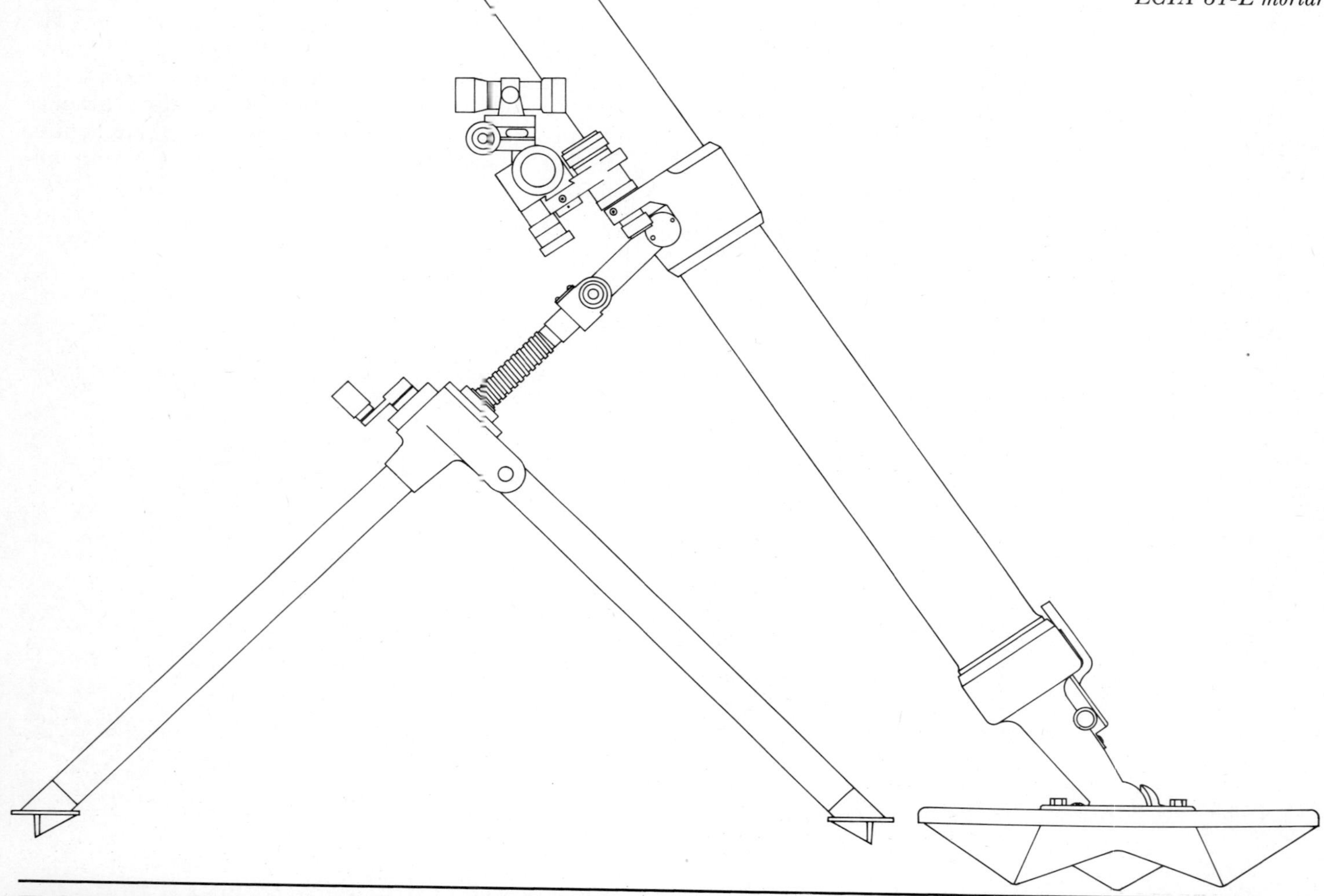

ECIA 105-L medium mortar

Manufacturer: **Esperanza y Cia SA (Spain)**

Calibre	105 mm
Barrel length	140 cm
Weight in firing position	97·6 kg
Carriage weight	Normal 205 kg (unloaded) Light 110 kg (unloaded)
Range	7000 m
Rate of fire	12 rpm
Operation	Automatic or manual
Sight	Optical self-levelling
Ammunition	HE (9·2 kg) Smoke (9·2 kg)
Ammunition packing	4 individual containers packed in a wooden box
Crew	4

This mortar is of similar design to the ECIA 81-L

mortar. The differences are in calibre, the strength of the various parts and a differently shaped baseplate, which is round in this case.

Due to the extra weight over the 81-L, two types of trailer have been designed for this weapon. The normal trailer is of box-type construction and is capable of carrying the complete weapon, its accessories and twelve rounds of ammunition. The light cart is designed for airborne operations, weighs about half and will carry the whole weapon, but no ammunition. Though it is normally transported on a trailer, this mortar can be carried by three men or by one mule.

The HE round has a damage radius of 150 m from its 1·75 kg charge of TNT. A smoke round is available.

In service with the Spanish forces.

ECIA 105-L mortar loaded on its normal transport cart

ECIA 105-L mortar loaded on its light cart

ECIA 120-SL heavy mortar

Manufacturer: **Esperanza y Cia SA (Spain)**

Calibre	120 m
Barrel length	160 cm
Weight in firing position	112 kg
Carriage weight	131 kg
Range	5000 m (N type round) 6660 m (L type round)
Rate of fire	12 rpm
Operation	Automatic or manual
Sight	Optical cross-levelling pendular type
Ammunition	N type HE and smoke (16·7 kg) L type HE and smoke (13·2 kg)
Ammunition packing	2 individual containers packed in a wooden box
Crew	Usually 4

The ECIA 120-SL has a similar configuration to other ECIA mortars, such as the 81-L and 105-L. A feature of this mortar, not apparent on the other members of the ECIA family, is an adjustable chain for limiting the leg spread of the tripod. Although normal transport is by trailer, the manufacturer claims that it is possible for the weapon to be manpacked by three men.

The types of ammunition designated N and L are available for this weapon. The N type bombs are heavier and longer, and carry a bigger charge (3·2 kg of TNT or smoke composition), then the L bomb (2·3 kg). The range of the N type is less at 5000 m against 6660 m of the L type. Packaging of ammunition is the same in each case. Two rounds are packed in individual containers in a wooden case.

Fragmentation of 120 mm calibre shell N. (Effective damage radius 150 m)

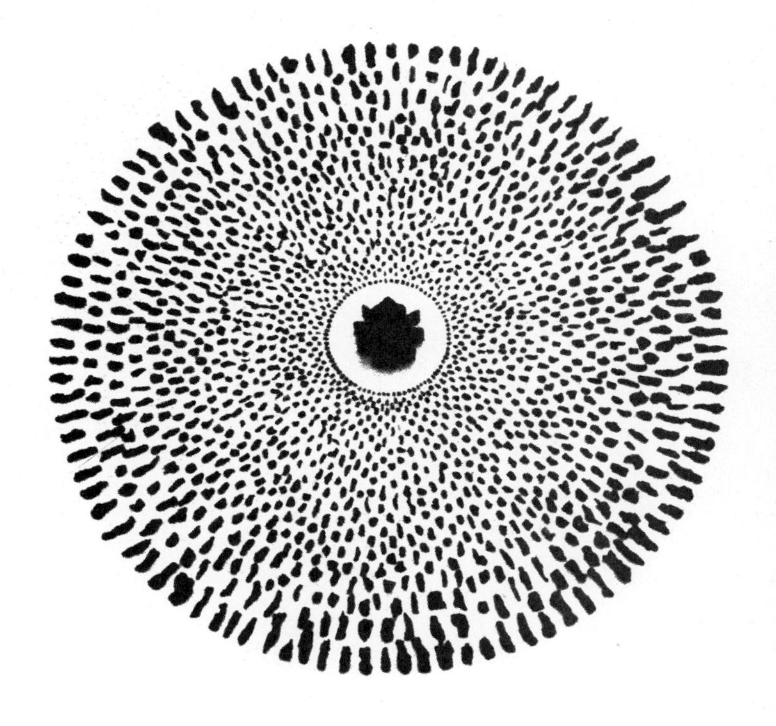

In service with the Spanish forces.

ECIA 120-L heavy mortar

Manufacturer: **Esperanza y Cia SA (Spain)**

Calibre	120 mm
Barrel length	160 cm
Weight in firing position	180 kg
Carriage weight	146 kg
Range	5700 m (N type round) 7100 m (L type round)
Rate of fire	10 rpm
Operation	Automatic or manual
Sight	Optical self-levelling
Ammunition	N type HE and smoke (16·7 kg) L type HE and smoke (13·2 kg)
Ammunition packing	2 individual containers packed in a wooden box
Crew	4

The ECIA 120-L is a longer range version of the 120-SL. The basic configuration is the same, although it has a larger baseplate and a heavier barrel. It fires the same ammunition as the 120-SL and is transported on a trailer. It is too heavy for man-packing. The other difference between the two mortars is that the 120-L does not have the adjustable chains to limit tripod leg spread.

In service with the Spanish forces.

M1937 (new type) medium mortar

Manufacturer: **State factories (USSR)**

Calibre	82 mm
Barrel length	122 cm
Baseplate dimensions	50 cm diameter
Barrel weight	19·6 kg
Bipod weight	20·1 kg
Baseplate weight	21·3 kg
Weight in firing position	56 kg
Range	3040 m (minimum 100 m)
Rate of fire	15–25 rpm
Operation	Automatic
Sight	MPM-44
Ammunition	HE (3·05 kg) and smoke
Crew	5

M1937 82 mm mortar being positioned for firing

M1937 82 mm mortar

Of the several 82 mm mortars produced by the USSR, immediately before and during World War II (the M1937, M1941, M1942/43 and M1943), only the M1937 has survived, modernised, to be the standard Warsaw Pact 82 mm mortar. There is little variation in the models of this mortar manufactured by the different communist countries, although some, but not the USSR, do produce an ingenious two-wheeled carriage which also transports the ammunition. The Chinese copy of the weapon is the 82 mm mortar type 53.

Whilst the 82 mm mortar is now rarely encountered in infantry units of the Soviet Army, being found mainly in airborne units, this mortar is still widely used by the infantry of the other Warsaw Pact countries, communist China and Albania. In the Soviet Army the infantry mortar is now the 120 mm mortar M1943. The 82 mm mortar M1937 (new type) and, indeed, all of its predecessors can fire the 81 mm mortar ammunition manufactured in many western countries.

In service with the Soviet, all other Warsaw Pact, communist Chinese, Albanian, North Vietnamese forces and the Viet Cong.

M107/M1938 heavy mortars

Manufacturer: **State factories (USSR)**

Calibre	107 mm
Barrel length	167 cm
Bipod length	120 cm
Baseplate dimensions	94 cm diameter
Weight in firing position	170 kg
Carriage weight	340 kg
Range	6300 m (minimum 800 m)
Rate of fire	10–15 rpm
Operation	Manual or automatic
Sight	Optical
Ammunition	Heavy HE (9 kg), light HE, smoke and chemical (7·9 kg)
Crew	6

The 107 mm mortar of both marks, M1938 and M107, is a scaled-down version of the Soviet 120 mm mortar, reduced in weight and size to suit its normal role, as the regimental mortar of mountain units. The mortar is usually transported by pack animals in difficult terrain, but is towed on a two-wheeled carriage over normal roads. For animal-packing, the weapon breaks down into three loads, barrel, bipod and baseplate.

The M107 is the improved model of this mortar and has replaced the M1938 in the Soviet Army, although the earlier version is still to be found in the non-Soviet Warsaw Pact countries and in South-East Asia.

In service with the Soviet, some other Warsaw Pact and North Vietnamese forces.

M1938 heavy mortar

Manufacturer: **State factories (USSR)**

Calibre	120 mm
Barrel length	185 cm
Baseplate dimensions	100 cm diameter
Weight in firing position	170 kg
Carriage weight	340 kg
Range	5700 m (minimum 400 m)
Rate of fire	12–15 rpm
Operation	Manual or automatic
Sight	MP-41/MP-42 collimating sight
Ammunition	HE (15·4 kg), smoke (16 kg), incendiary (16·7 kg)
Crew	5 or 6

The 120 mm mortar M1938 was the standard Soviet infantry mortar until it was replaced recently by the 120 mm M1943. A unique design when originated, the mortar can be quickly broken down into three parts, barrel, bipod and baseplate, for movement over short distances. For normal travel the whole weapon folds together and is towed on a two-wheeled carriage or, if necessary, can be animal-packed in its three parts. The mortar can be either drop- or trigger-fired by lanyard, as required, and an anti-double-loading device is provided for attachment to the muzzle. See also the M1943 mortar.

In service with the Soviet, all other Warsaw Pact, communist Chinese and Albanian forces.

M1943 heavy mortar

Manufacturer: **State factories (USSR and People's Republic of China)**

Calibre	120 mm
Barrel length	185 cm
Baseplate dimensions	100 cm diameter
Weight in firing position	170 kg
Carriage weight	340 kg
Range	5700 m (minimum 400 m)
Rate of fire	12–15 rpm
Operation	Manual or automatic
Sight	MP-41/MP-42 collimating sight
Ammunition	HE (15·4 kg), smoke (16 kg), incendiary (16·7 kg)
Crew	5 or 6

The 120 mm mortar M1943 has virtually replaced the M1938 as the regimental mortar of the Soviet infantry and is found, with the M1938, in the other countries listed, being manufactured also in communist China as the 120 mm mortar type 55.

Whilst the ballistic and performance details and methods of handling are the same for both models, the outward appearance differs slightly: the shock absorber cylinders of the M1943 are much longer than those of the M1938, and in the later model the elevating and traversing gear is rather more sophisticated.

The outer casing of the HE ammunition can be made of either wrought or cast iron, the latter being more effective against personnel but being slightly reduced in maximum range.

In service with the Soviet, all other Warsaw Pact, communist Chinese and Albanian forces.

M1943 120 mm mortar

2 inch mortar

Manufacturer: **Ministry of Defence (United Kingdom)**

Calibre	50 mm
Barrel length	55 cm
Weight in firing position	10·5 kg
Range	430 m
Rate of fire	5 rpm
Operation	Manual
Sight	White line on barrel
Ammunition	HE (0·9 kg), signal, illuminating
Ammunition packing	6 rounds in fibre container, 3 containers in a steel box
Crew	1–2

2 inch mortar team in action.

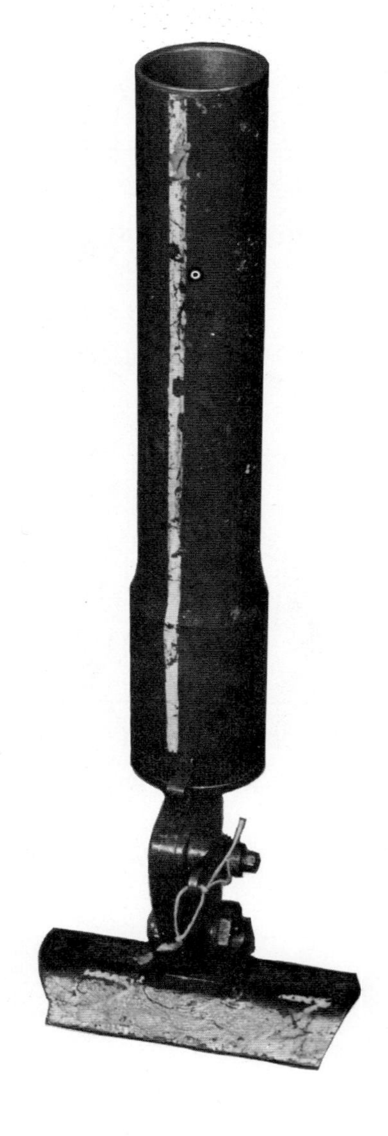

2 inch mortar

The 2 in mortar was once the main support weapon of the British infantry weapon platoon. Latterly, and as a result of the introduction of weapons like the Carl Gustav (see Missiles and Rockets), it is now virtually obsolete, though still used for illumination and signal purposes. During its years of service, a number of Marks were produced, but the variations are now history. The weapon is basically a smooth-bored, hand-held, manually-fired weapon, capable of launching a 0·9 kg HE bomb out to approximately 430 m. Though stocks of HE bombs are still thought to exist, the only rounds issued today are illuminating and smoke rounds. The latest Mark of 2 in mortar has no fixed sighting system, but merely a white line painted on the top of the barrel which gives the firer a means of judging direction. Different ranges are achieved by varying the angle of the barrel, using high or low angle as necessary.

In service with the United Kingdom forces.

3 inch mortar

Manufacturer: **Ministry of Defence (United Kingdom)**

Calibre	76 mm
Barrel length	129·5 cm
Weight in firing position	56 kg
Range	1500 m
Rate of fire	10 rpm
Operation	Automatic
Sight	Optical dial
Ammunition	HE (4·5 kg), smoke (4·5 kg)
Ammunition packing	3 rounds in a fibre carrier, 3 carriers in steel box
Crew	3

3 inch mortar

This weapon has been replaced by the 81 mm L1A1 medium mortar, but is still to be found in some Middle East countries. The 3 in is a smooth-bore mortar designed to give a good rate of sustained fire, yet be light enough for three men to carry. The weapon consists, basically, of a steel tube, screwed to a breech block, containing all the necessary elevation and traversing gears and a rectangular machined baseplate. Three types of ammunition were available for this weapon—HE, smoke and illuminating.

In service in the Middle East, but obsolescent.

81 mm L1A1 mortar

Manufacturer: **Ministry of Defence (United Kingdom)**

Calibre	81 mm	*Rate of fire*	15 rpm
Barrel length	128 cm	*Operation*	Automatic
Barrel weight	12·3 kg	*Sight*	Optical cross-levelling
Bipod length	114 cm	*Ammunition*	HE L15A3 (4·4 kg)
Bipod weight	11·8 kg		Smoke WP L19A1 (4·5 kg)
Baseplate dimensions	54·6 cm diameter		Practice L22A1 (4·4 kg)
Baseplate weight	11·4 kg	*Ammunition packing*	2 rounds per plastic container; 2 containers in a steel box
Weight in firing position	36·6 kg		
Range	5600 m	*Crew*	3

Firing the 81 mm mortar

This is the current medium mortar in service with the British forces and has seen action around the world. The weapon is operated by a crew of three, and is specifically designed to break down into three one-man loads, the heaviest load being the barrel, which weighs 12·3 kg.

The barrel is made of high-strength steel and has cooling fins incorporated to dissipate heat, and thus withstands sustained firing with maximum charges. The bipod mount is made of special steel and light alloys in order to combine strength with lightness. The elevating and traversing gear is sealed for long life and low maintenance. The baseplate is of Canadian origin, and is forged in light alloy with four deep webs. The C2 sight unit for this weapon is also of Canadian origin.

There are three types of ammunition available: the HE bomb (L15A3), the white phosphorous smoke round (L19A1) and a practice round, (L22A1).

In service with United Kingdom and Commonwealth forces.

T18E6 light mortar

Manufacturer: **Department of the United States Army**

Calibre	60 mm
Barrel length	56 cm
Baseplate	12·7 cm × 7·6 cm
Weight in firing position	9·1 kg
Range	750 m
Rate of fire	30 rpm
Operation	Manual
Ammunition	HE, smoke, illuminating

This novel type of mortar is designed to be used like a grenade launcher. The baseplate is, in effect, a small, curved shoulder-pad and a M15 grenade launcher-sight is fitted near the tube muzzle. The mortar is trigger-fired, using a lanyard connected to the tube base. The normal HE, smoke, illuminating and practice bombs can be used with an additional initial propellant and ignition cartridge. For transportation a sling is attached to the sight-bracket and shoulder-pad, making this mortar a portable and versatile weapon for ranges up to half a mile.

In service with the United States forces.

M2 light mortar

Manufacturer: **Department of the United States Army**

Calibre	60 mm
Barrel length	72·4 cm
Barrel weight	5·6 kg
Weight in firing position	19 kg
Range	1850 m
Rate of fire	30 rpm
Operation	Automatic
Ammunition	HE, smoke, illuminating

60 mm M2 mortar

The same mortar, with negligible differences, has been manufactured by three countries. It has a square, flat, pressed-steel baseplate with the toothed spade under the rear edge, the short smoothbore tube, two-piece traversing gear, elevating gear hand-crank and bipod with single-spiked collars. The differences lie in the markings, hand-cranks and bipod feet. The United States version (the M2) and the French version (the Stokes-Brandt M1953), the original, are identical (except for markings) and have steel bipod feet and a folding hand-crank. The Chinese version (the M31) has brass bipod feet and a fixed hand-crank. All three weapons are muzzle-loaded and fire HE, illuminating, and smoke bombs, but the range of the M2 is a little better than the other two mortars. The rate of fire quoted would drop to around 20 rpm if extended for any length of time. All three mortars can use the same ammunition, as can also the T18E6 and M19 mortars, with an ignition cartridge and four propellant charges.

In service with the United States, communist Chinese, Taiwanese, North and South Vietnamese forces and the Vietcong.

M19 light mortar

Manufacturer: **Department of the United States Army**

Calibre	60 mm
Barrel length	81·3 cm
Barrel weight	7·3 kg
Weight in firing position	19·1 kg
Range	2100 m
Rate of fire	20–30 rpm
Operation	Manual
Ammunition	HE, smoke, illuminating

The US 60 mm M19 mortar was designed to serve a limited purpose. With its light weight it can be very effective and delivers the same weight of shell as the similar but shorter M2 mortar an extra 270 m. The M19 is also a muzzle-loading, smoothbore weapon, but is trigger-fired. This and the extra tube length are really the only differences in appearance between the M19 and the M2, as the projecting trigger mechanism necessitates a narrow elongation of the tube base. The standard HE, smoke and illuminating rounds, interchangeable with the M2 and T18E6 mortars, are used, with an ignition cartridge and four propellant charges.

In service with the United States forces.

M1 medium mortar

Manufacturer: **Department of the United States Army**

Calibre	81 mm
Barrel length	127 cm
Barrel weight	20·2 kg
Bipod weight	19·2 kg
Baseplate weight	20·4 kg
Weight in firing position	60·1 kg
Range	3000 m
Rate of fire	20–30 rpm
Operation	Automatic
Ammunition	HE, HE light (3·2 kg), smoke, illuminating

Although at first sight there appears to be nothing to distinguish the M1 mortar from many other mortars of this size, there are two singular features incorporated in the rectangular baseplate—the base of the tube is received by any of a row of three ball-sockets (a feature shared by the French M44 mortar) and the single carrying-handle has a leather-covered grip. Otherwise the M1 is a standard smoothbore weapon, firing HE (light and heavy), illuminating and smoke (WP and FS) ammunition. The maximum range shown can only be achieved by the light (3·2 kg) HE rounds, all of the other bombs being capable of around 2300 m.

In service with the United States, South Vietnamese and certain Middle Eastern forces.

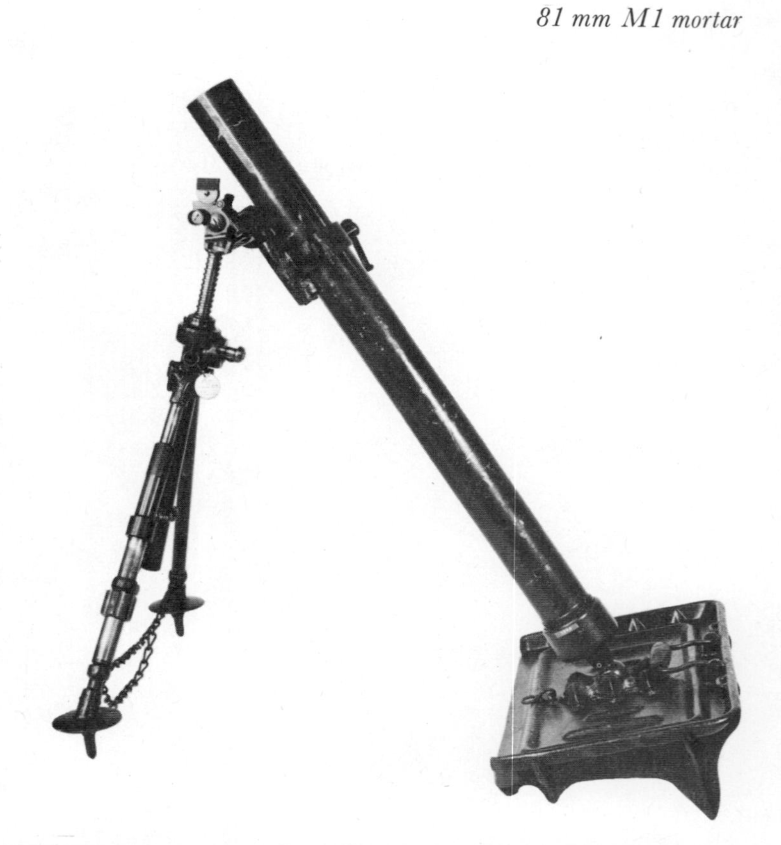

81 mm M1 mortar

M29 medium mortar

Manufacturer: **Department of the United States Army**

Calibre	81 mm
Barrel length	130 cm
Barrel weight	12·7 kg
Bipod weight	14 kg
Baseplate weight	21·7 kg
Weight in firing position	48·5 kg
Range	3500 m
Rate of fire	30 rpm
Ammunition	HE, HE light (3·2 kg), smoke, illuminating

The M29 81 mm mortar is lighter and more effective than its predecessor the M1, using a slightly longer barrel to fire exactly the same HE, smoke (FS and WP) illuminating rounds an extra 460 m. There are two slightly different versions, the M29 and M29E1, and both use two slightly differing bipod and baseplate assemblies, the M23 and M23A1. These differ in that three latches, present on the M23 baseplate, are absent from the M23A1, and the traversing gear of M23 is a burnbuckle and clamp, but on M23A1 an adjustable slide on the bipod left leg performs this task. The range and rate of fire quoted above are maximum and apply to the HE round—a reduction will be found when other types of ammunition are used and when sustained fire is carried out. This is the first US medium mortar to use a round baseplate, on the underside of which are small wedge-shaped spades.

In service with the United States forces.

81 mm M29 mortar

M8 light mortar

Manufacturer: **State factories (Yugoslavia)**

Calibre	50 mm
Barrel length	56 cm
Baseplate spade length	51 cm
Weight in firing position	7·3 kg
Range	480 m (minimum 135 m)
Rate of fire	25–30 rpm
Operation	Manual
Sight	White line on barrel
Ammunition	HE, smoke, illuminating, signal (all 0·9 kg)
Crew	2

The 50 mm Yugoslav mortar is a slightly modified version of the British World War II 2 in mortar Mk 8. It is the smallest of the series of very small, light mortars developed by the Yugoslavs and derived mainly from Western European and American mortars. It is particularly useful for guerrilla warfare in mountainous regions, such as Yugoslavia. This mortar has no baseplate and comprises instead a spade, hinged to the breech, and a barrel on which the sight consists merely of a line painted along it. The M8 is necessarily trigger fired as the round is not sufficiently heavy to be fired by the drop method. The very short range is due to the shortness of the barrel, and it can be fired from the hip.

In service with the Yugoslav forces.

M57 light mortar

Manufacturer: **State factories (Yugoslavia)**

Calibre	60 mm
Barrel length	70 cm
Barrel weight	5·5 kg
Bipod weight	4·5 kg
Baseplate weight	8·8 kg
Weight in firing position	19·7 kg
Range	1690 m (minimum 74 m)
Rate of fire	25–30 rpm
Operation	Automatic
Sight	Optical
Ammunition	HE (1·4 kg)
Crew	2

The 60 mm mortar M57, copied from the United States World War II M2 mortar of the same calibre, is the next to smallest of the light mortars built by the Yugoslavs for use in guerrilla warfare in their own mountainous terrain. With a total weight of only 19·7 kg, the mortar can be easily and quickly manoeuvred and transported by one man while his partner carries the ammunition. Great flexibility is given the M57 by its speed of manoeuvre, fast rate of fire, and wide variety of range—the minimum range of 74 m could even be dangerous to the firer.

In service with the Yugoslav forces.

M57 light mortar

M31 medium mortar

Manufacturer: **State factories (Yugoslavia)**

Calibre	81 mm
Barrel length	131 cm
Barrel weight	21 kg
Bipod weight	19 kg
Baseplate weight	20 kg
Weight in firing position	61·5 kg
Range	4100 m (minimum 85 m)
Rate of fire	25 rpm
Operation	Automatic
Sight	Optical
Ammunition	Heavy HE (4·2 kg), light HE, smoke and illuminating (3·2 kg)
Crew	3

The Yugoslav M31 81 mm mortar is the older of the two

mortars of this calibre based on French models. The M31 has now been largely replaced by the 60 mm M68 mortar, probably also of French origin but, having been produced extensively for export, is likely to be found in Near Eastern and African countries, as well as being held in reserve in the parent country. This mortar also closely resembles the United States 81 mm mortar M1, and is distinguished by a rectangular baseplate and a comparatively long, thin barrel, held by the bipod clamp at almost half-way. This mortar can be manpacked by the three crew members or otherwise transported in a light vehicle.

In service with the Yugoslav forces.

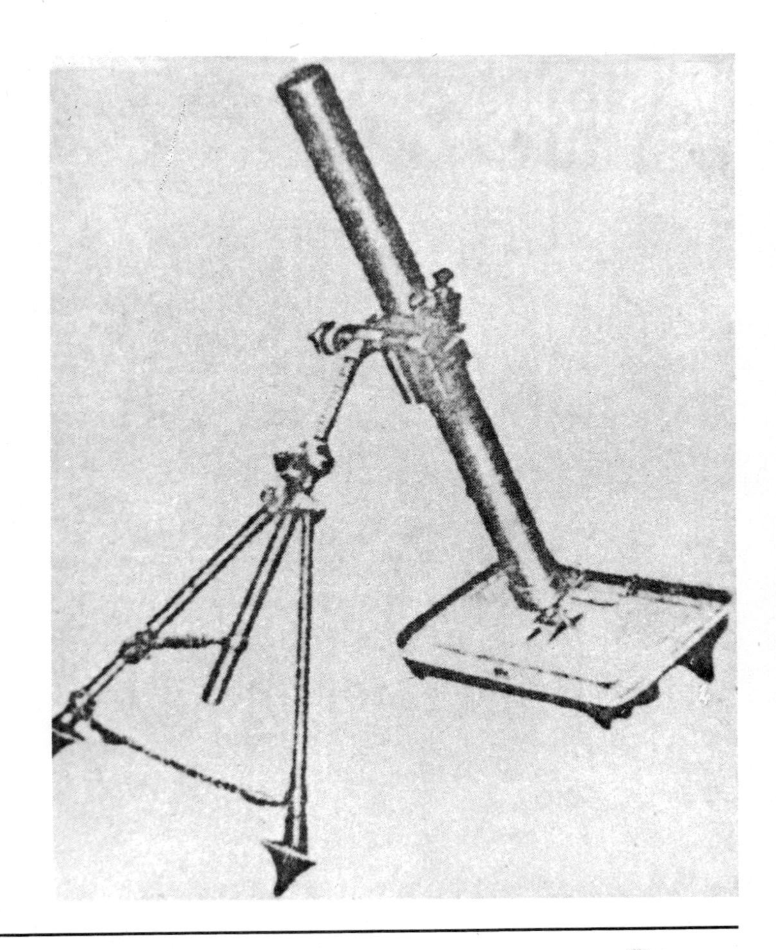

M31 medium mortar

M68 medium mortar

Manufacturer: **State factories (Yugoslavia)**

Calibre	81 mm
Barrel length	164 cm
Barrel weight	16 kg
Bipod weight	13 kg
Weight in firing position	41·5 kg
Range	4800 m (minimum 90 m)
Rate of fire	25 rpm
Operation	Automatic
Sight	Optical
Ammunition	Heavy HE (4·2 kg), light HE, smoke and illuminating (3·2 kg)
Crew	3

M68 medium mortar

The fragile-looking 81 mm mortar M68, being an almost identical copy of the French standard mortar 81-61L of the same calibre, is a very much improved version of the 81 mm mortar M31, and was also produced with export in mind. In contrast to its predecessor, an increase in range of 700 m has been coupled with a decrease in overall weight of 20 kg by replacing the old rectangular baseplate with a smaller triangular baseplate, reducing the bipod to absolute minimum dimensions and producing the barrel (now even longer than before) from a light alloy. Mobility when used in a manpack role is thus considerably enhanced.

In service with the Yugoslav and some Near Eastern and African forces.

BB1 medium mortar

Manufacturer: **State factories (Yugoslavia)**

Calibre	82 mm
Barrel length	120 cm
Barrel weight	21 kg
Bipod weight	20 kg
Weight in firing position	62 kg
Range	4200 m (minimum 82 m)
Rate of fire	20–25 rpm
Operation	Automatic
Sight	Optical
Ammunition	HE (3·5 kg)
Crew	5

Yugoslavia has so far produced only one 82 mm mortar, but its name is not yet known. It is most likely the design of the mortar is based on the Soviet 82 mm mortar M1937 (New Type), the only visible differences being the changed shape of the baseplate (rectangular instead of round) and the connection of the bipod centre spindle to the bipod leg below the right (instead of to the opposite) leg. The Yugoslav 82 mm mortar is slightly heavier than the Soviet version and fires a slightly heavier round over 1000 m further (although a special propulsion charge is required to attain maximum range). 81 mm ammunition can also be used in this weapon. As with other mortars, the 82 mm can be man-packed by the crew.

In service with the Yugoslav forces.

UBM52 heavy mortar

Manufacturer: **State factories (Yugoslavia)**

Calibre	120 mm
Barrel length	129 cm
Weight in firing position	400 kg
Carriage weight	420 kg
Range	6000 m (minimum 195 m)
Rate of fire	25 rpm
Operation	Manual or automatic
Sight	Optical
Ammunition	Heavy HE (15·9 kg), light HE, smoke and illuminating (12·2 kg)
Crew	5

Although the Yugoslav 120 mm mortar UBM52 can fire the same ammunition as the Soviet 120 mm mortars, the resemblance ends there. The UBM52 was designed as a heavy mobile weapon for use both in normal operations and in mountainous terrain. It is thus semi-permanently mounted on its own two-wheeled carriage for firing, but can be taken apart for pack transport by five mules. It also possesses a muzzle attachment to permit towing by either two mules or a vehicle. The cleverly designed spiked rectangular baseplate and hydro-elastic recoil system allow the mortar to be halted and fired almost immediately, no ground preparation for the baseplate being necessary. In spite of its shorter barrel, the UBM52 can outshoot the Soviet M43. If the UBM52 uses its light HE ammunition, it has an extra 300 m range and a far higher rate of fire.

In service with the Yugoslav forces.

UBM52 heavy mortar (note the recoil system)

60 mm Tampella light/commando mortar

Manufacturer: Not divulged

Calibre	60·75 mm
Barrel length	74 cm
Barrel weight	6·6 kg (with sight)
Bipod weight	4·5 kg
Baseplate weight	3·4 kg
Weight in firing position	14 kg (10 kg in commando mode)
Range	2550 m
Rate of fire	Variable
Operation	Automatic
Sight	Optical cross-levelling collimator
Ammunition	HE (1·5 kg) Smoke—plastic phosphorous or titanium chloride (1·5 kg)
Ammunition packing	3 fibre containers, together holding 6 bombs

The 60 mm Tampella mortar is a dual-purpose weapon designed to be used with or without the bipod. Either way it is light enough to be carried by one man.

The barrel is made of steel alloy with a fine honed bore and has a breech-piece attached which contains a fixed firing pin. A ball extension from the breech fits into a socket in the baseplate. This allows the weapon to be traversed through 360 degrees without moving the baseplate. In addition an adjustable clamping ring on the baseplate can be locked to fix the barrel in a single position. This is particularly important in the commando role when the barrel is supported by the firer's hand. The bipod is of tubular steel construction and incorporates the elevation, azimuth and fine adjustment gears as well as a recoil buffer. A collar ring is used to mount the sight on the barrel which does not have to be removed for firing. An elevation and an azimuth scale with a collimator and levelling bubbles make up a simple robust sight unit.

The HE round for this mortar has a forged steel body and an alloy fin-stabilising assembly designed to eliminate the problem known as sporadic shorts. A filler of TNT is used and the whole is propelled by a primary and up to four secondary charges. A smoke round is available which has the same ballistic properties as the HE round and comes with two types of filler, titanium chloride or plastic phosphorus. The plastic phosphorous version doubles as a night ranging round.

In service with the Israeli forces.

60 mm Tampella mortar with bipod

60 mm Tampella mortar in the commando role

81 mm Tampella mortar

Manufacturer: Not divulged

Calibre	81 mm
Barrel length	115·5 cm (short), 145·5 cm (long), 145·5 cm (split)
Barrel weight	11·6 kg (short), 14·5 kg (long), 17·5 kg (split)
Bipod weight	12·3 kg
Baseplate weight	13·2 kg
Weight in firing position	37 kg (short), 40 kg (long), 43 kg (split)

Range	4000 m (short), 4600 m (long and split)
Rate of fire	20 rpm
Operation	Automatic
Sight	Optical cross-levelling collimator
Ammunition	HE, smoke and practice (4 kg) and illuminating
Ammunition packing	One round in a fibre container, 4 containers in a wooden box
Crew	3

The 81 mm Tampella mortar is a smooth-bore weapon with three choices of barrel. A short, light barrel with a slightly reduced range of 4000 m against 4600 m of the others, a long barrel for conventional operations and, thirdly, a split barrel consisting of two parts of roughly equal length joined by an overlapping interrupted screw for use by airborne units. Whatever the barrel configuration, the other parts are the same, and the weapon can be man-packed in three loads. Like other Tampella mortars, the barrels are made from steel alloy to close tolerances, with breech blocks having fixed firing pins and ball butts. In addition, the 81 mm mortar, like the 120 mm light mortar, has an optional safety system. The baseplate is of circular design and manufactured from sheet steel with welded spades. The socket in the centre accommodates the ball butt and the mortar can cover a 360 degree arc without movement of the base-plate. A collapsible bipod of similar design to the 60 mm mortar has a recoil system and the gearing is dust-proofed. The sight unit is the same as that of the 120 mm mortars and is described under the Standard 120 mm.

The HE round is of forged steel and contains 540 gm of TNT. Other rounds, with identical ballistic patterns, include three types of smoke and a practice bomb. The fuses on all Tampella mortar rounds are point detonating and incorporate an impact or delay setting.

In service with the Finnish and Israeli forces.

81 mm Tampella split barrel mortar

120 mm light Tampella mortar

Manufacturer: Not divulged

Calibre	120 mm
Barrel length	173 cm
Barrel weight	43 kg
Bipod length	100 cm
Bipod weight	27 kg
Baseplate dimensions	74 cm diameter
Baseplate weight	38 kg
Weight in firing position	108 kg
Carriage weight	110 kg
Range	7000 m
Rate of fire	5–10 rpm
Operation	Automatic
Sight	Optical cross-levelling collimator
Ammunition	M 58F HE, smoke and practice (12·9 kg) and illuminating M 58FF HE, smoke and practice (13 kg) and illuminating
Ammunition packing	One round in a fibre container, 2 containers in a wooden box
Crew	3

The 120 mm light Tampella mortar is a smooth-bore weapon, with a retractable firing pin. The barrel is made of steel alloy, and is externally threaded at the breech to take the breech block containing the firing pin. A ball

120 mm light Tampella mortar

extension on this block makes the joint with a central socket in a circular welded baseplate and enables the mortar to be fully traversed without re-bedding. The bipod is of similar design to all the Tampella mounts, and incorporates a recoil buffer, dustproof gearing for elevation, azimuth and fine adjustment. The sight unit is the same as that of the 120 mm standard, and of the 81 mm Tampella mortar, and is covered in the description of the former.

The optional carriage is of tubular construction and can be towed at speeds up to 40 kph. The weapon, all its accessories and six rounds of ammunition can be carried. The mortar can be man-packed by three men or one mule.

A special range of ammunition designated M 58FF has been produced for this mortar, though it will also fire the M 58F ammunition. The HE bomb is filled with 2·3 kg of TNT. Other rounds include three types of smoke, and illuminating and practice bombs. All rounds have the same ballistic properties, so only one range table is necessary.

In service with the Israeli forces.

The sight used on the 81 mm and 120 mm Tampella mortars

The mortar carriage

120 mm standard Tampella mortar

Manufacturer: Not divulged

Calibre	120 mm
Barrel length	194 cm
Barrel weight	82 kg
Bipod length	174 cm
Bipod weight	66 kg
Baseplate dimensions	96 cm diameter
Baseplate weight	72 kg
Weight in firing position	220 kg
Carriage weight	129 kg
Range	8300 m
Rate of fire	5–10 rpm
Operation	Automatic
Sight	Optical cross-levelling collimator
Ammunition	M 58F HE, smoke and practice (12·9 kg) and illuminating
Ammunition packing	One round in a fibre container, 2 containers in a wooden box
Crew	3/4

The 120 mm standard Tampella is a smooth-bore mortar made to high tolerances and is designed for simplicity in both operation and maintenance. Though normally towed, it can be carried by mule, or man-handled over very short distances.

The barrel is made of high-tensile steel alloy and has a close tolerance bore. It is internally threaded at the breech end to take the breech block which contains the firing mechanism. The firing mechanism is of the spring-loaded striker type actuated by a lanyard and has a safety lever. The bipod incorporates the recoil buffer with the barrel collar, elevation, azimuth and correction

120 mm standard Tampella mortar

gears. Leg spread is limited by an adjustable chain. Welded sheet steel is used for the baseplate, in the centre of which is a socket to take the breech-piece ball end. The mortar can be traversed 360 degrees without moving the baseplate. The sight unit consists of an elevation and azimuth mechanism, one range and two cross-levelling bubbles and a collimator. Quick releases for large adjustments are fitted and the mils-graduated dials can be freed for rapid and large adjustments. A quick release dovetail mount on the bipod facilitates removal of the sight, though this is not necessary when firing. A steel box chassis trailer is normally used to move the weapon.

Four types of ammunition are available, though any 120 mm mortar ammunition can be used. The M 58F-18 round is a HE bomb containing 2·3 kg of TNT and utilises up to eight secondary charges, giving a maximum range of 6200 m. Three types of smoke round of the same designation are available; also illuminating and practice rounds. With the Super Tampella (ST) bomb, a range of 8300 m is possible.

In service with the Israeli and Finnish forces.

Missiles and Rockets

General

The infantry in a modern war needs weapons for three main purposes: to destroy tanks, to destroy other infantry and to destroy aircraft. It makes little difference if the weapons are employed in an offensive or a defensive role so far as their design is concerned. Probably the most important of these three purposes is the destruction of enemy tanks; thus it will be found that in this review of missiles and rockets the anti-tank weapon predominates.

The original weapon for use against a tank was the gun, which was large and unwieldy, not particularly accurate and not an infantry weapon. It soon became evident that what was required was a lighter, more mobile weapon which could be used by soldiers in the field, so the rocket was developed, followed by the guided missile.

A rocket is launched from a variety of containers, often mounted on a simple support on the ground, or from the shoulder. Rockets are propelled by the jet stream from a motor or from the combustion of cordite or other explosive. The NATO standard for rockets calls for a flight time of not more than 1·25 sec when used in the infantry role. This limits their range to under 400 m. Other armies allow a longer flight time, but in general rockets have ranges of less than a quarter of those of guided missiles. Most rockets have hollow-charge warheads and are as capable of penetrating tank armour as are missiles. They are smaller and more portable then missiles and considerably less expensive. They are undoubtedly useful weapons, but are easily outranged by tank guns; thus they tend to be used more as a clandestine weapon fired from behind cover and, unlike a gun, make no noise or flash on being launched.

With the modern highly mobile tank it is not easy to hit the target with a rocket which, once it is launched, is committed to one trajectory only. Further, there is the requirement for the infantry to outrange the enemy's tank fire. This led to the development of the missile which, because it had a much longer range, had to be guided in flight to take account of the target's movements.

Wire-guidance

The majority of anti-tank missiles in use today are wire-guided. That is to say, they unreel a length of very fine wire (or sometimes two wires) behind them and the operator uses this wire to pass electrical signals to the missile in order to steer it. The operator must have the target in sight all the time and the range of the missile is limited, both by the amount of wire it can carry and the endurance of its propulsion motor.

Wire-guidance is used because it is not subject to enemy electronic countermeasures, and is less expensive than fitting the missile and launcher with sophisticated radio or other electronic equipment. With wire-guidance, the operator must have a clear view of the target and he must remain in position for the time of flight of the missile. Further, in most systems, the operator is actually steering the missile from the launcher, which thus becomes an obvious target for the enemy. Britain, with her SWINGFIRE system, has managed to separate the launcher and the operator by up to 100 m, and it is possible for the launcher to be behind cover, provided the operator is in a position from which he can see the target.

The original guidance was purely optical; the operator observed the target, launched his missile, which he was able to see, and steered it manually by means of a joystick.

Recently a more sophisticated method of guidance has been introduced. The missile carries infra-red flares in its tail, and at the launcher there is an infra-red sensor which measures the angle between the missile's path and the direct line of sight. If the missile deviates from this line, correcting signals are automatically passed down the wire to bring it back. All the operator has to do is to keep the target on the cross-wires of his sight. Examples of this method are the Franco-German MILAN and the United States TOW.

Non-wire Systems

Efforts are now being made to get away from the wire-guidance systems and at least two new ideas are under development, both depending upon lasers.

Britain and Belgium are working together on a system called ATLAS in which a laser beam illuminates the target. The missile flies down this beam, and has a laser receiver in its nose which picks up the reflected laser light from the target and uses it to guide itself to hit.

ATLAS has a range of only 1000 m, but the United States are developing a similar system —HELLFIRE—with a much longer range. They are hoping to adapt the principle used with their 'smart' bombs where the target is illuminated by a laser from any convenient point, not necessarily the launch point. The missile homes on the reflected laser light, even though the illuminator may be many degrees off the line of sight from the launcher. This allows the missile to be used in indirect fire when it cannot 'see' the target on launch. It merely rises, searches with its laser receiver until it picks up the reflected laser energy, and then locks on and homes. These new devices are not with us yet, and all present systems require the operator to keep his sight on the target during the time of flight. This more or less precludes night action; hence, the search for other methods of guidance.

An ideal weapon, both for infantry and airborne use, would be one where no form of external guidance whatsoever was required, ie the missile is launched in the general direction of the target and thereafter homes itself, thus leaving the operator, or the launching aircraft, free to move or take cover. Work is proceeding on this, and it is possible that either an infra-red homing or a radar-homing missile may take its appearance before long. Apart from allowing the 'shoot and skoot' technique to be employed, it would also enable missiles to be launched at night.

One-man Missiles

There are a number of 'one-man' missiles on the market and most of them have a range of about 2000 m, which is probably sufficient as a lone infantryman is unlikely to be able, or permitted, to pick out a tank at a longer range. The missiles can be launched either directly off a small launcher on the ground, or from the shoulder.

In the 1973 Middle East war, the Egyptians did considerable damage to the Israeli tanks by the use of a very small anti-tank missile contained in a box no larger than a suitcase. Small weapons of this type and rockets are particularly suited to guerrilla-type operations. They can be easily concealed and can do considerable damage. With the NATO nations faced with a 3 to 1 preponderance of Warsaw Pact tanks, anti-tank weapons are assuming tremendous importance and there is an encouraging school of thought that NATO should be concentrating more on the very small missile or rocket for use by tank-hunting groups and in harassing operations.

Helicopter-mounted Weapons

With NATO's forces being so much smaller numerically than those of the Warsaw Pact and with the latter's free choice of the attack point, it is difficult for the Allied infantry to be in the right place at the right time. Mobility becomes all important. Thus NATO is at last concentrating on arming helicopters with anti-tank weapons.

Although the French, and later the British, had the SS11 mounted in their helicopters for a long time, it was the Americans, with their Vietnam experience, who eventually took the lead in this form of warfare, and fitted a number of their Huey Cobra helicopters with the TOW anti-tank missile. These aircraft can carry two or four missiles on each side in launcher pods. The Franco-German HOT has been test-fired from an Alouette, but will probably eventually be fitted in a German BO 105 or a French SA 360, either of which could carry four to six missiles plus a crew armed with the hand-portable MILAN.

The British are experimenting with the SWINGFIRE mounted in a Puma helicopter and have renamed the missile in this role HAWKSWING. So far the trials have not progressed very fast, but it is hoped eventually to fit it into Gazelle and Lynx helicopters. HAWKSWING should have a range of 4000 m, where the United States TOW has a range of only marginally over 3000 m. A helicopter needs a missile with as long a range as possible to enable the target to be engaged outside the range of hostile anti-tank or anti-aircraft fire.

The principle of operating helicopters in the anti-tank role is to form small battle groups of perhaps one or two reconnaissance helicopters with up to six attack machines. The group would endeavour to keep out of sight behind hills or houses and would send up one reconnaissance vehicle to find the enemy and to call up the attack helicopters by radio. They then literally pop up, deliver their missiles, and pop down behind cover again as soon as possible.

With wire-guided missiles, such as TOW and SWINGFIRE, the helicopter has to remain in position during the flight of the missile so that it can be guided to hit. Pilots would much rather launch their missiles and get behind cover with the least possible delay; hence the requirement for a self-homing missile which would not require pilot guidance.

Vulnerability of Helicopters

Helicopters are, of course, particularly vulnerable at the low heights at which they must operate to small anti-aircraft missiles, and in particular to the one-man shoulder-launched missile. Such missiles did considerable damage to Israeli aircraft in the recent Middle East war. Nearly all missiles of this type home on the heat emitted from the aircraft's engines, and all that the aimer has to do is to point the missile in the general direction of the aircraft, press a button and the missile does the rest. An exception to this is the British BLOWPIPE, which is automatically guided for the first 2 or 3 sec of its flight and then manually guided by the operator, who has to continue to track the target through his sight. As a result BLOWPIPE is of limited use at night.

One-man missiles do not have a great range, something of the order of 3 km is normal, but they are invaluable to the infantryman undergoing direct aircraft attack for dealing with helicopters and for clandestine work in the vicinity of enemy airfields. Being small they might not necessarily shoot down an aircraft, but they should certainly deliver a powerful enough explosion to cause a forced landing. One of the problems with hand-held missiles is the difficulty of carrying a supply of missiles, and some missile and rocket launchers are now designed to fire only one or two missiles/rockets and are then abandoned. It follows that to produce an effective volume of fire it is necessary to arm a large number of soldiers with launchers.

Standardisation

As will be seen, the NATO countries and France have developed some 10 vehicle or ground-launched anti-tank missiles and 8 hand-held ones plus numerous different types of rockets. Many of the missiles perform almost identical functions and it seems a great waste of time and effort to have done so much work, not to mention the production which is now being carried out, when one, or at the most two, standard weapons could have sufficed. The Franco-German HOT, the United States TOW and the British SWINGFIRE all have very similar performances, and the German COBRA, the United States DRAGON, the Franco-German MILAN, the Italian MOSQUITO are all weapons designed for the same purpose—one-man launching.

Standardisation inside NATO has never really got off the ground, but anti-tank and ground-to-air missiles are both examples of the waste of effort and money due to the fact that the nations cannot agree amongst themselves.

Sophisticated infantry weapons are likely to increase in numbers and complexity, and if mobility is to be NATO's keyword, the infantryman may find himself in Turkey at one moment and in Norway at the next. He would like to find stocks of weapons in which he has been trained in both countries. At present this is highly unlikely unless the NATO countries drastically revise their procurement methods.

JOHN MARRIOTT

RL-83 (Blindicide) multi-purpose free flight missile launcher

Manufacturer: **MECAR SA (Belgium)**

Calibre	83 mm
Dimensions	Length 92 cm (folded), 170 cm (open)
Weight	8·4 kg (with optional telescopic sight)
Range	Up to 900 m
Sight	Optical and mechanical
Mount	Bipod and shoulder-fired
Ignition	Mechanical
Muzzle velocity	100 m/sec
Ammunition	HE hollow charge, HE anti-personnel, parachute illuminating, smoke and incendiary
Effect	Penetrates any known armour
Crew	2
Environment	Pan climatic

This weapon has been the standard rocket launcher in many armed forces for a number of years. As a first generation anti-tank weapon, it is now obsolescent. However, it is still widely used by both regular and other forces because of its cheapness and simplicity.

The tube folds down for easy carriage to just over half its total length. Without any modification, the weapon will fire the complete range of ammunition available. Firing is mechanical, and there are three sighting systems: mechanical to 400 m, optical to 400 m with angular corrections, and an auxiliary sight for ranges to 900 m.

The rounds available are a HE hollow-charge rocket, anti-personnel, combined anti-tank/anti-personnel, parachute illuminating, smoke and incendiary.

In service with the Belgian forces.

RL-83 (Blindicide)

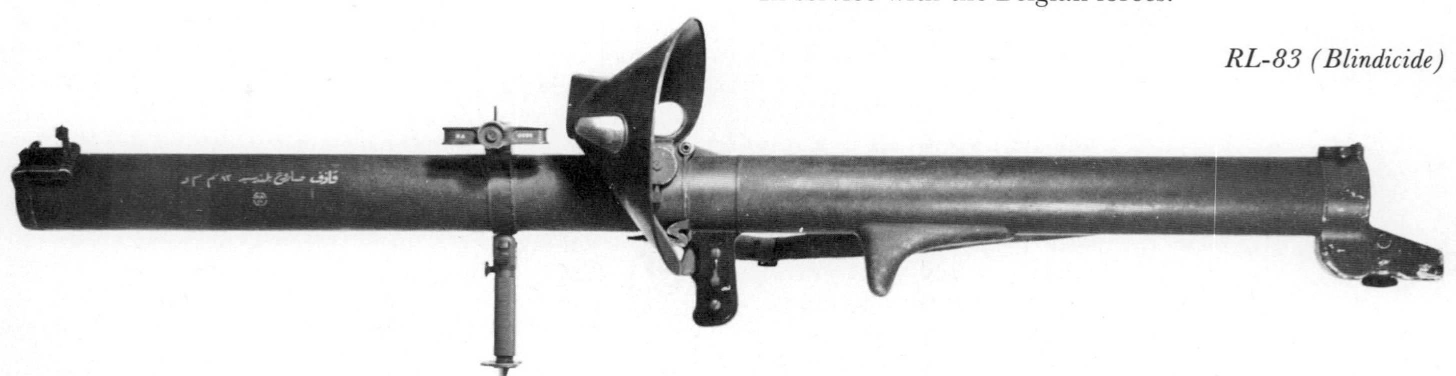

RL 100 multi-purpose free flight missile launcher

Manufacturer: **MECAR SA (Belgium)**

Calibre	101 mm
Dimensions	Length 102 cm (folded), 188·5 cm (open)
Weight	12·9 kg
Range	2000 m (effective 400 m)
Sight	Mechanical 100 m–500 m Optical 100 m–500 m (with angular corrections)
Mount	Bipod
Ignition	Percussion
Muzzle velocity	195 m/sec
Ammunition	HEAT, HE, HEPAT, smoke, incendiary, illuminating
Effect	HEAT penetrates 375 mm of armour plate or 1200 mm of concrete

This simple, rugged weapon has been in service with a number of countries for many years. Although it was initially designed to be for use in main defence positions, its low weight allows it to be carried easily by one man. The launching tube is smooth bored and made from aluminium alloy. A centrally situated hinge allows the weapon to be folded for carriage and easy stowage. Attached to the tube are a retractable bipod, an adjustable shoulder pad, a folding hand-grip and a pistol-grip containing the firing mechanism. A protective guard is attached to the optical sight to protect the firer from exhaust particles. Firing is initiated mechanically, thus eliminating the problems of electrical systems. To fire, a rocket is inserted into the rear of the weapon and automatically locked into place to prevent movement when the tube is tilted. The double safety mechanism on this weapon requires the loader to release a catch on the firing mechanism as well as the firer to release a trigger safety. Only when both safety requirements have been complied with can the weapon be fired.

A range of ammunition available includes a fragmentation round, a combination anti-tank and fragmentation round, smoke incendiary and illuminating rounds, as well as the primary anti-tank round.

In service, but obsolescent.

Type 51 anti-tank free flight missile launcher

Manufacturer: **State factories (People's Republic of China)**

Calibre	87 mm
Length	152 cm
Weight	9·5 kg
Range	90 m–180 m
Sight	Optical
Effect	Penetrates some 130 mm of armour plate

Although the United States M20 3·5 in rocket launcher was the original from which the Chinese communists developed the type 51, only the general shape of the tube is common to both. The type 51 consists of a one-piece cylinder with a small curved blast-shield at each end (half of the front shield being multi-perforated), a curved metal shoulder-rest connected to the cylindrical pistol-grip which contains the electric batteries and firing mechanism, an optical sight over the left of the pistol-grip, and a forward-folding bipod connected to the pistol-grip by the tubular metal carrying handle. The rocket launcher is a smooth-bore, breech-loaded weapon, capable of firing its HEAT rounds at a rate of up to 4 rpm. These can penetrate about 130 mm of armour.

In service with the communist Chinese forces.

Type 56 anti-tank gun

Manufacturer: **State factories (People's Republic of China)**

Calibre	75 mm
Length	213 cm
Weight	86 kg (weapon 51·7 kg, carriage 34·3 kg)
Range	6600 m
Sight	Optical
Ammunition	HEAT and HE
Effect	Penetrates 80 mm of armour plate

The type 56 recoilless rifle is another weapon developed by the Chinese communists from United States equipment. In this case the original was the M20 recoilless rifle, and once again only the general form of the tube and breech remain. The mechanism of the breech is, however, considerably altered. Whilst retaining the conventional long, clean barrel and curved conical breech, the type 56 is mounted on a distinctive curved tubular axle with a single forward tubular support ending in a transverse towing bar. The tube is connected to the carriage by a single ring clamp with the prominent elevating and traversing screws set at right angles to each other behind and in front of the ring clamp respectively. The new type 56 (or type 62) sight, mounted on the left above the clamp, permits either direct or indirect fire, using either HEAT or HE rounds, at a rate of up to 10 rpm. It is possible to penetrate some 80 mm of armour. The weapon can be fired without removing the detachable solid-tyred wheels, but is, of course, more accurate and stable without them.

In service with the communist Chinese and North Vietnamese forces and the Vietcong.

75 mm Type 56

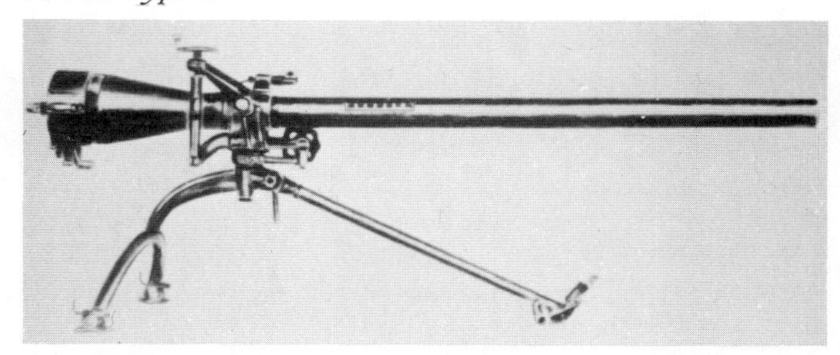

H-12 anti-personnel free flight missile

Manufacturer: **State factories (People's Republic of China)**

Calibre	107 mm
Dimensions	Length 83·8 cm
Weight	19 kg
Range	8300 m
Warhead	HE

The communist Chinese H-12 rocket is very similar to the type 63, only differing in that it can be fired without the aid of a launcher and the warhead unscrews about 5 cm forward of the screwing band whereas, in the case of the type 63, the join is level with the edge of the band. Launching is carried out with the aid of any improvised chute, the motor being started electrically by wire, and spin-stabilisation is imparted by the six canted jet nozzles in the rocket's base. As with the type 63, there is a nose-mounted fuse, which can be set to either impact or delayed-action detonation by adjustment of a screw in the side of the fuse. Like all similar missiles, the H-12 is designed to be very easily portable, but is equally not very accurate and its fragmentation warhead is really effective only against towns and military camps, to which it does offer a considerable threat.

In service with the Vietcong.

Type 63 anti-personnel free flight missile launcher

Manufacturer: **State factories (People's Republic of China)**

Calibre	107 mm
Dimensions	Length of rocket 33·8 cm
Weight	22·6 kg (2 tube set)
Range	8300 m
Warhead	HE

The communist Chinese light (250 kg) type 63 rocket launcher is another weapon developed with guerrilla warfare in mind. When fully assembled it comprises a 12 round launcher mounted in three banks of four on a tubular alloy four-legged stand, which can be carried in the rear of a light truck easily. For carriage in difficult country, however, the launcher breaks down into six one-man loads—one set of four tubes, four sets each of two tubes, and the mount. It appears that a popular method of utilising this weapon is to use one double tube, set on its own. The rockets, which are spin-stabilised, are electrically fired and have an adjustable fuse which can be set for impact or delayed-action detonation. The rockets are 83·8 cm in length, weigh 19 kg and have six jet nozzles set into the base. A crew of as few as two could therefore provide a considerable threat from a range of 8 km although, as with most of these weapon types, the broken-down launcher is not very accurate and can really only be used against a large target such as a camp or village.

In service with the communist Chinese and North Vietnamese forces, and the Vietcong.

M488 anti-personnel free flight missile launcher

Manufacturer: **State factories (People's Republic of China)**

Calibre	102 mm
Dimensions	Length 81 cm
Weight	11·3 kg
Range	5000 m
Warhead	TNT

The M488 is the smallest of several single-tube rocket launchers used in guerrilla warfare by the Vietcong. As with most of the others, the launcher is a single modified tube taken from a multi-barrelled rocket launcher—in this case the Chinese communist type 50-5 launcher. Normally the tube is mounted on a bipod, or tripod, and is fired electrically, but can also be mounted on a makeshift bipod made of two sticks. The spin-stabilised rockets are 71 cm in length and weigh 15·4 kg. They are fitted with a nose-mounted impact jet fuse, are of a dull olive colour and have eight jet-nozzles set in the base. These rockets are not very accurate and are intended for area fire only against large targets such as towns and military camps. The launcher (with or without bipod) can easily be carried by one man, but ammunition is heavy, and it is unlikely that porters could carry more than two rounds each by back-pack for any distance. In appearance the fin-stabilised version differs from all other similar missiles in the form of the base section with its narrow neck and six thin fins. This last model is more usually fired from the original type 50-5 launcher.

In service with the Vietcong.

T21 (Tarasnice) anti-tank gun

Manufacturer: **State factories (Czechoslovakia)**

T21 (Tarasnice) 82 mm RCL

Calibre	82 mm
Length	147 cm
Weight	20 kg (with carriage)
Range	300 m (direct) 2800 m (indirect)
Sight	Optical and battle
Ammunition	HEAT
Effect	Penetrates 230 mm of armour plate

The Czech T21 recoilless anti-tank gun is a very versatile weapon, capable of being fired from its small two-wheel carriage, from the shoulder or from a fixed mount on the Czech tracked OT62 armoured personnel carrier, and in both direct and indirect roles.

It is a smooth-bore weapon. firing a shaped-charge HEAT fin-stabilised round, which is breech-loaded, and fired electrically—as with the P27 anti-tank grenade launcher, the trigger action works a magneto. To cope with the direct and indirect fire capability, the T21 is equipped with ordinary iron sights graduated in 50 m intervals and also a telescopic sight graduated at 100 m intervals.

The HEAT round, 2·1 kg in weight, can penetrate up to 230 mm of armour at an effective range of 300 m if if the target is moving, and up to 650 m if the target is stationary. Rate of fire is about 5 rpm, but this is adversely affected by the absence of a used round extractor in the breech, which has to be cleared manually with the aid of an asbestos glove.

The T21 is usually transported in a truck or armoured personnel carrier, but can be towed for short distances using the long tubular towing handle, normally kept folded over the top of the tube.

In service with the Czechoslovak, North Vietnamese, and Near Eastern forces and the Vietcong.

M59 and M59A anti-tank gun

Manufacturer: **State factories (Czechoslovakia)**

Calibre	82 mm
Length	381 cm
Weight	386 kg
Range	7550 m
Sight	Optical (PB04K)
Ammunition	HEAT and HE
Effect	Penetrates 250 mm of armour plate
Crew	5

The Czech M59A recoilless gun is unique in that it is the only weapon of this type used by Warsaw Pact countries to have a spotting rifle, the semi-automatic 12·7 mm ZH59. Although designed basically as an anti-tank gun for use in the infantry regiment, the very long barrel and provision of both HEAT and HE rounds enable this weapon to be used as a field gun. The M59A is distinguished by its long barrel, spotting rifle and the small flared blast-shield behind the breech and is visibly different from the original M59 only by reason of the ribbing on the breech.

The PB04K sight, mounted on the left-hand side in front of the breech, is employed for both the indirect and direct fire roles. The 6 kg projectile is breech-loaded and the HEAT round can pierce up to 250 mm of armour. Both versions of this gun are usually mounted on a light two-wheeled, rubber-tyred carriage, towed by a vehicle, and can also be moved easily for short distances manually by the small hand-towing bar on the muzzle. The weapon has also been found mounted on armoured personnel carriers and light trucks, but in all cases the rate of fire is around 6 rpm, and a crew of five are needed to serve the gun.

In service with the Czechoslovak and some Third World countries' forces.

P27 (Pancerovka) anti-tank free flight missile launcher

Manufacturer: **State factories (Czechoslovakia)**

Calibre	45 mm (missile 120 mm)
Length	103 cm
Weight	6·4 kg
Range	100 m
Sight	Tangent leaf and hooded post
Ammunition	HEAT
Effect	Penetrates 250 mm of armour plate

The Czech P27 launcher was produced initially at about the same time as the Soviet RPG2 which it resembles. The P27 incorporates a tube, 103 cm long, sometimes fitted with a small, flared blast-shield at the rear end and an insulated guard covering most of the rear half, a

Close-up of P27

pistol-grip with trigger and electrical firing mechanism, large fore and back sights and a bipod.

The bipod and the large size and sophistication of the sights are the main differences between this weapon and the RPG2. The fin-stabilised, shaped-charge HEAT round is loaded by hand into the muzzle and is electrically fired—the trigger action powers a magneto. The missile will penetrate up to 250 mm of armour, but can only be used effectively against a moving vehicle at about 80 m. Beyond 100 m targets must be limited to men or soft-skinned vehicles. Up to five rounds can be fired in one minute. The front sight is a hooded post, and the rear sight a tangent leaf graduated at 50 m, 75 m, 100 m, 125 m and 150 m, the two folding together for carriage, for which a sling is provided.

In service with the Czechoslovak, North Vietnamese, and Near Eastern forces and the Vietcong.

P27 (Pancerovka) 45 mm missile launcher

89 mm Strim F1 anti-tank free flight missile launcher

Manufacturer: **Luchaire SA (France)**

Calibre	88·9 mm
Dimensions	Length 160 cm (ready to fire), 117 cm (transportable)
Weight	7·3 kg (loaded)
Range	2300 m (effective 400 m)
Time of flight	1·5 sec to 400 m
Sight	Optical
Mount	Bipod
Ignition	Electrical
Muzzle velocity	290 m/sec
Ammunition	Shaped charge
Effect	Penetrates 400 mm of armour plate or 1300 mm of concrete
Crew	2

The F1 is a light (anti-tank) rocket launcher designed to replace the 3·5 in M20A1, previously in service with the French Army. The extensive use of plastics in the F1's manufacture has led to a low-weight anti-tank weapon with considerable strike effect.

The launcher consists of the tube on which an adjustable shoulder piece foregrip, electrical firing mechanism and telescopic sight are mounted. The rocket is carried in a container which is fitted directly to the tube, thus extending its length and ensuring that all the propellant is burnt before the missile leaves the muzzle. All the necessary electrical connections are made automatically as the round is loaded. The rocket is a shaped-charge round equipped with a piezo-electric detonator and stabilised by nine unfolding fins. The propelling charge is of the so-called 'brush' type, that is to say, a number of sticks of propellant are supported by perforated discs at each end. Due to the small spaces created between the individual sticks a faster and more even burning of the charge is ensured. This rapid burning of the propellant results in there being no exhaust particles and a high muzzle velocity of approximately 300 m/sec, and a flatter trajectory out to the 400 m operational range.

In service with the French forces.

89 mm Strim rocket launcher

89 mm Strim round (note the unfolding fins)

Sarpac anti-tank free flight disposable missile launcher

Manufacturer: **Hotchkiss-Brandt (France)**

Calibre	68 mm
Dimensions	73·4 cm (closed), 99·7 cm (open)
Weight	2·3 kg (ready to fire) 2·7 kg (protected for carriage in transport)
Range	150 m–200 m (anti-tank) 650 m (anti-personnel)
Sight	Mechanical parallelogramic; telescopic for longer ranges
Mount	Shoulder-fired
Ignition	Percussion
Muzzle velocity	150 m/sec
Ammunition	Rochar HE hollow charge (1 kg) Rocap HE and fragment (1·8 kg) Roclair illuminating (1·3 kg)
Effect	Rochar penetrates 300 mm of armour
Crew	1
Simulator	Indoor and outdoor are available

Sarpac is a light individual weapon intended for use at short ranges. The weapon is supplied ready for use and consists of a telescopic fibre glass tube which doubles as a carrying case and projector. The launcher/rocket unit is an expendable watertight assembly which cannot

Sarpac launcher closed

Sarpac launcher in firing mode

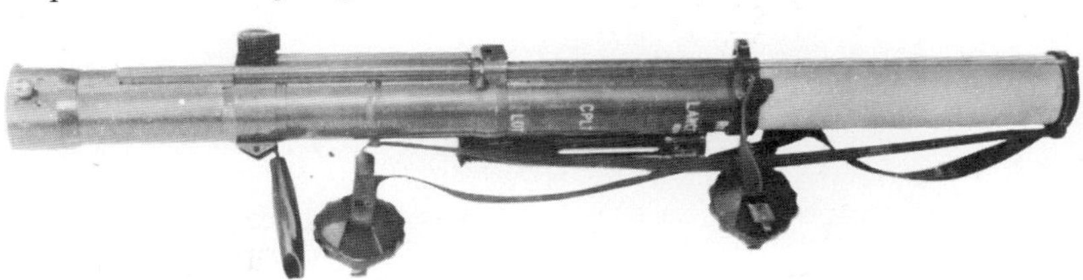

Examples of Sarpac ammunition

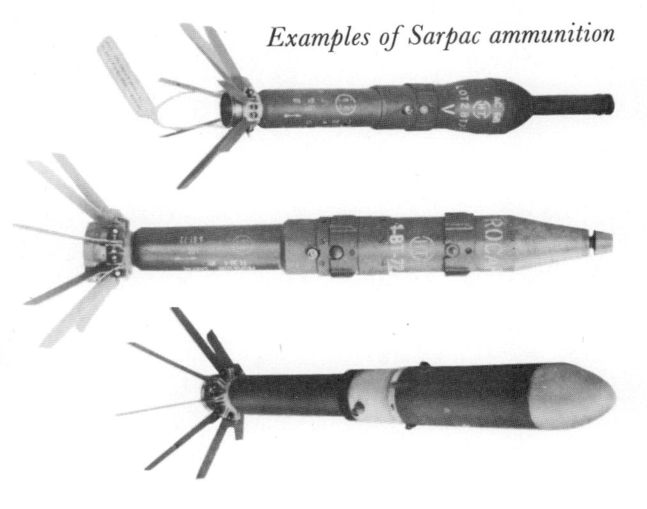

be fired until the tube is extended, thus arming the percussion firing mechanism. A folding sight unit of parallelogramic design is designed to enable an inexperienced operator to obtain good results.

Although the primary round is Rochar (a HE hollow-charge, fin-stabilised rocket)) Sarpac can be used to fire Rocap HE and Roclair illuminating rounds. The hollow charge warhead is equipped with a piezo-electric detonator and a delay unit inhibits the arming of the rocket until it has reached approximately 6 m from the muzzle.

Rocap explodes scattering 800 gm of splinters, while Roclair burns at 180,000 cp for 30 sec.

In service.

MAS Type A (Arpac) anti-tank free flight disposable missile launcher

Manufacturer: **Groupement Industriel des Armements Terrestres (France)**

Calibre	72 mm
Dimensions	Length 55 cm (ready to fire), 40 cm (transportable)
Weight	1·3 kg
Range	100 m
Time of flight	0·86 sec to 50 m
Sight	Two-position peep
Ignition	Percussion
Muzzle velocity	7 m/sec (76 m/sec after 10 m)
Ammunition	Shaped charge
Effect	Penetrates 250 mm of armour plate
Crew	1

The MAS Type A is one of the several new disposable rocket launchers now becoming available. It is intended for anti-tank combat at ranges of 100 m or less. The missile consists of a shaped-charge warhead equipped with a point-detonating fuse and a six-nozzled rocket motor which is expelled from a small launcher by a propellant charge. This charge is only sufficient to start the missile on its flight path and is said to have no more recoil than a rifle.

The launcher is made mostly from plastic and comprises a short tube closed at one end by a shaped butt piece and at the other by a hinged cover. A percussion firing mechanism projects from the top of the tube and incorporates a two-position peep-sight. Within the tube is a barrel which contains the initial propellant charge. This barrel is a sliding unit which recoils on firing. However, by the time it strikes the closed end of the tube, the missile is in flight, so the recoil does not in any way affect the firer's accuracy. Once the missile is clear of the tube the motor ignites and accelerates the missile from its launch velocity of 7 m/sec to 76 m/sec. There is no flash or blast from this weapon and it can be safely fired from an enclosed position or through an aperture no larger than 10 cm × 25 cm. The smoke and noise levels are very low and it takes only about 6 sec to prepare for firing.

Not yet adopted for service.

MAS Type A (Arpac) in action

MAS Type A (Arpac) front view

ACL/APX 80 multi-purpose free flight missile launcher

Manufacturer: **Groupement Industriel des Armements Terrestres (France)**

Calibre	80 mm
Dimensions	Length 145 cm
Weight	8·6 kg (with sight), 16·7 kg (with sight and round)
Range	550 m
Time of flight	1·2 sec at 550 m
Sight	Optical
Mount	Bipod and shoulder-fired
Ignition	Electrical
Muzzle velocity	400 m/sec
Ammunition	HE hollow charge, HE anti-personnel, illuminating and smoke
Effect	Penetrates 120 mm of single armour plate (40 mm and 10 mm of double plate)
Crew	2
Environment	−40 C to +50 C

The research and development programme of this weapon, initiated in 1964, was completed in 1970. It is designed to meet a French army requirement for a low-weight, multi-purpose weapon, with priority given to the anti-tank role. ACL/APX 80 is now in full production.

The weapon consists of a strong, rifled steel tube which incorporates a novel breech mechanism designed to facilitate rapid loading. A carrying handle, telescopic bipod and adjustable shoulder-rest assist carriage and use. A detachable optical sight is provided.

The basic round for this weapon is a hollow-charge anti-tank projectile of unusual design in that the payload is located behind a secondary propulsion unit. The complete round consists of a cartridge case which contains the initial propulsion charge and also serves to protect the stabilising fins of the projectile. The projectile body contains the hollow charge, the sustainer rocket and a piezo-electric generator.

On firing, the primary propulsion unit expels the projectile leaving the cartridge case behind in the breech. The empty case is then ejected separately by the loader. In flight the projectile, spun by the rifling, is further stabilised by the unfolding fins. After a pre-determined delay, secondary, or sustained, propulsion is initiated and the projectile is accelerated to its maximum velocity of 545 m/sec. The warhead is detonated on impact by the piezo-electric generator.

To fulfil the multi-role requirement, HE anti-personnel, illuminating and smoke rounds are available. A high velocity is not so necessary with these rounds, so the secondary propulsion unit is replaced by additional pay load.

A sub-calibre firing device has been developed.

In production.

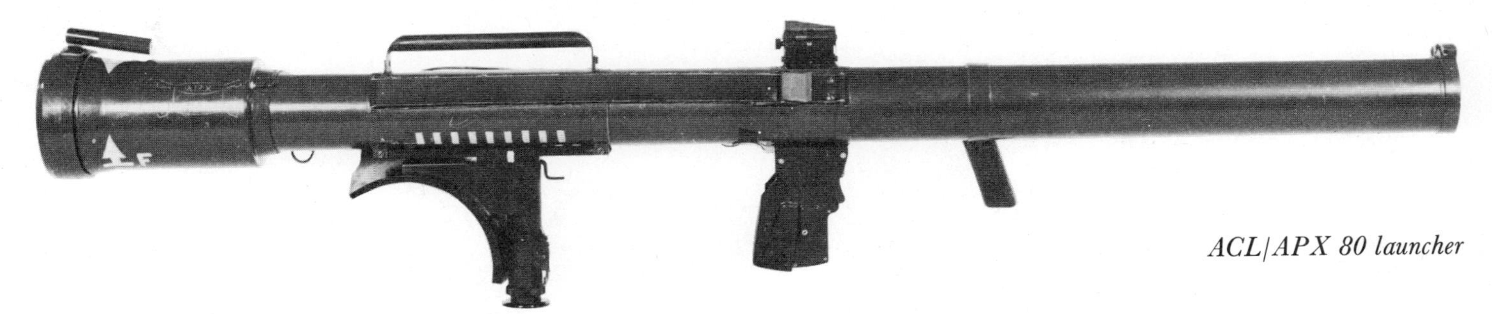

ACL/APX 80 launcher

Armbrust 300 anti-tank free-flight disposable launcher

Manufacturer: **Messerschmitt Bölkow-Blohm GmbH (Germany)**

Calibre	80 mm
Dimensions	Length 82 cm
Weight	4·8 kg
Range	300 m
Time of flight	1·5 sec to 300 m
Sight	Reflex
Ignition	Percussion
Muzzle velocity	220 m/sec
Ammunition	Shaped charge. Anti-personnel and illuminating rounds available
Effect	Penetrates 300 mm of armour plate
Crew	1

Armbrust 300 in action

Armbrust 300 is a private development by the manufacturer and is intended for close combat against armoured vehicles, though anti-personnel and illuminating versions are also available. The weapon is supplied as a pre-loaded, one-shot disposable system.

Its most unusual feature is the virtual elimination of smoke, noise and flash, thus enabling a soldier to engage targets without giving away his position. Precise information on the operating principles of the weapon have not been released. However, it is claimed that an all-up weight of 4·8 kg enables a soldier comfortably to carry up to six rounds and, using the reflex sight fitted, to engage an enemy with an excellent chance of success. The primary anti-tank round is a hollow-charge rocket which is armed after 10 m of flight and is capable of penetrating 300 mm of armour plate.

Not yet adopted for service.

Armbrust 300

PZF44 anti-tank free flight rocket launcher

Manufacturer: **West German Federal Ministry of Defence**

Calibre	Rocket 81 mm Launcher 42·8 mm
Dimensions	Length 88 cm
Weight	6·9 kg
Range	200 m
Sight	Optical
Ignition	Percussion
Muzzle velocity	107 m/sec
Ammunition	Shaped charge
Effect	Penetrates 320 mm of armour plate
Crew	1–2

The PZF44 is a recoilless weapon with a similar configuration to that of the Czechoslovakian P27 and the Russian RPG7. As far as is known from the limited information released, it operates in a similar manner, and has an effective range of 200 m.

The projectile consists of an 81 mm, shaped-charge warhead equipped with a tail boom of 42·8 mm. The tail boom incorporates the rocket motor which is probably initiated by a percussion firing mechanism.

In service with the West German forces.

81 mm PZF 44 Panzerfaust

BO810 Cobra 2000 anti-tank guided missile

Manufacturer: **Messerschmitt–Bölkow–Blohm GmbH (Germany)**

Dimensions of missile	Length 95·2 cm Diameter 20 cm Wingspan 48 cm
Weight	Missile 10·3 kg Aiming unit 4·1 kg
Range	400 m–2000 m
Speed	300 kph
Sight/aiming	Optical with joystick
Operation	Line of sight, command by wire
Warhead	Hollow charge and fragmenting hollow charge
Effect	Anti-tank warhead penetrates 475 mm of armour; Anti-tank shrapnel warhead penetrates 350 mm of armour and is lethal out to 10 m
Crew	1
Separation	50 m
Simulator	Indoor available and dummy warhead

Cobra 2000s deployed on the ground. (Note operator right foreground.)

Cobra is a wire-guided missile of low weight designed for operation by one man who can easily carry, set up and launch two missiles. An unusual feature is that it can have two interchangeable warheads. The hollow-charged warhead is claimed to be effective against all known armour, whilst the anti-tank/shrapnel warhead has both a penetration effect of some 350 mm as well as a blast effect which scatters fragments over 15 m from the point of detonation.

The Cobra is conventionally shaped, and consists of a cylindrical body with a cruciform wing arrangement. However, launching of the missile is different from most other comparable weapons in that no launcher is used. The missile is placed on the ground so that a booster, located between two of the wings, points downwards. When the missile is launched, the booster propels it upwards and forwards at an angle of 20 degrees. At a given moment, the sustainer motor in the rear section cuts in and the missile is accelerated towards the target.

The operator is equipped with a control box which can be connected to as many as eight missiles, using separation cables and a junction box. The control box incorporates all the devices for launching and guiding the missile, including the battery power supply. Guidance is by the target coincidence method Immediately after launch, the missile is gathered on to the operator's line of sight. Using the optical sight on the control box, the operator continues to track the target, sending commands to the receiver gyro assembly in the missile by means of a joystick control, via the wire dispensed by the missile. The receiver-gyro interprets these signals and activates spoilers on the wings, which alter the flight path accordingly. A visual flight monitor is provided by the flare assembly located in the rear of the missile.

Cobra 2000s

In service with the West German and Argentinian forces.

Milan anti-tank guided missile

Manufacturer: **Aerospatiale and Messerschmitt–Bölkow–Blohm GmbH (France/Germany)**

Dimensions of missile	Length 750 cm Diameter 10·3 cm
Dimensions of tube	Length 120 cm
Weight	Missile 11 kg Launcher/guidance unit 15 kg Ready to fire 26 kg
Range	25 m–2000 m
Speed	180 m/sec
Sight/aiming	Optical tracking with semi-, auto-IR homing
Operation	IR guidance, with command by wire
Warhead	Hollow charge
Effect	Penetrates all known armour
Crew	2
Simulator	Field trainer under development
Environment	Pan climatic

Milan launcher/guidance unit

Milan is a joint Franco–German-developed, wire-guided, anti-tank missile system consisting of three separate units: an aiming unit incorporating the sighting and firing mechanism; the missile in its launch tube; and a light tripod support. The missile is contained, with its wings folded, in the launch tube which also serves as a container for transport and storage. The tube is equipped with an electrical- and mechanical-locking device for attachment to the sight unit. A battery in the tube supplies power to the aiming unit.

The missile consists of a warhead containing a hollow charge and fuse, a two-stage rocket motor which forms the body, and the rear section which contains the jet deflection system and guidance equipment. This last consists of a cartridge-driven gyro, and IR tracer, a bobbin holding the two-strand wire, a signal decoder and a battery.

On launch, a gas generator in the tube gives an initial boost to the missile and accelerates it to a speed of some 76 m/sec. Recoil from the generated gas throws the spent tube from the launcher back some feet behind the firing point. After launch, the rocker motor accelerates the missile to a final speed of 174 m/sec. Once in flight, the aiming unit, which contains a sighting telescope and IR sensor, as well as the guidance control system, generates signals which are transmitted to the missile along the wire dispensed behind it. The signals are interpreted and passed to a single deflector in the jet nozzle which is synchronised with the rotation of the missile.

Much attention has been paid to operator safety. The missile is locked in its tube and as long as this is the case, ignition of the gas generator and rocket motors is impossible. Only pressing the trigger can unlock the missile, and the warhead is armed only when it has left the tube and the rocket motor is ignited. In combat conditions, the weapon is claimed to be extremely difficult to locate because of the absence of the flash, noise or smoke normally associated with the firing of such weapons. With a second man to assist in reloading, a rate of fire as high as 5 rpm can be achieved against targets at long ranges.

In service with the French and West German forces.

Milan in action

Milan launched

Mamba anti-tank guided missile

Manufacturer: **Messerschmitt-Bölkow-Blohm GmbH (Germany)**

Length	99·5 cm
Diameter	10 cm
Fin span	40 cm
Weight	11·2 kg
Warhead	HEAT (2·5 kg)
Range	300 m (minimum), 2000 m maximum)
Guidance	Optical/wire
Simulator	Indoor
Environment	−40° to +60°C
Simulator	Indoor available

The West German MBB company have developed the Cobra system (produced by Bölkow from the first generation missile Cobra 810) to their latest, the Mamba, which has an improved guidance system, and a double motor which allows course corrections and easier gathering during a slower initial flight phase which is followed by great acceleration. Flight time is shortened considerably, thereby reducing the chances of evasion by the target. The single-chamber motor expands via a downwards-angled jet and thus compensates for the weight of the missile during both the start and cruise phases. By using the beam-riding principle, guidance is very much improved, enabling the missile course to be corrected equally well in all directions. As a thermal battery is used in the missile, it is permanently ready for use, and can operate equally easily in temperatures from −40° to +60°C.

In service with the West German forces.

Mamba in its packing case

Mamba, packing case open

Indoor simulator (for Mamba)

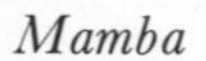

Mamba

Mosquito anti-tank guided missile

Manufacturer: **Contraves Italiana SpA (Italy)**

Dimensions of missile	Length 111 cm Diameter 12 cm Wingspan 60 cm
Weight	14·1 kg
Range	350 m–2400 m
Speed	90 m/sec
Sight/aiming	Optical, with joystick
Operation	Manual gathering, command by wire
Warhead	Hollow charge, fragmentation
Effect	Penetrates 660 mm of armour plate. Fragments
Crew	1–2

The Mosquito missile is capable of carrying either a hollow charge or fragmentation warhead. These warheads are packed separately from the conventionally designed glass-fibre missile which is powered by a two-stage, solid-propellant motor. The missile is housed in a launch/transport container with its wings folded. To launch the missile the container is placed on the ground and opened. A pre-selected warhead is attached and, by means of a separation cable, the operator connects the sight, control unit and container.

The control unit contains a joystick control and an electronic package and mounts a binocular sight. Once launched the missile is manually gathered and subsequently guided to the target. Course corrections are initiated by the operator's movements of the joystick and transmitted to the trailing-edge spoilers on the cruciform wings of the missile via the wires dispensed in flight. The system of roll-stabilisation of the missile in flight is probably similar to that of the Bantam.

In service with the Italian forces.

Mosquito in its container

Mosquito ready for launch

KAM 3D (Type 64 ATM) anti-tank guided missile

Manufacturer: **Kawasaki Heavy Industries (Japan)**

Dimensions	Length 102 cm Diameter 12 cm Wingspan 60 cm
Range	350 m–1800 m
Speed	306 kph
Sight/aiming	Optical, with push-button control
Warhead	Hollow charge
Operation	Line of sight, command by wire
Effect	Penetrates all known armour
Crew	2
Environment	Pan climatic

The Kam 3D is a wire-guided, anti-tank missile, the development of which started in 1957 under a contract awarded to the Technical Research and Development Institute of the Japanese Defence Agency. It was later adopted as standard equipment for the Japanese Self-Defence Force, and has the official designation Type 64ATM.

The Kam 3D has an orthodox configuration with a cylindrical metal body and cruciform metal wings incorporating full-scale trailing edge spoilers for control. Propulsion is provided by a dual-thrust, solid-propellant, double-base rocket motor, the booster stage of which accelerates the missile to its cruising speed in 0·8 sec, after which the sustainer stage maintains velocity. Launched at an elevation of 15 degrees, the operator tracks his target with an optical sight and brings the missile into line using a push-button control box which transmits signals along the wire dispensed from the missile. Visual tracking of the missile is achieved by a flare during daylight, and by the glow of the sustainer rocket exhaust at night. A gyro stabilisation system automatically compensates for pitch and yaw.

The missile can be fired singly or in multiples.

In service with the Japanese Ground Self-Defence Force.

KAM 3D

KAM9 anti-tank guided missile

Manufacturer: **Kawasaki Heavy Industries (Japan)**

Dimensions of missile	Length 150 cm Diameter 15 cm Wingspan 33 cm
Dimensions of container	Length 160 cm Diameter 16 cm
Weight	Missile 3 kg (in container) Tracking unit 50 kg Computer 20 kg Sight 20 kg
Range	2000 m
Sight aiming	Optical
Operation	Automatic homing, command by wire
Warhead	Shaped charge
Effect	Penetrates all known armour
Crew	3

KAM9

KAM9 is an improved performance, longer range version of the KAM 3D. It has been under development since 1966 on a contract from the Technical Research and Development Institute of the Japanese Defence Agency.

The KAM9 is launched from its tubular transport/storage container. Before launch this container is placed on the launch tracking unit which contains the firing device, sight and check system. On firing, a primary solid-propellant motor ejects the missile from the container to a safe distance. A secondary motor then ignites and accelerates the missile to its cruising speed.

The operator, by constantly tracking the target, allows sensors in the tracking system to observe the missile's position in relation to the target, thereupon course deviations are fed into a computer and corrective signals are passed to the missile gyros via wires dispensed by the missile. The shaped-charge warhead is equipped with a piezo-electric fuse system and is capable of penetrating all known armour.

Not yet in service.

140 mm anti-personnel free flight missile launcher

Manufacturer: **State factories (North Vietnam)**

Calibre	140 mm
Dimension	Length 114·3 cm
Weight	9·1 kg
Range	1060 m
Warhead	HE

The 140 mm single-tube rocket launcher is another of the several launchers made by extracting one tube from a multi-barrelled launcher. Here the Vietcong and North Vietnamese have taken a tube from the Soviet RM14 launcher and mounted it crudely (but effectively) on two adjustable brackets on a wooden board. The launcher is set up for firing on a log or pile of earth, and small adjustments to elevation and traverse can be made using screws set in the brackets. A quadrant can be fitted to aid sighting. Although of greater calibre than the DKZ-B rocket, this missile is much shorter and lighter with a similar range, but is much less accurate. The rocket weighs 39·5 kg, is 109 cm long, and is fitted with a nose-mounted fuse capable of being set at impact or delayed-action detonation. It is readily identifiable by its size, the narrow groove cut round the outside of the base, and the canted jet-nozzles set into the base to impact the spin stabilisation.

In service with the Vietcong.

SR Carl-Gustav M2 multi-purpose free flight rocket launcher

Manufacturer: **Forenade Fabriksverken (Sweden)**

Carl-Gustav M2 in action

Calibre	84 mm
Dimensions	Length 113 cm
Weight	14·2 kg (29·5 kg protected for carriage in transport)
Range	450 m (anti-tank) 1000 m (HE and smoke) 2000 m (illuminating)
Time of flight	1·79 sec to 400 m
Sight	Open or telescopic
Mount	Sprung bipod and shoulder-fired
Ignition	Percussion
Muzzle velocity	350 m/sec
Ammunition	HEAT, HE, smoke and illuminating
Effect	Penetrates 400 mm of armour plate
Crew	2
Environment	Pan climatic

This is a recoilless weapon designed primarily for use against tanks, but can also be used in a variety of roles. In this form it has been adopted by a number of NATO countries. However, a new sighting system has recently been developed and is described separately under Carl-Gustav M2-550.

The weapon consists of a rifled tube with a rear-mounted, up-rotating venturi, a sprung bipod-cum-shoulder rest, a pistol-grip firing mechanism and a forward handgrip. An open or a telescopic sight can be fitted, the latter incorporating a temperature-compensating device.

The weapon is normally operated from the shoulder, like a rifle. A round is loaded from the rear into the breech with the venturi open. Firing is mechanical by a hand-cocked, percussion-operated detonator located in a tube on the right side of the barrel. It is worth noting that the weapon venturi has to be securely closed and locked before firing is possible. In addition, a two-pressure trigger and safety catch are provided.

As with other multi-purpose systems, a variety of ammunition types is manufactured. The main round is a hollow-charge HEAT projectile, but anti-personnel, smoke and illuminating rounds are also available. The basic design of these rounds comprises a warhead and a light alloy cartridge case which has a plastic blow-out disc in the base to achieve the recoilless effect.

In service with United Kingdom, Swedish, Norwegian, Canadian, Danish, Eirean and Austrian forces.

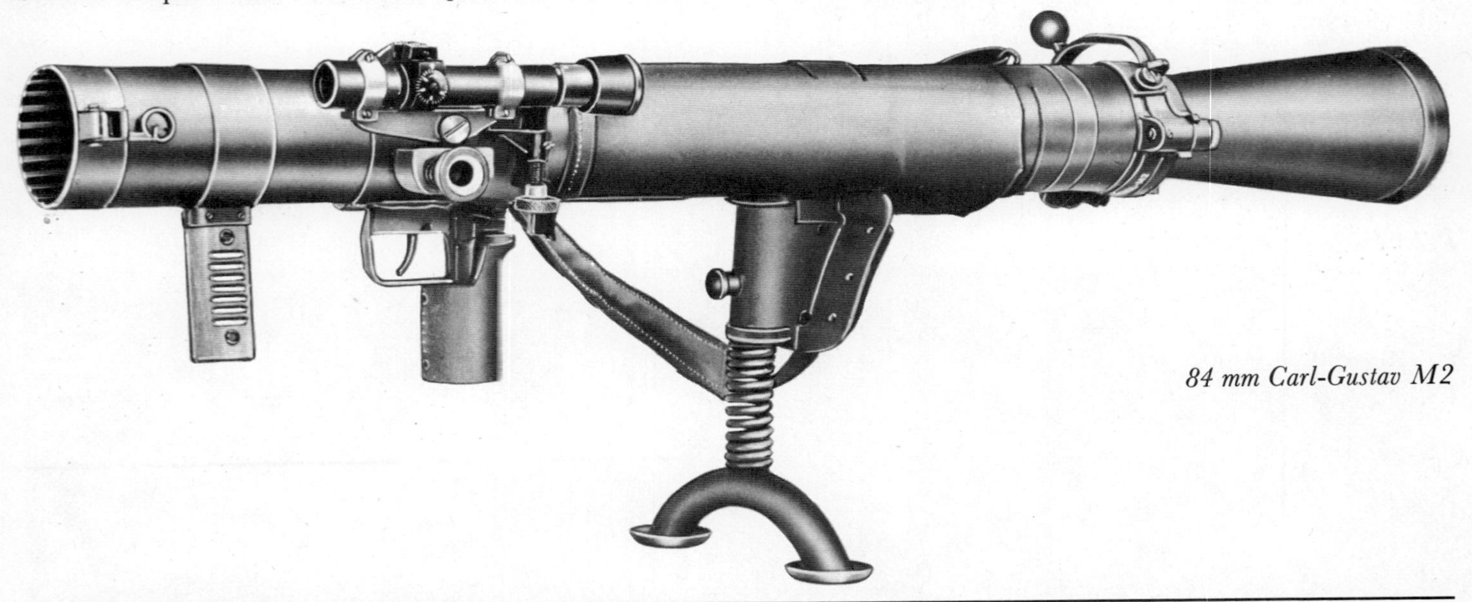

84 mm Carl-Gustav M2

Carl-Gustav M2-550 multi-purpose free flight rocket launcher

Manufacturer: **Forenade Fabriksverken (Sweden)**

Calibre	84 mm
Dimensions	Length 113 cm
Weight	17·6 kg
Range	700 m (HEAT), 1000 m (HE and smoke), 2000 m (illuminating)
Time of flight	2·2 sec to 700 m
Sight	Optical-electronic
Mount	Sprung bipod and shoulder-fired
Ignition	Percussion
Muzzle velocity	260 m/sec
Ammunition	HEAT, HE, smoke and illuminating
Effect	Penetrates 400 mm of armour plate
Crew	2

In this version, the breech-locked percussion arrangement of the Carl-Gustav M2 is retained. However, modifications to the sight support bracket and the fore-grip have been made in order to mount the new sighting system designated FFV 555. This sight has been developed to make it easier for the operator to determine

84 mm Carl-Gustav M2-550 (with the HEAT 551 r ound)

Carl-Gustav M2-550 in action

HEAT 551 round

Details of HEAT 551 round

accurately both the range and the aim-off required to hit a moving target. The new sight is telescopic and incorporates in its design a drum-operated coincidence range finder effective between 175 m and 1000 m. A selector lever can be set to compensate for the ballistic variations of different ammunition. With the range to the target set on the range drum, and the selector lever adjusted, a lead (aim-off) compensator is automatically programmed to admit a light pulse in the firer's sight picture. By noting target movement between consecutive light pulses, the required lead can be ascertained.

To maximise the advantages of this new sight a fin-stabilised HEAT round (FFV 551) of improved performance has been produced. It consists of a light alloy cartridge case and a hollow charge shell fitted with an auxiliary rocket motor, which ignites 5 m–18 m from the muzzle. Since the round is fired from a rifled barrel, a Teflon slip ring is used to limit its rotation and six tail fins provide additional stabilisation in flight. On impact, detonation is initiated by a piezo-electric fuse system. Alternative ammunition types are as supplied for the SR Carl-Gustav M2. A sub-calibre training aid is available.

In service with the Swedish forces.

Bantam anti-tank guided missile

Manufacturer: **A B Bofors (Sweden)**

Dimensions of missile	Length 84·8 cm Diameter 11 cm Wingspan 40 cm
Dimensions of container	97 cm × 177 cm × 177 cm
Weight	Missile 7·6 kg Control unit 5·5 kg Ready to fire 20 kg
Range	300–2000 m
Speed	85 m/sec
Sight/aiming	Optical with joystick
Operation	Manual gathering, command by wire
Separation	20 m
Warhead	Hollow charge
Actuation	Impact
Effect	Penetrates 500 mm of armour
Crew	1–2
Simulator	Indoor available
Environment	−40 C to +60 C

Bantam is a wire-guided, anti-tank missile intended for operation by one man. However, mounts for vehicles and small aircraft have been developed. The basic configurations consist of the missile with its hollow-charge warhead in a combined launch and transport container, a control unit with separation cable and a special harness which doubles as a launching ramp.

About 30 sec is said to be needed to bring the system

Bantam launched

Bantam in flight

into action. The container and harness are placed on the ground pointing towards the expected threat. The 20 m separation cable is connected to the control unit which consists of an optical sighting device and a control box, with a joystick-type control. Two 2000 m spools of wire, each with a micro-switch, start to unwind from the missile when it is launched. After 40 m, the micro-switch in one of these spools ignites the sustainer and up to four pre-selected tracer flares in the rear of the missile. The other micro-switch arms the warhead after 230 m. Command signals are also conveyed through the wires during flight.

Once in flight the folded wings of the missile open and are designed to give the missile rotation and stability. Vibrating spoilers on the trailing edges of the wings carry out direction control. On each quarter rotation of the missile, they switch from elevation to traverse and vice versa. The missile gyro is activated on firing by a powder pellet which, after the missile has travelled 30 m, withdraws a pin that unlocks the gyro. Guidance commands are amplified by a transistor amplifier in the missile and channelled to the spoilers via a commutator connected to the gyro.

The missile can be guided 1 m from the launcher, and the sustainer and tracers ignite after 40 m; at 45 m the booster goes out and acceleration is finished. After 230 m, the fuse is armed and the missile guided to the target where impact initiates the piezo-electric fuse system and the hollow-charged warhead is detonated.

In service with the Swedish and Swiss forces.

Miniman anti-tank free flight disposable launcher

Manufacturer: **Forsvarets Fabriksverk (Sweden)**

Calibre	74 mm
Dimensions	Length 90 cm
Weight	2·9 kg
Range	250 m
Sight	Plastic graduated grid
Mount	Shoulder-fired
Ignition	Percussion
Muzzle velocity	160 m/sec
Ammunition	HEAT (0·9 kg)
Effect	Penetrates 340 mm of armour plate
Crew	1
Environment	−40 C to +60 C

Miniman is one of the several lightweight disposable weapons available today. It is designed for use by one soldier against armour or emplacements. The barrel is made of a glass-fibre reinforced plastic material, and external parts such as sights, firing mechanism housing and shoulder piece are also plastic. The entire weapon comes as a pre-loaded unit in a two-round container. The barrel acts as a missile container and is weatherproof. Two complete missiles are supplied in an aluminium and polyethylene pack, with a carrying handle, weighing 7·1 kg.

Unlike more conventional systems a propellant-filled combustion chamber is connected to the projectile by a frangible joint. This joint retains the missile in position until the gases escaping from the combustion chamber produce sufficient pressure to snap the joint. The missile in this weapon is an aluminium-cased, hollow-charge projectile with a piezo-electric detonating device. Stabilisation in flight is achieved by its shape and assisted by small unfolding wings. In order to fire, the operator removes the muzzle cover, mechanically cocks the firing mechanism, raises the sights and presses the thumb-operated trigger. Having fired, he discards the launcher.

A 9 mm sub-calibre practice weapon is available.

In service with the Swedish forces.

Miniman ready to fire

Miniman

SPG82 anti-tank free flight missile launcher

Manufacturer: **State factories (USSR)**

Calibre	82 mm
Length	215 cm
Weight	37·8 kg
Range	700 m (300 m effective)
Ammunition	HEAT or HE
Effect	Penetrates 230 mm of armour plate
Crew	2

The Soviet-made SPG82 was the standard infantry battalion rocket launcher of several Warsaw Pact countries in the immediately post-war years, but was replaced by the B10 and is now normally found in use only in the Middle East. The SPG82 has a very long tube with a flared muzzle, a shoulder-pad on the left side, a small two-wheeled mount, and a long tubular towing bar attached behind the muzzle. The large shield with two vision ports is intended to protect the user against the rocket blast, not enemy fire. Normally the weapon is fired on its mount, but can be freed to be fired by two men, one firing the launcher and the other helping to support it. Both HE and HEAT rockets are provided, both weighing 5 kg, and the launcher possesses two different sets of sights, one for each ammunition type—the HEAT round can pierce 230 mm of armour, and is used up to 300 m, whilst the HE sight is graduated every 100 m as far as 700 m.

In service with the Syrian and Afghan forces.

B10 (or RG82) anti-tank gun

Manufacturer: **State factories (USSR)**

Calibre	82 mm
Length	191 cm
Weight	85·5 kg
Range	4700 m (effective 400 m)
Sight	Optical (PBO2)
Ammunition	HEAT and HE
Effect	Penetrates 300 mm of armour plate
Crew	4

82 mm B10 (RG82)

The Soviet-made B10 (or RG82) recoilless gun replaced the SPG82 rocket launcher as the battalion anti-tank weapon in about 1950 and, although now largely replaced in its turn by the SPG9, is still to be found in some satellite countries and China. Considerably heavier than its predecessor, the B10 is equipped with the more modern PB02 sight for both direct and indirect fire and using a 7·3 kg, shaped-charge, fin-stabilised HEAT round, and an 8·2 kg HE round, is capable of much more effective fire—the HEAT round can penetrate up to 300 mm of armour at 400 m.

The B10 is breech-loaded and percussion-fired, the trigger and bolt being accommodated in a pistol-grip located above and to the right of the tripod mount, whilst the optical sight is on the opposite side in front of a rectangular, perforated guard. The gun is usually transported in a truck or armoured personnel carrier, but can be towed by its four-man crew on its small two-wheeled carriage using the conspicuous towbar fitted below the muzzle. The small castor wheel below the towbar is designed to prevent the muzzle touching the ground while the gun is being manœuvred or set up for firing on the tripod. The latter can be adjusted to give either a low silhouette or a better field of view, but the weapon can, if necessary, also be fired whilst still on the wheeled mount. A rate of fire of 6–7 rpm is attributed to the B10

In service with the Polish, Bulgarian, East German, North Vietnamese, Near Eastern and communist Chinese forces and the Vietcong.

B11 (or RG107) anti-tank gun

Manufacturer: **State factories (USSR)**

Calibre	107 mm
Length	350 cm
Weight	305 kg
Range	6650 m (450 m effective)
Sight	Optical (PB04)
Ammunition	HEAT and HE
Effect	Penetrates 350 mm of armour plate
Crew	5

The B11 (or RG107) is the biggest recoilless gun manufactured by the USSR, having been developed (along with the B10) from knowledge gained from captured United States weapons during the Korean War. Whilst the B11 is designed mainly as an anti-tank gun, able to pierce 350 mm of armour at 450 m, it is light and mobile enough on the two-wheeled carriage to be manœuvred in battle by its five-man crew using the light towbar attached below the muzzle. Although the B11 can, like the smaller but similar B10, be fired from its wheeled mount, the motor-car-type wheels are awkward and are often removed whilst the gun is raised on its tripod.

The two main recognition features of this weapon are the tripod which, while travelling, is spread with the front leg attached to the tube and the two rear legs raised and carried at an angle to the rear, and the limber loop above the muzzle by which the gun is connected to its towing truck.

The B11 is breech-loaded, using a 16·8 kg shaped-charge, fin-stabilised HEAT round or a 21·3 kg HE round, both types of ammunition being served by the same PBO4 direct and indirect fire sight, which is mounted high and centrally on the gimbal mounting of the barrel. The USSR no longer uses this, or any similar calibre recoilless gun, in its first-line divisions.

In service with some Warsaw Pact, North Vietnamese, and Near Eastern forces and the Vietcong.

107 mm B11 (RG107)

SPG9 anti-tank gun

Manufacturer: **State factories (USSR)**

Calibre	75 mm
Length	200 cm
Range	1000 m
Sight	Optical
Ammunition	HEAT
Crew	2

The SPG9 recoilless gun is a breech-loading weapon which is now gradually replacing the B10 in several Warsaw Pact countries. The SPG9 has a long, clear tube with a carrying handle (to allow manœuvring while the tube is hot) set about 25 cm from the muzzle. It is mounted permanently on a tripod mount, of which the legs fold forward for packing. No wheels are provided, as the weapon is usually transported in an armoured personnel carrier, although it is light enough to be carried by two men. The missile, probably a shaped-charge HEAT round, is similar to that used by the PRG7V, having an initial propellant cartridge and fin-stabilisation. An optical sight is located on the left of the tube above the mount, and the foresight is also on the left attached above the forward carrying handle.

In service with the Soviet and most other Warsaw Pact forces.

75 mm SPG9

RPG2 anti-tank free flight missile launcher

Manufacturer: **State factories (USSR and the People's Republic of China)**

Calibre	40 mm (missile 82 mm)
Length	95 cm
Weight	2·7 kg
Range	100 m
Ammunition	HEAT
Effect	Penetrates 180 mm of armour plate
Crew	1

The original Soviet PRG2, now obsolescent, is a very simple and cheaply produced, infantry section anti-tank grenade launcher. It is a later version of the RPG1, developed from the German World War II Panzerfaust system. It consists of a cylindrical tube with an awkward-looking pistol-grip containing the trigger, bolt and firing pin, a small foresight and tall rear sight, and a wooden covering round most of the tube behind the pistol-grip. The reason for the large rear sight, which is graduated for 50 m, 100 m and 150 m, is the high trajectory of the the 2·7 kg shaped-charge HEAT round, which has a maximum anti-tank range of only 100 m, and a penetration capability of 180 mm of armour. The fin-stabilised round is muzzle-loaded and percussion-fired. A safety-catch is provided. The weapon can be fired standing, kneeling or lying but only from the right shoulder, as there is a gas-ejection port on the right side of the tube above the pistol-grip. Later models have a small, flared blast-shield on the open rear end of the tube and can be fitted with the Soviet NSP2 infra-red night sight. Rate of fire is about 4 rpm.

The RPG2 is similar to the Czech P27, but has simpler sights and no bipod. The Chinese communists make a copy of the RPG2 which they call the anti-tank grenade launcher Type 56, and in North Vietnam the weapon is known as the B40.

In service with some Warsaw Pact, the communist Chinese and North Vietnamese forces and the Vietcong.

RPG2 with missile

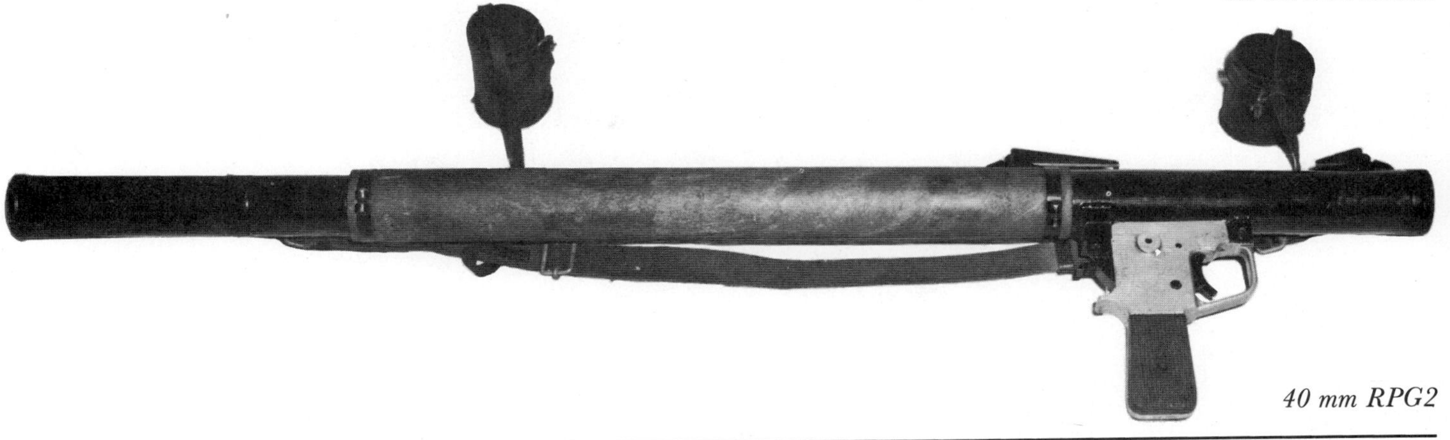

40 mm RPG2

B40 anti-tank free flight missile launcher

Manufacturer: **State factories (USSR and the People's Republic of China)**

See the RPG2.

In service with the North Vietnamese forces.

RPG7V, RPG7, RPG7D anti-tank free flight missile launcher

Manufacturer: **State factories (USSR)**

Calibre	40 mm (missile 85 mm)
Length	100 cm
Weight	8·5 kg (loaded)
Range	500 m
Sight	Telescopic (× 2½) and battle
Ammunition	HEAT
Effect	Penetrates 320 mm of armour plate

The Soviet RPG7V anti-tank grenade launcher is the replacement for the RPG2, affording improved range and penetration. Although still operating on the basic German Panzerfaust principle of a tube open at both ends with a pistol-grip and trigger-firing mechanism, there are several technological improvements over RPG2, some of which convey a marked difference in the new weapon's appearance. These include the blast-shield of the RPG7V which is large and conical; to provide greater thrust the centre tube section covered by part of the wooden heat shield has been expanded; to improve handling there are now two pistol-grips; there are now two relatively small iron sights graduated every 100 m from 100 to 500, and in addition a × 2½ telescopic sight can be used as well as the NSP2 infra-red night sight.

The 1·7 kg rocket-assisted, fin-stabilised, shaped-charge HEAT round is muzzle loaded and percussion fired, although the projectile itself utilises a piezo-electric fuse which self-destructs at at 900 m and the PRO7 telescopic sight can be illuminated for night use. The RPG7V missile is launched from the tube by the normal propellant but a short distance from the launcher the rocket motor cuts in, thus giving the missile greater accuracy from the resultant increased thrust and lower trajectory; 320 mm of armour can be penetrated at the much increased range. The original RPG7 was slightly larger than the RPG7V, and fired a slightly smaller projectile. RPG7D is the paratroop version of RPG7V, which can be divided in two for compact transportation.

40 mm RPG7

40 mm RPG7V

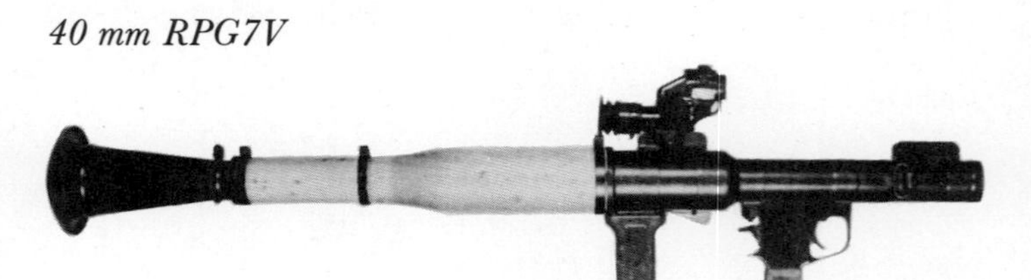

RPG7V round

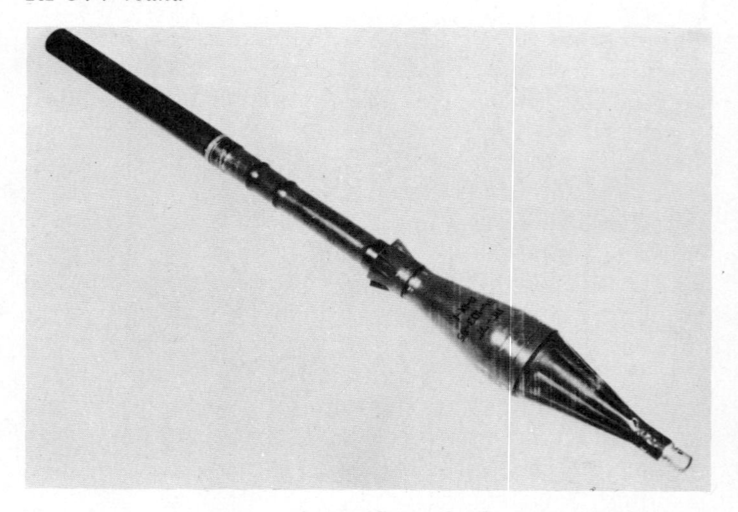

In service with the Warsaw Pact, North Vietnamese, Syrian, Iranian and Egyptian forces and the Vietcong and IRA.

Sagger AT-3 anti-tank guided missile launcher

Manufacturer: **State factories (USSR)**

Dimensions of missile	Length 81·5 cm Diameter 12 cm
Weight	11 kg
Range	2500 m
Sight/aiming	Optical with joystick
Operation	Automatic gathering, command by wire
Warhead	HEAT
Actuation	Impact
Effect	Penetrates 400 mm of armour plate
Crew	3

The infantry version of the Sagger anti-tank guided

missile is operated by a team of three men, normally from an unprepared site on the ground, but the weapon can be fired from an armoured personnel carrier or truck. The weapon kit consists of a two-part missile (HEAT warhead and body), carried in a glass-fibre case which serves as the launch pad, and a control box. As the missile is of lightweight construction, the crew can carry several at once. For normal operation the missiles, which are wire-guided, are set up, facing the direction of enemy advance, on the light launch rail contained in the carrying case. Maximum range is about 2500 m and the HEAT warhead will penetrate up to 400 mm of armour at 0° impact angle on impact at any distance up to that range. The control box incorporates activation and flight control switches set in front of the optical sight. On being fired by electrical impulse from the activation switch, the missile is gathered in the optical sight and guided on to the target by manipulation of the flight control switch.

A similar version of this missile is also used by the countries listed, in fixed mounts on various armoured vehicles.

In service with all the Warsaw Pact, Yugoslav, Egyptian and Syrian forces.

Sagger in action. (Missile is behind the optical sight.)

Sagger

DKZ-B anti-building and anti-personnel free flight missile launcher

Manufacturer: **State factories (USSR)**

Calibre	122 mm
Dimensions	Length 246 cm
Weight	49·4 kg
Range	10 900 m
Warhead	HE

The DKZ-B rocket launcher is yet another example of a single-tube launcher taken from a multiple-tube rocket launcher, in this case the original being the Soviet BM21. As with the other similar weapons, the purpose has been to produce a launcher which can be easily transported in difficult country by guerrilla forces, using a minimum crew. It breaks down into two loads—the 21·7 kg, 246 cm long tube, and the mount, folding to a compact 96·5 cm × 30·5 cm × 43·2 cm, weighing 27·7 kg. The HE fragmentation rocket is the longest (190·5 cm) and heaviest (46·3 kg), and has the longest range of all the known single-shot launcher missiles. It is fin-stabilised but, additionally, spin is imparted by a rifling slot along the tube (visible on the outside). These assets, together

122 mm DKZ-B

with the solid tripod mount, panoramic sight and fitted quadrant, give the launcher a good degree of accuracy not achieved by the other similar weapons. The nose-mounted fuse can be set to impact or delayed-action detonation. The rocket is easily distinguished by its long pencil shape, folding fins round the base, six jet-nozzles set in the base, and the small spin-imparting lug 76 cm from the base.

In service with the Vietcong.

SAM-7 anti-aircraft guided missile

Manufacturer: **State factories (USSR)**

Dimension of launcher	150 cm
Weight	10 kg
Range	Out to 3700 m
Speed	Mach 1·5
Operation	Heat-seeking
Sight	Battle
Warhead	HE
Actuation	Impact
Crew	1
Environment	Pan climatic

The SAM-7 heat-seeking, low-level surface-to-air missile was developed by the USSR to counter the threat of ground-attack aircraft and helicopters armed with anti-armour and anti-aircraft weapon systems It has proved its use against such targets in Vietnam and during the 1973 Arab-Israeli war but, because of its lack of radar target acquisition facilities, the hand-held system of operation and the small size of the warhead, it is not effective against larger and faster aircraft Additionally, the essentially heat-seeking nature of the projectile means that it must attack the exhausts of the target and can be diverted by ejection of flares and other manœuvres, such as flying below 150 m. The system consists of a launching tube about 150 cm in length, fitted with a solid shoulder-pad behind the pistol-grip firing mechanism, a thermal battery forward of the pistol-grip and simple battle-sights mounted above the left side of the tube. A distinctive heavy strengthening band is fitted round the muzzle, and a canvas sling is provided for carrying purposes. The SAM-7 system equates to the United Kingdom Blowpipe and the United States Red Eye and is alternatively referred to as SA7, Grail and Strela (Russian—'Arrow').

In service with the Soviet, other Warsaw Pact, Egyptian, Syrian and North Vietnamese forces and the Vietcong.

SAM-7 in action

Mobat (BAT L4) and Wombat anti-tank gun

Manufacturer: **Royal ordnance factories (United Kingdom)**

Mobats in action

Wombat in action

Calibre	120 mm
Length	400 cm
Weight	766 kg (Wombat—275 kg)
Range	780 m
Crew	3

The Mobat is the bigger of the two recoilless anti-tank guns used by the British Army, the smaller gun being the Wombat. The Mobat was developed from the original BAT L1 and comprises an L6A1 recoilless gun fitted with a 7·62 mm Bren light machine gun on the left-hand side of the barrel and mounted on a two-wheel L2A1 towed carriage. The Bren is primarily a fixed line of fire weapon for spotting purposes. The outstanding visual characteristic of the Mobat is the vertical rectangular sliding-wedge breech with its operating levers on both sides and the large conical blast-shield projecting from the lower part of the breech rear. The HE-P rounds are, of course, breech-loaded, utilising the loading tray fitted on top of the blast-shield, no additional propellant

Close-up of Wombat, vehicle mounted

cartridge being necessary. The gun is trigger-fired, using an electrical firing pin: the power supply is obtained from two batteries housed in the firing-mechanism frame. Over longer distances the Mobat is towed by the permanently attached limber-ring above the muzzle, but can be manœuvred for short distances by means of the small handles on the short box-girder trail.

The Wombat, though based on the Mobat, is simpler, weighs only 275 kg and is carried in a light truck. It can be manhandled by its crew, but cannot be towed more than a few metres. The breech is a swinging collar type, and carries the venturi. A ·50 spotting rifle replaces the Bren.

The Wombat is in service with the United Kingdom forces. The Mobat is obsolescent.

Vigilant anti-tank guided missile

Manufacturer: **British Aircraft Corporation Limited (United Kingdom)**

Dimensions of missile	Length 98·5 cm Diameter 13·1 cm Wing span 27 cm
Dimensions of sight case	15·5 cm × 9 cm × 26·7 cm
Dimensions of launcher box	98·5 cm × 26·7 cm × 26·7 cm
Weight of missile	14·8 kg
Weight of sight/aiming system	4·2 kg
Range	200 m–1375 m
Time of flight	12·5 sec to 1375 m
Sight/aiming	Optical with thumb control
Operation	Manual gathering, command by wire
Separation	63 m
Warhead	Hollow charge
Actuation	Impact
Effect	Penetrates 550 mm of armour plate
Crew	2
Simulator	Classroom and field trainers available
Environment	−32 C to +52 C

Vigilant is a first generation man-portable, wire-guided, anti-tank missile that can be set up and launched by one man, and is claimed to be effective against any known battle tank. A number of configurations have been produced for Vigilant, the most basic of which consists of a launcher box containing the missile, a sight controller unit, a battery and a separation cable. Other configurations include various vehicle mounts and a remote traversable ground mount.

To use the system in its basic mode, the launcher is placed on the ground pointing in the general direction of an expected threat. The operator connects the separation cable (up to 63 m) and takes up a suitable fire position. Any target within a ±10 degree elevation and ±35 degree azimuth bearing can be engaged.

The sight controller is held in both hands, the finger of one hand operating the firing trigger and the thumb of the other resting on the guidance button. The target is held in the optical sight and the missile is launched. The operator retains the target in his sight, gathers the missile on to its flight path by using the thumb control which passes elevation or azimuth corrections to the

Vigilant showing all components

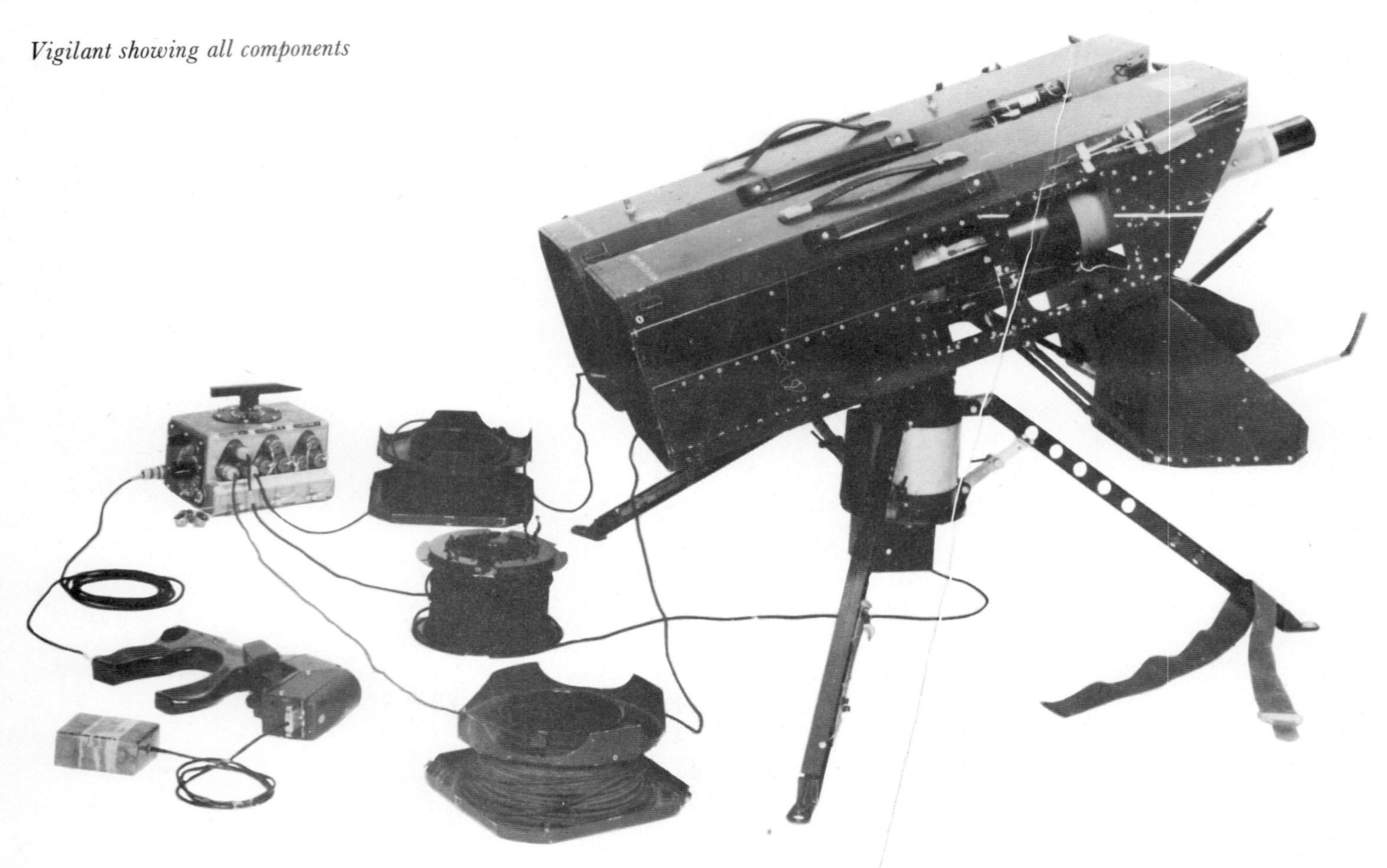

Vigilant sight-control unit

Vigilant vehicle-mounted

Pen etration effect of Vigilant

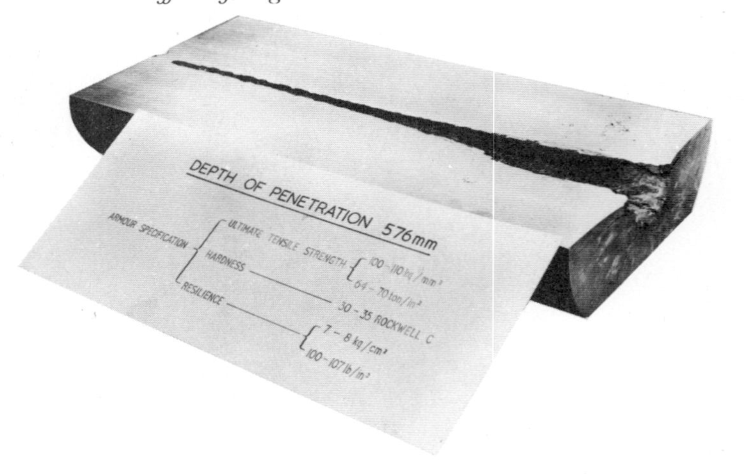

missile, as required, via the wire dispensed from the missile. So long as the marker flare of the missile is framed in the sight picture, the control is centred and the missile will remain on the flight path.

The Vigilant employs its own velocity control system of which the essential feature is a gyro auto-pilot. Flight corrections are received by the auto-pilot which measures the changes in the missile's flight. The missile responds only to thumb-control signals, therefore a reversal process to put the missile back on a parallel path once elevation and azimuth corrections have been made is automatically carried out by the auto-pilot. In addition, the auto-pilot automatically compensates for high winds and buffeting.

A variety of optional extras is available for the Vigilant, including a selector box enabling one man to operate up to six missiles, a remote traversable launcher, holding two missiles, which can be moved through an arc of 340 degrees in 8 sec, and a selector box permitting the control of three such launchers by a single operator.

In service with the United Kingdom, Finnish, Kuwaiti, Abu Dhabi and Swiss forces.

Vigilant at the moment of launch

Swingfire (and Beeswing) anti-tank guided missile

Manufacturer: **British Aircraft Corporation Limited (United Kingdom)**

Dimensions of missile	Length 106 cm Diameter 17 cm Wingspan 37·3 cm
Weight	Missile and launching box 10 kg
Range	150 m–4000 m
Sight/aiming	Optical with joystick control
Operation	Auto-gathering, command by wire
Separation	50 m plus
Warhead	Hollow charge
Actuation	Impact
Effect	Penetrates all known armour
Crew	1–3
Simulator	Multi-purpose and field trainers
Environment	− 32 C to + 52 C

Swingfire is a second generation wire-guided missile designed primarily for installation in any kind of military vehicle. It is also possible to carry it in, or under, a Wessex helicopter or one with comparable performance.

The Swingfire missile, which can be treated as a conventional round of ammunition, is launched direct from its launching box which is hermetically sealed up to the moment of launch. The missile is automatically programmed on to the operator's line of sight both in elevation and azimuth. This means that the operator does not have to gather the missile manually. It also means that the missile can be launched out of line with the target from, say, behind a building. However, the operator must have a clear line of sight; thus a separation unit has been designed to allow the operator to fire missiles 50 m or more from the launch vehicle.

Once the missile is in the operator's line of sight, command signals are given by a joystick on the sight unit and transmitted via a wire dispensed from the missile. The signals are interpreted by the missile gyros and

Swingfire at launch

Beeswing mounted, ready for action

enforced by deflection of the main motor thrust or 'Jetavator'. The gyros operate in a similar manner to those in the Vigilant system and will maintain the missile's course in the absence of commands from the operator.

A development of Swingfire, the Beeswing, is also available. It can be divided into convenient packages which permit a three-man crew to carry the system up to 500 m and then bring it into action. The Beeswing packages can also be transported by a standard load-carrying vehicle of similar capacity to a long wheelbase Land-Rover. In addition, the Swingfire system is being adapted for helicopter launching, as Hawkswing, which will give maximum opportunity for exploiting its 4000 m range from a wide variety of helicopters.

In service with Belgian and United Kingdom forces.

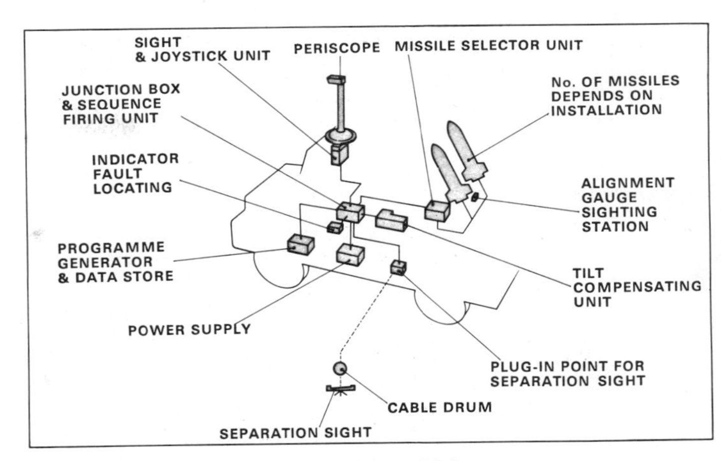

Swingfire equipment as stowed in vehicle

Beeswing major assemblies

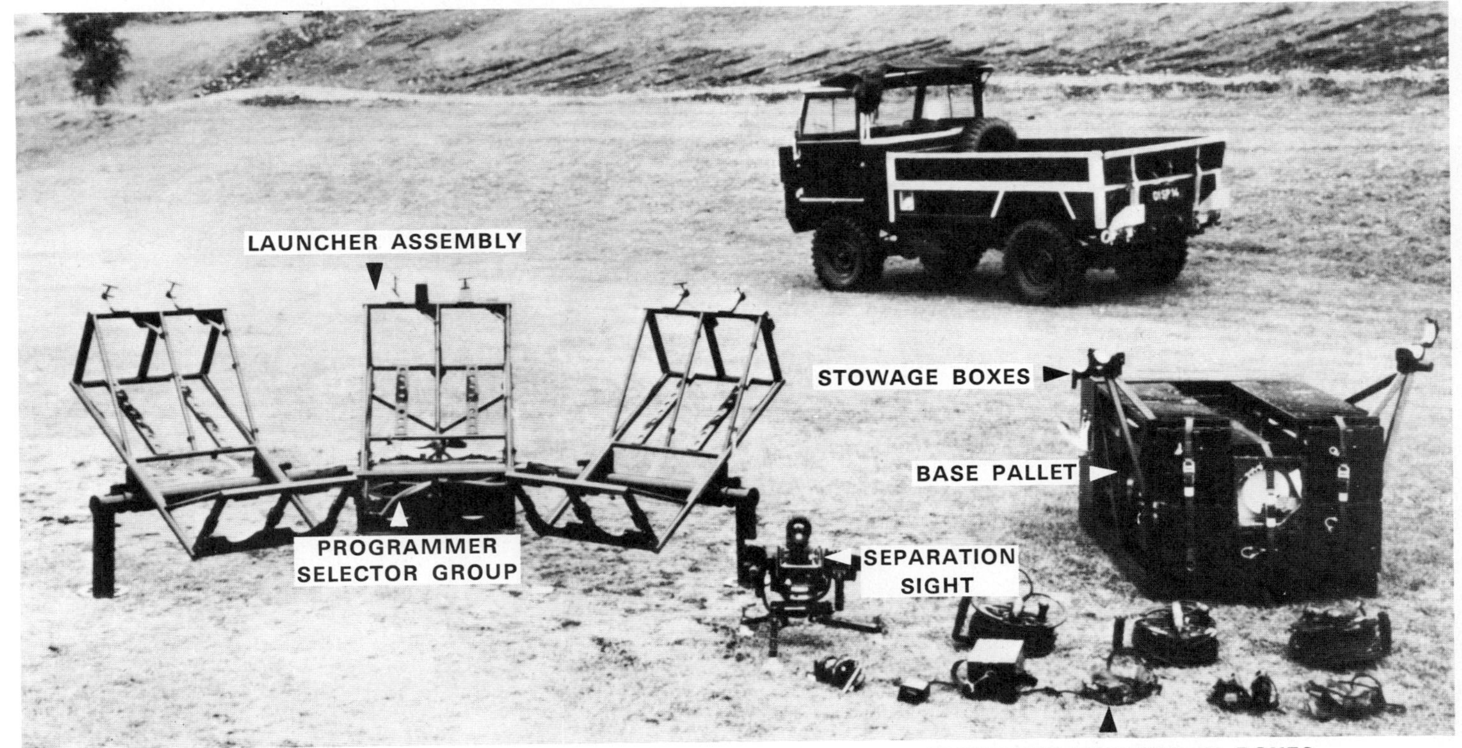

Blowpipe anti-aircraft and anti-vehicle guided missile

Manufacturer: **Short Brothers and Harland Limited (United Kingdom)**

Blowpipe at launch

Dimensions of canister	Length 140 cm
Weight	Missile 14 kg (in canister) Aiming unit 7 kg Ready to fire 21 kg
Range	Out to 3000 m
Speed	Supersonic
Sight/aiming	Electro-optical with optional IFF
Operation	Auto-gathering with radio, and part auto, guidance
Warhead	HE
Actuation	Impact or proximity
Effect	Aircraft destruction and damage to small craft and vehicles
Crew	1–2
Simulator	Classroom and field trainers available
Environment	Pan climatic

Blowpipe is a relatively inexpensive and simple weapon system which can be operated by one man. It consists of a launch canister containing a supersonic missile and the aiming/guidance unit. Together the two units weigh 21 kg and only a few seconds are needed to fit them together. The weapon is then ready to engage approaching aircraft, small naval craft or soft-skinned vehicles.

The operator places the weapon on his shoulder and supports the canister with his left hand. With his right, he holds the grip on the aiming unit. One finger operates the trigger and the thumb rests on the control button. A monocular sight on the aiming unit enables the target to be sighted and tracked. Squeezing the trigger generates electrical impulses to activate the batteries in the canister which supply power to the aiming unit and the missile. A sequence device within the aiming unit checks that all the missile systems are activated and then fires the first-stage motor. This motor ejects the missile, but is burnt out before the missile clears the launcher. Thus, the missile coasts to a safe distance before the second motor ignites and accelerates the missile to supersonic speed.

After launch, the operator must continue to track the target because the aiming unit incorporates a sensor which detects the relative position of the missile to the operator's line of sight. The sensor is designed mainly to facilitate the gathering of the missile, and has a range limited both to the output of the flares in the missile, and to the sensitivity of the sensor itself. Deviations are received by the sensor and new instructions are beamed back to the missile by radio. The missile flies on automatic guidance for 2–3 sec, during which the operator continues to track the target. After this time, the missile is under manual control and the thumb-operated guidance button is used. On manual control, guidance is relatively simple since it is not necessary to centre the target in the monocular sight. So long as the target is retained in the field of view, the missile can be guided to it.

The Blowpipe warhead is situated in the centre section of the missile and is basically a blast device, with a small armour-piercing capability. In the nose of the missile there is a proximity fuse which will trigger the warhead, provided the missile passes within a certain distance of the target. If the missile is on target, the warhead is detonated on impact.

Having fired and guided a missile, the operator must detach the empty canister and attach a second one before he is ready to engage another target.

About to enter service with the United Kingdom and Canadian forces.

Blowpipe

Blowpipe front view

Atlas anti-tank guided missile

Manufacturer: **British Aircraft Corporation Limited (United Kingdom) and Fabrique Nationale Herstal (Belgium)**

Warhead	HEAT
Operation	Optical and laser beam
Range	1000 m

The lightweight anti-tank laser-assisted system (Atlas) is being developed jointly by British Aircraft Corporation and the Belgian FN Herstal as a possible replacement for the Carl Gustav, Wombat and Vigilant. The Atlas is, in effect, a combination of rocket launcher and guided missile, as the launcher can be used over short ranges without the assistance of the laser guidance system. The Atlas consists of three components in a tube-type launcher (similar to the Carl Gustav—with a hinged breech and conical venturi, a solid shoulder-pad above the curved Y-shaped bipod behind the pistol-grip firing mechanism, and grenade launcher-type sights on the top of the tube above the pistol-grip); the rectangular laser guidance system on a small tripod; and the cylindrical missile with folding fins, solid fuel double motor, laser sensors and HEAT warhead, transported in a narrow rectangular box. The missile is breech-loaded and trigger-fired. Where the range is too great to ensure a certain hit, using the grenade-launcher-type sights, the target is collected on the laser guidance system, to which the laser sensors on the missile react in the final flight phase, activating small jets on the missile body to correct its course.

Not yet in service.

Atlas

M18A1 anti-tank free flight missile launcher

Manufacturer: **Department of the United States Army**

Calibre	57 mm
Dimensions	Length 157 cm
Weight	20·2 kg
Range	4000 m (effective 450 m)
Sight	Optical
Mount	Rear-mounted bipod and centrally mounted monopod
Muzzle velocity	360 m/sec
Ammunition	HEAT
Effect	Penetrates most known armour
Crew	2

The M18A1 is no longer in service with the United States forces. However, it is still occasionally to be encountered amongst her allies. By today's standards this weapon, which saw service in Korea, is heavy and lacking in performance. However, in its time it very adequately served as an effective defence against armour.

In service, but obsolescent.

M20 and M20A1 anti-tank free flight missile launcher

Manufacturer: **Department of the United States Army**

Calibre	88·9 mm
Dimension	Length 153 cm
Weight	5·9 kg
Range	100 m–150 m
Sight	Optical
Ignition	Electrical
Muzzle velocity	160 m/sec
Ammunition	HEAT
Effect	Penetrates 280 mm of armour plate
Crew	2

The M20Al is better known as the 'Super Bazooka'. It was adopted by many NATO countries, including the United Kingdom, where it was known as the 3·5 in rocket launcher M20 Mk 2. It has now been relegated to reserve units and is occasionally encountered in the hands of insurgent forces.

Much of its success and popularity was due to its simple design. The launcher consists of two lengths of tube which are connected together with interlocking lugs of the twist-bayonet type. The shoulder rest, magnetic-type firing mechanism and optical sight are all attached to the tube. The rocket is loaded from the rear and two wires are connected to externally-mounted terminals. In cold weather, there is some risk from exhaust particles and in wet weather it is often necessary to dry the terminals to avoid any risk of hang-fire. Nevertheless, though this weapon has now been largely superseded by more sophisticated devices, it remains an efficient and effective defence against armour.

In service with some United States, United Kingdom, Canadian, Italian, French, Portuguese and other forces.

M20A1 in action

M72, M72A1, M72A1GI anti-tank free flight disposable missile launcher

Manufacturer: **Department of the United States Army**

M72 folded. Sectioned to show working

Calibre	66 mm
Dimensions	Length 65·3 cm Ready to fire 89 cm
Weight	Launcher 1·1 kg Complete 2·1 kg
Range	1000 m (effective 200 m)
Sight	Front—reticle with lead markings Rear—peep
Ignition	Percussion
Muzzle velocity	144·8 m/sec
Ammunition	HEAT
Effect	Penetrates 260 mm of armour plate
Crew	1

The M72 is a self-contained disposable anti-tank system consisting of a rocket loaded in a telescopic tube launcher. This tube serves as a watertight container as well as housing the percussion firing mechanism.

The launcher is composed of two concentric tubes, the inner of which is aligned to the outer by a slot in the trigger housing. To fire the weapon the protective caps are removed and the inner tube is withdrawn to a locked position. The sights are raised and the target can then be engaged.

The 66 mm HEAT round for this weapon is a fin-stabilised rocket basically consisting of a M18 warhead, a M54 rocket and an impact detonating fuse (M412). Since all the rocket propellant is burnt in the launch tube there is no danger to the firer from exhaust particles.

In service with the United States, Canadian and United Kingdom forces.

66 mm M72

M67 anti-tank recoilless rifle

Manufacturer: **Department of the United States Army**

Calibre	90 mm
Dimensions	Length 134·6 cm Height 43 cm (on ground mount)
Weight	15·8 kg
Range	2100 m (effective 450 m)
Sight	Optical
Mount	Rear bipod and forward monopod
Ignition	Percussion
Muzzle velocity	218 m/sec for HEAT (376 m/sec for A/P)
Ammunition	HEAT, anti-personnel also available
Effect	Penetrates all known armour
Crew	2

The M67 is the heaviest man-portable recoilless rifle in service with the United States armed forces, though it is now largely confined to reserve units. It is primarily an anti-tank weapon, but can be used in an anti-personnel role with a canister round.

It is designed to be fired from the ground using the rear bipod mount and a forward monopod for stability, but it can be fired from the shoulder. The weapon is manually loaded via a rear breech and as such fires fixed ammunition with a perforated casing. Firing is accomplished by a percussion system and an × 3 optical sight (M 103) is provided. This sight is graduated in 50 m intervals up to 400 m, every 100 m up to 800 m.

In service with the United States reserve forces.

90 mm M67 RCL gun

M40A1 anti-tank gun

Manufacturer: **Department of the United States Army**

Calibre	106 mm
Length	340 cm overall
Weight	130 kg
Range	2750 m
Muzzle velocity	500 m/sec
Ammunition	HEAT and anti-personnel
Crew	3—4

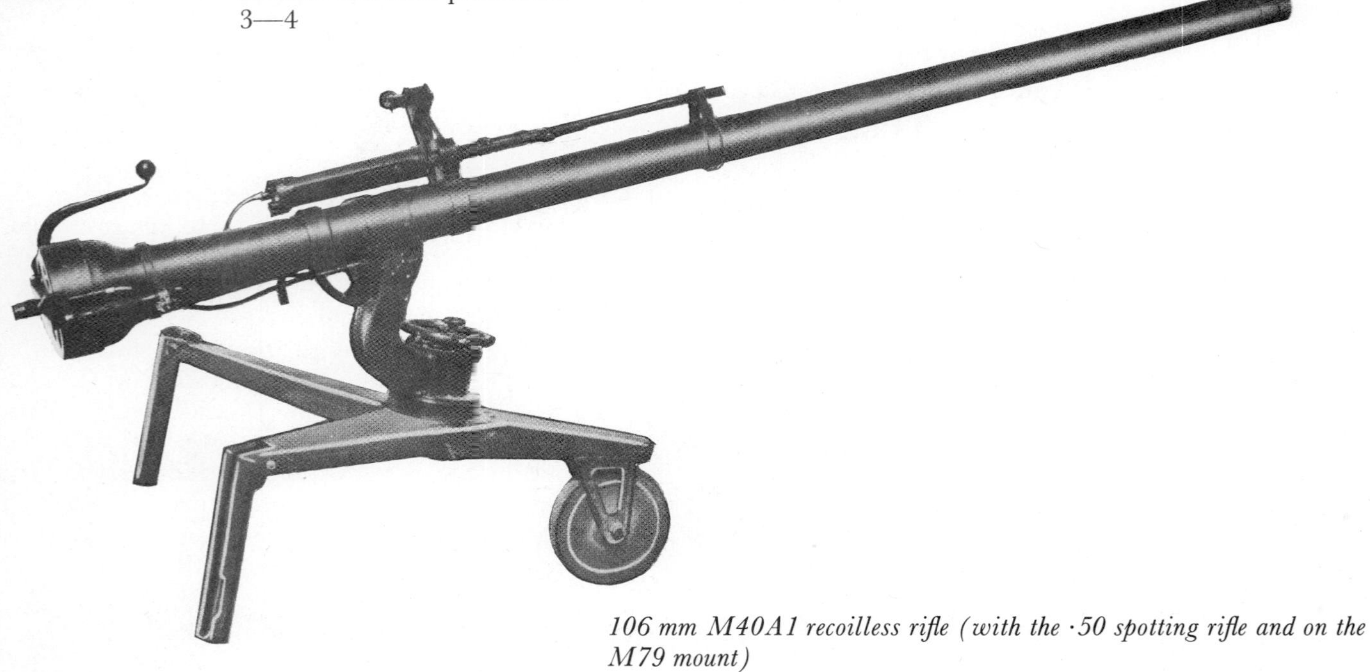

106 mm M40A1 recoilless rifle (with the ·50 spotting rifle and on the M79 mount)

The M40A1 recoilless rifle is produced in two slightly differing variations—the basic model and the M40A1C, which has a slightly improved breech mechanism, and carries a projectile indicator on its barrel. This weapon is a conventional smooth bore, breech-loading gun equipped with a ·50 in calibre spotting rifle, mounted on top of the rear portion of the barrel, and fitted with an interrupted thread-type breech block. The M79 mount sometimes used with this gun differs from the standard M92 mount (a plain, short-legged tripod with a 360° traversing ring) in that its three flat, box-girder legs are attached horizontally to the central pedestal, with a large castor-wheel below the end of the forward leg. On the left side above the pedestal is the large elevating gear-wheel. The weapon is percussion-fired, using both HEAT and HEP-T rounds, and can be relied on to fire 2500 rounds before the barrel needs to be replaced.

In service with the United States, Iranian and Israeli forces.

Tow (XM-71A) anti-tank guided missile

Manufacturer: **Hughes Aircraft Company (United States)**

Dimensions of missile	Length 116·8 cm Diameter 15·2 cm
Weight	Missile 18·1 kg
Range	65 m–4000 m
Speed	1000 kph
Sight/aiming system	Optical and auto-sensor
Operation	Manual gathering, command by wire
Actuation	Impact
Warhead	Shaped charge
Effect	Penetrates all known armour
Crew	2
Environment	Pan climate

Tow, which stands for Tube-launched, Optically-tracked, Wire-guided missile, is currently in service with the United States Army and others. It saw extensive combat in Vietnam, where in the first 77 combat launches from a UH-1-B (Huey Cobra) helicopter, 62 hits were claimed.

The basic mount is man-portable and capable of being split into four units. These units are the tripod, launcher, electronic signals generator and the tracing optical and optical sensor. Mounts for a variety of vehicles are being developed.

The missile in its container, is loaded into the launcher, and electrical connections are made through the container as it is loaded. The wings and control surfaces are folded at this stage but open on ejection. In flight, two wires, through which command signals are transmitted, unreel from the missile. So long as the operator tracks the target in his sight, automatic corrections are made by a sensor to keep the missile on the correct course and the operator does not have to make any range or lead calculations.

In service with the United States, West German, Dutch, Iranian and Kuwaiti forces.

Tow at launch

Tow in action

Tow gyro-stabilised sight

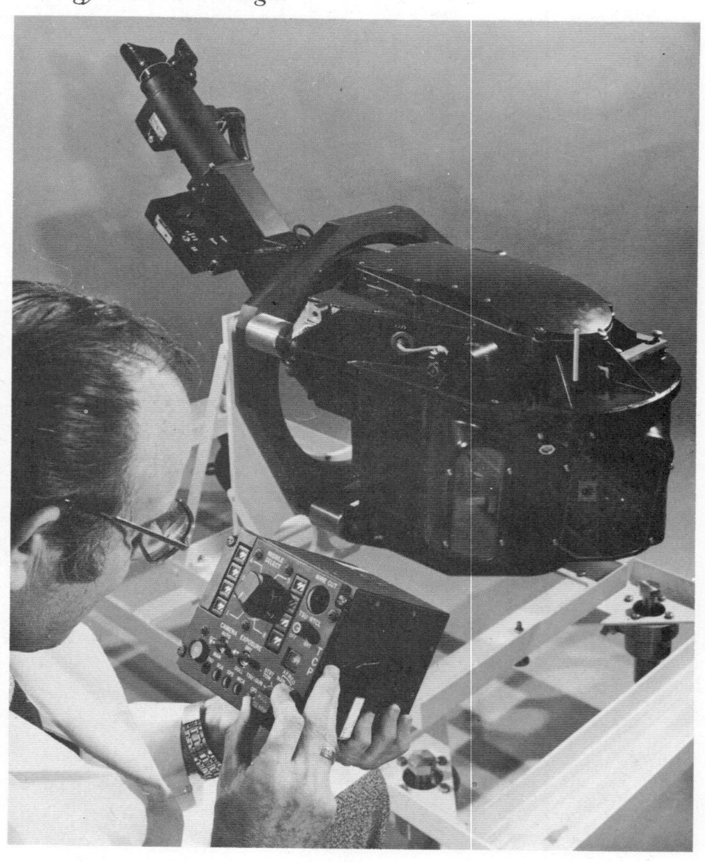

Tow mounted on a mule

Tow being fired from a Huey Cobra

Dragon (XM-47) anti-tank guided missile

Manufacturer: **McDonnell-Douglas Corporation (United States)**

No details available

The Dragon system is composed of two main components—the round and the tracker system. The basic guidance principle is similar to that of the Tow missile, and it is intended as a replacement for the 90 mm recoilless rifle at platoon level. It has a range of 1000 m.

The round is packed in a container, which serves as both a carrying case and recoilless launcher. Operationally, the carrying case is attached to the tracker which contains a telescope, a sensor device and some electronics.

To fire Dragon, the operator simply lines his telescopic sight on to the target and launches the missile. Provided he keeps his sight on the target until the round hits, a light source on the rear of the missile will be picked up by an optical sensor mounted on the tracker. This sensor monitors the deviation of the missile from the gunner's line of sight, and automatically sends correcting signals to the missile over two wires dispensed from it. Within the missiles these signals are interpreted as bursts from the rocket motor which are vented through nozzles around the missile's circumference. Thus, like Tow, the missile will follow on the command-to-line-of-sight principle, as long as the operator continues to track his target in his sight. The launcher is discarded after firing.

Dragon carried slung

Not yet in service, but production of Dragon has now been assured.

Dragon at launch

Redeye (XM-41EZ) anti-aircraft guided missile

Manufacturer: **General Dynamic Corporation (Pomona Division) (United States)**

Dimensions of missile	Length 120 cm Diameter 76 mm
Weight	13 kg
Range	3000 m
Speed	Supersonic
Sight/aiming	Optical
Operation	IR homing
Warhead	HE
Effect	Blast
Crew	1–2

Redeye is a shoulder-fired, surface-to-air missile designed for defence against low-flying aircraft. It carries a conventional HE warhead and is powered by a two-stage solid propellant motor which accelerates it to supersonic speed.

The missile is housed in a carry/launch tube which is fitted to an optical sight and firing mechanism assembly equipped with an audio-device to inform the operator when the missile homing system is energised. Once the IR homing device has locked on to the target, the missile is launched. On firing, a booster motor expels the missile from the tube. It coasts for about 6 m whereupon the main motor ignites. An infra-red sensor in the missile homes on the heat of the aircraft engines.

In service with the United States and West German forces.

Redeye at launch

Stinger anti-aircraft guided missile

Manufacturer: **General Dynamic Corporation (Pomona Division) (United States)**

Dimensions of missile	Length 152·4 cm
Weight	14·5 kg (ready to fire and with IFF)
Range	No information available
Speed	Supersonic
Sight/aiming	Optical
Operation	Passive homing with proportional navigation ('fire and forget')
Warhead	HE
Effect	Blast and aircraft destruction
Crew	1
Environment	Pan climatic

Stinger

The Stinger weapon system is under development for the United States Army and Marine Corps, and is still subject to security restrictions. The system which utilises much of the Redeye technology is intended to provide all arms with a man-portable air defence system primarily in forward areas, or on the move.

Stinger is designed to counter high speed, low-level aircraft, but is also effective against slower aircraft. It is shoulder-launched, and straightforward. The weapon is pointed, the target is identified and ranged, and the weapon is fired. Once the missile has been launched, its guidance devices, which are of the passive homing and proportional navigation type, become operational. No further guidance is necessary.

It is understood that, at present, the weapon consists of a missile in a launch tube. The sealed tube serves as a storage handling container, and cannot be opened in the field except by firing. A sighting and firing unit on to which the tube is fitted can be supplied with an optional IFF device.

Under development.

RB57 anti-tank free flight missile launcher

Manufacturer: **State factories (Yugoslavia)**

Calibre	44 mm (missile 90 mm)
Length	96 cm
Weight	8·3 kg
Range	1200 m (effective 400 m)
Sight	Folding tangent leaf and battle
Ammunition	HEAT
Effect	Penetrates 270 mm of armour plate

The Yugoslav RB57 anti-tank grenade launcher was produced in 1957 as a result of research into the German Panzerfaust system and has subsequently replaced the United States World War II launchers used until then by the Yugoslav forces. The RB57 has thus a certain resemblance to the Soviet RPG2, but is much more sophisticated and is almost comparable in performance to the RPG7V (but having a longer maximum range).

The RB57 is, however, considerably heavier and the 1·8 kg shaped-charge, fin-stabilised HEAT round is not rocket assisted, having a maximum effective range against a stationary target of only 400 m, which is reduced to 200 m if the target is in motion, and only 270 mm of armour can be penetrated. Rate of fire is 4 rpm. The projectile is muzzle-loaded and fired by means of a primer set(at a right angle to the direction of flight) in the lower side of the tail boom. The primer is detonated by a spring-loaded striker housed in the cylinder set in front of the pistol-grip assembly. The striker is activated and automatically reset by a double-action trigger. The standard sights are of the folding tangent leaf type, graduated every 100 m up to 400 m and, for fast close-range action, a small battle sight graduated to 200 m is provided. The weapon has occasionally been seen with an optical sight fitted.

In service with the Yugoslav forces.

44 mm RB57

M60 anti-tank gun

Manufacturer: **State factories (Yugoslavia)**

Calibre	82 mm
Length	220 cm
Weight	122 kg
Range	4500 m (effective 500 m)
Sight	Optical (PTDM60) and battle
Ammunition	HEAT and HE
Effect	Penetrates 220 mm of armour plate
Crew	5

The Yugoslav M60 recoilless gun is similar to the Soviet B10 of the same calibre, but is longer and heavier and has a longer maximum anti-tank range. The M60, like the RB57 anti-tank grenade launcher, is one of three anti-tank weapons (the third is the M65 105 mm recoilless gun) developed by the Yugoslavs to take the place of the United States anti-tank weapons on which they had relied since World War II.

A breech-loading smooth-bore weapon, the M60 uses a 4·3 kg shaped-charge, fin-stabilised HEAT round which will penetrate 220 mm of armour at ranges up to 500 m, and also a HE projectile up to the maximum range of 4500 m. This round resembles an artillery shell at first sight, but the finned boom is protected by a perforated sheet casing which is released on launching.

The optical PTDM60 sight is set level with the tube on the left side and is graduated up to 1500 m, but additionally, as in the case of the RB57, there is a battle sight fitted for quick action.

Normally the M60 is towed behind a light truck on its light, curved, tubular, two-wheeled carriage, but it can also be either towed easily by its five-man crew by the double-headed towbar below the muzzle, or quickly broken down for pack transport by the crew or by mule. This is a common feature of most Yugoslav made weapons.

In service with the Yugoslav forces.

82 mm M60

M65 anti-tank gun

Manufacturer: **State factories (Yugoslavia)**

Calibre	105 mm
Length	415 cm
Weight	280 kg
Range	6000 m (effective 600 m)
Sight	Optical
Ammunition	HEAT
Effect	Penetrates 330 mm of armour plate

Whereas the USSR has now given up large-calibre recoilless guns, Yugoslavia, with its problem of finding effective weapons of sufficient manœuvrability to be of use in mountainous terrain, has, in addition to the two lighter anti-tank weapons, the RB57 and the M60, developed its own large recoilless rifle, the M65. Among communist countries' weapons, the M65 is unique in that it is fitted with a 12·7 mm spotting machine gun, the UB, used at ranges up to 600 m (the M65's maximum effective anti-tank range) and employing a 20 round belt, fired either automatic or single shot. The M65 is a breech-loading weapon with a very long rifled barrel, allowing the gun to fire its HEAT projectiles a distance of 6000 m. HE rounds have not yet been seen with this weapon. Six rounds can be fired in one minute and the shaped-charge warhead will pierce 330 mm of armour plate.

The gun is mounted on a tripod, the two wheels attaching to the base of two of the legs, whilst the third leg extends to the rear and also acts as a towbar. A small, square shield which protects the firer's face from blast is fitted in front of the optical sight. This weapon can travel in the normal manner towed by a truck or armoured personnel carrier, or can be broken down for carriage by mule.

105 mm recoilless M65

In service with the Yugoslav forces.

Grenades

Space does not permit a lengthy history of the grenade from the time the first one was conceived, neither is there much merit in giving it. So, a convenient point in history at which to begin is the outbreak of World War I in August 1914. At this time, the British forces had only one official grenade. This was the Hand Grenade No 1 which had been introduced into the British forces as a result of lessons learned at Port Arthur during the Russo-Japanese War. In August 1914, the grenade was in very short supply and production in quantity was not achieved until the middle of 1915 due to the complication of its manufacture and particularly of its detonator. This absurd shortage led to the production in the field of three types of improvised grenade, which was given considerable impetus on 27 December 1914 when the Germans first threw grenades into the British trenches.

The first improvised type was called the Jam-Tin bomb which was made by infantry from jam or milk tins filled with ammonal, or gun-cotton, obtained from the Royal Engineers. The grenade was fused by a short length of Bickford fuse which had to be lit before throwing. The second type consisted of glass bottles filled with Jelliteer JL, a lethal mixture of prussic acid, chloroform and triacelyl cellulose, sealed with a rubber stopper through which a fuse was inserted. The third type consisted of a tin, filled with explosive and shrapnel balls attached by two tapes to a wooden throwing handle. The time fuse protruded from the centre of the lid. The manufacture of these three types of grenade, and possibly others, was officially forbidden in December 1915, when quantities of the No 1 Grenade became more readily available. It is reported that there was much relief at this.

The No 1 Grenade consisted of a glass cylindrical body encircled by a narrow cast-iron ring, serrated to break into 16 fragments. The body was mounted on a wooden block to which a cane handle was attached. Four webbing streamers were nailed to the top of the handle. This grenade had a number of 'safety' devices, including a glass or aluminium removable cap upon which were stamped the words 'Fire', 'Travel', and 'Remove'. It also had a firing pin held in position by a whipcord bracket and a leather tag. Inevitably, this grenade had to be handled with some respect for it was filled with 3 oz of explosive and detonated upon impact—if not before.

Later, Hand Grenade No 2 (the Mexican or Tonite Hales grenade) and the Rifle Grenade No 2 percussion were introduced. Over 12½ million of these were produced during the war.

Finally, in the spring of 1915, the No 5 Grenade (or Mills Hand Grenade), which was a time-fused grenade, was introduced, and over 33 million of them were issued before it was superseded by No 23 Grenade. This grenade was very similar to the 36 Grenade which has just become obsolescent in the British Forces. It was probably one of the most famous series of hand grenades ever to be produced.

It is interesting to note, perhaps, that, at the outbreak of war, only the Royal Engineers, so far as the British Army was concerned, were trained in the use of grenades. However, trench warfare forced a change, although the training of infantry as bombers did not start seriously until May 1915. During World War II, a very great number of grenades was manufactured. Many had considerable similarity to the grenades of World War I, but many did not. In addition to the more conventional HE-filled grenades, there were phosphorus, incendiary, sticky and gas grenades. Considerable use was made of grenades fired from rifles and, indeed, considerable use was made of grenades during training. Battle inoculation, as it was called, became a very important aspect of training during the period of the phoney war and just after it. Realism, quite rightly, was considered to be an essential part of training. For this reason, and so far as the British forces were concerned, the 69 Grenade was a training aid, yet nowadays it would be considered to be an offensive hand grenade.

Since World War II great strides have been taken in three main areas: first, the rifle grenade. This has become a thoroughly sophisticated weapon culminating in the ability to use live ball ammunition as a means of projecting it. Clearly, this has some advantage for it avoids the manufacture, and the need to carry, special ballistite, or blank ammunition.

The second area is one in which multi-purpose, or polyvalent, grenades have been developed. These mainly consist of 4 or 5 grenade parts namely, the fuse and its cover, the body, a pre-fragmented metal sleeve and the tail assembly. Together with a clever fuse-setting system, it is possible to produce three main configurations—offensive hand, defensive hand and rifle grenades. To these can be added an 'impact only', 'delay only' or 'impact and delay' fuse.

In the third area, ingenuity and philosophy are strange bedfellows. Here there are the mini grenade, and the limited effect, or offensive, grenade.

These last two types, together with some of the others described in the book, are designed to produce a slight variation in the concept of war. This is that it is probably better to wound than to kill—on the grounds that overflowing hospitals will have a greater effect on the morale of the civilian population than the crowded, but unseen, cemeteries miles from home. Hence, a growing number of the modern grenades tend to be hand offensive rather than hand defensive.

As the reader will quickly notice, we have, in this section, given only a typical cross-section and selection of grenades. Many countries have been omitted for repetition can be boring. Gas grenades of all sorts have been excluded for other reasons. Space prevents us from illustrating the frighteningly wide variety of homemade grenade devices in service in Ulster, the Lebanon or in Portuguese Africa. But you will find enough to interest you for a while if you read on.

John Owen

PRB-423 controlled fragmentation hand grenade

Manufacturer: **sa PRB (Belgium)**

Dimensions	Diameter 57 mm Height 103 mm
Weight	235 gm
Body material	Plastic
Charge	Composition B (60 gm)
Arming	Pin, lever and striker
Fuse	4 sec pyrotechnic train
Effect	900 fragments out to 20 m
Safety	Manual pin
Environment	Pan climatic
Packing	40 grenades in a 'Nonail' box and 100 grenades in a 'Nonail' box. Fuses packed separately

PRB-423 hand grenade.

The PRB-423 grenade was developed at the request of the Benelux countries as an offensive/defensive grenade and based on NATO standards.

The body of the grenade consists of a plastic case enclosing spirally wound pre-fragmentated steel coil and an explosive composition. The initiation system is of the pin-and-lever type, equipped with a 4 sec delay. The lethal radius is 9 m from the point of detonation and fragments are ineffective after 20 m. PRB consider a fragment effective only if it perforates a 1 in thick pine panel and thus the safety radius of this grenade is presumably based on this criterion.

In service with the Belgian and Luxembourg forces.

PRB-103 polyvalent hand and rifle grenade

Manufacturer: **sa PRB (Belgium)**

Dimensions	Diameter 50 mm Length 296 mm (PRB-7 and PRB-8 – 85 mm)
Weight	665 gm (PRB-7 – 116 gm; PRB-8 – 440 gm)
Body material	See text
Charge	Pressed TNT (80 gm)
Arming	1·5 sec delay and impact
Sight	None
Calibre	50 mm
Method of discharge	Rifle with 22 mm diameter muzzle (PRB-7 and PRB-8 – manual)
Propellant	Ballistite round
Muzzle velocity	58 m/sec
Range	250 m–275 m
Fuse	See text
Effect	500 fragments out to 40 m plus (PRB-7 – blast)
Safety	Manual pin
Environment	Pan climatic
Packing	24 grenades are packed in an expanded polystyrene form which is heat-sealed in a waterproof bag. The fuses are similarly packed and both packages are placed in a 'Nonail' box, weighing 24 kg, which floats.

The PRB-103 is one of the new polyvalent grenades which are made of standardised components that can be separated to perform three different roles. This grenade consists of four basic components. First there is a tail assembly which consists of a fin-stabilised boom containing a holder for the propellant cartridge. Then, a grenade body which is made of thermal plastic material and filled with 80 gm of pressed TNT. Thirdly, a spirally wound steel wire, notched to disperse some 500 fragments. Last, there are the two types of fuse: the PRB-8 impact fuse which is used for launching the grenade by rifle and contains a self-destructing mechanism in the event of failure on impact, and the **PRB-3** time fuse which has a delay of 4·5 sec and which is used mainly with the offensive and defensive configured grenades. Both these fuses are of the block-striker lever and pin-safety type.

In order to use the PRB-103 as a rifle grenade, the PRB-8 fuse is used together with the three other components, and the entire grenade is launched from a rifle with a muzzle diameter of 22 mm. On detonation, the 500 fragments fly out and are claimed to be 100% effective within 12 m, 50% effective at 13·5 m, but ineffective over 40 m from the point of impact.

The defensive grenade (**PRB-8**) uses the PRB-3 fuse with its 4·5 sec delay, and the tail assembly is removed. The fragmentation effects are the same as those of the rifle-launched version. The offensive grenade (**PRB-7**) is obtained by unscrewing a retaining ring from the defensive version and removing the fragmentation sleeve. In special circumstances the PRB-8 fuse can be used with the offensive version.

PRB-8 hand grenade.

PRB-103 polyvalent grenade (with fin).

The components of the PRB-103 polyvalent grenade.

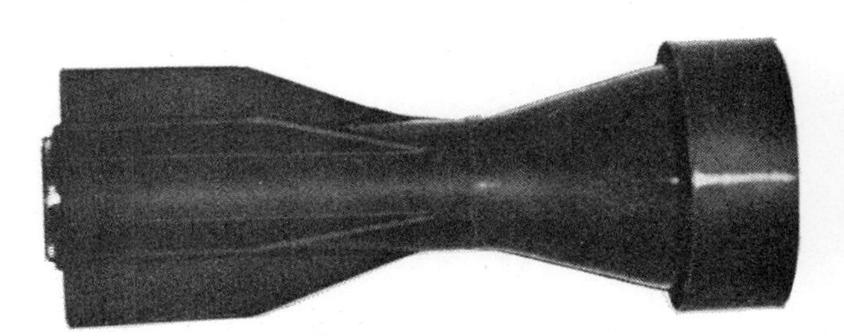

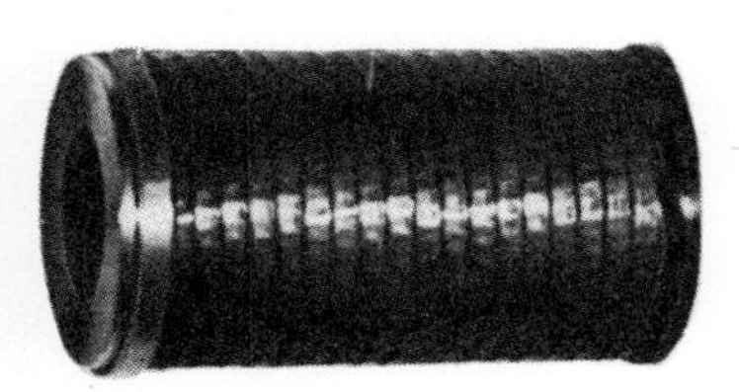

50 mm offensive/defensive hand grenade

Manufacturer: **MECAR SA (Belgium)**

Dimensions	Diameter 50 mm Height 80 mm
Weight	220 gm
Body material	Plastic
Charge	Composition (with 900 steel balls)
Arming	Pull pin and lever
Fuse	4 sec pyrotechnic train
Effect	90% casualties at 4 m
Safety	Manual pin
Environment	−32C to +60C

The MECAR 50 mm is a controlled-effect grenade which has been developed as the result of a study within the FINABEL countries, to meet the requirements of the Belgian Army for an offensive/defensive hand grenade.

The grenade consists of a body, believed to be made of a plastic material, filled with 60 gm of explosive composition. Embedded in the explosives are about 900 steel balls of limited aerodynamic capability. The initiation system is of the pin, lever and pyrotechnic train type.

When the grenade explodes, the steel balls are thrown outwards but, due to their deliberately poor aerodynamic qualities, lose any damaging effect within 20 m. At 4 m from the point of detonation, however, a 90% casualty probability can be expected. It is the limited effective zone characteristic of this grenade that makes it highly suitable for both offensive and defensive tasks.

In service but obsolescent.

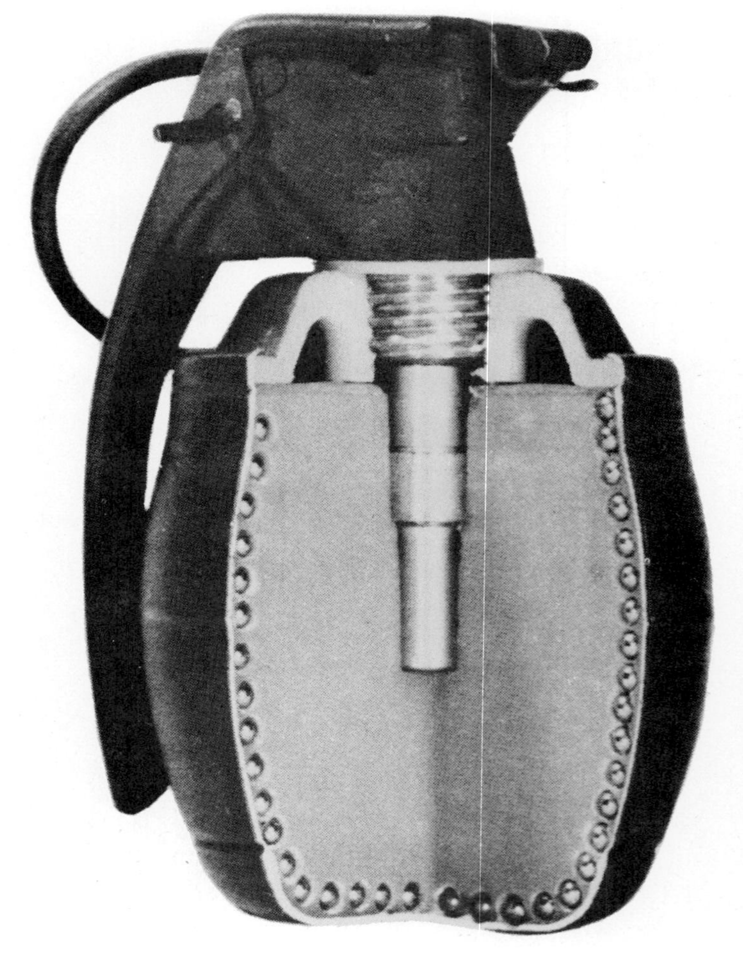

50 mm hand grenade.

HE-RFL-60N anti-personnel rifle grenade

Manufacturer: **MECAR SA (Belgium)**

Dimensions	Length 250 mm
Weight	470 gm
Body material	Metal
Charge	HE
Arming distance	12 m
Sight	Graduated grid
Calibre	60 mm
Method of discharge	Any rifle
Propellant	Ballistite round
Muzzle velocity	65 m/sec
Range	300 m
Fuse	Impact
Effect	500 fragments out to 50 m
Environment	−32 to +52C

The HE-RFL-60N was developed as the anti-personnel weapon complementary to the Energa anti-tank grenade and is lethal up to 8 m from the point of detonation. Fragments are effective out to 50 m. Thus its maximum range of 300 m, together with its 500-plus fragments, permit effective fire to be put down by infantrymen either on targets in the open or, by indirect fire, on targets behind cover.

In service with the Belgian forces.

HEAT-RFL-73N Energa anti-tank rifle grenade

Manufacturer: **MECAR SA (Belgium)**

Dimensions Length 367 mm
Weight 725 gm
Body material Aluminium alloy with copper cone
Charge Shaped
Arming distance 9 m
Sight Grid, with grenade
Calibre 73 mm
Method of discharge Any rifle
Propellant Ballistite round
Muzzle velocity 50 m/sec
Range Operational 100 m to 150 m; Maximum 260 m
Fuse Impact
Effect Penetrates 275 mm of armour or 600 mm of concrete
Environment −35C to +52C
Packing 10 grenades in a crate (480 mm × 215 mm × 495 mm) weighing 22 kg. A crate of 50 grenades weighing 69 kg also available

This 73 mm anti-tank grenade was developed to supply infantry with a low-cost weapon capable of penetrating armour plate up to 275 mm thick, or concrete up to 600 mm. It is fitted with a point-detonating fuse which operates at up to a 70 degree angle of incidence. On impact, the fuse detonates a shaped charge of the Energa type.

A propelling cartridge and a sighting grid are provided with each grenade. It is usual to fire this grenade from the underarm position, using the rifle sling as a brace. Although it is capable of a range of 260 m, the best effective ranges are 75 m on moving targets and 100 m on stationary targets. Launching is possible from any rifle equipped with a grenade-launching capability of 22 mm diameter.

Inert practice grenades are available, equipped with a re-usable marker which permits a check of the firer's accuracy by means of a visible coloured chalk mark on the target.

In service with the Belgian and some African forces.

HEAT-RFL-75N Energa anti-tank rifle grenade

Manufacturer: **MECAR SA (Belgium)**

Dimensions Length 376 mm
Weight 655 gm
Body material Metal
Charge Shaped HE
Arming distance 6 m
Sight Graduated grid
Calibre 75 mm
Method of discharge Any rifle
Propellant Ballistite round
Muzzle velocity 54 m/sec
Range Operational 75 m–100 m; Maximum 275 m
Fuse Impact
Effect Penetrates 275 mm of armour or 600 mm of concrete
Environment −32C to +52C

The HEAT-RFL-75N is the well-known Energa grenade which has been in service for some years. It has a considerable reputation, though constant improvements in the design of rifle grenades are leading to its gradual obsolescence. It will, however, be in service for some time yet.

It is a hollow charged grenade equipped with an impact fuse operating on the same principle as that of the HEAT-RFL-73N, which, it is thought, was introduced as a less expensive substitute.

There is a target practice nose-marker version which leaves a coloured chalk mark on impact.

HEAT-RFL-75N rifle Energa anti-tank grenade.

Energa grenade ready to fire from a G3 rifle.

In service with the United States, United Kingdom, Swiss and West German forces.

HEAT-RFL-73 Jet HP self-propelled Energa anti-tank rifle grenade

Manufacturer: **MECAR SA (Belgium)**

Dimensions	Length 418 mm
Weight	770 gm
Body material	Metal
Charge	Shaped HE
Arming distance	12 m
Sight	Graduated grid
Calibre	73 mm
Method of discharge	Any rifle
Propellant	Ballistite round
Muzzle velocity	80 m/sec
Range	Operational 150 m–200 m Maximum 550 m
Fuse	Impact
Effect	Penetrates 300 mm of armour or 600 mm of concrete
Environment	−32C to +52C
Packing	10 grenades in a crate (530 mm × 215 mm × 495 mm) weighing 23 kg. A crate of 50 grenades (72 kg) is also available.

This grenade is an extended-range version of the HEAT-RFL-73N. Apart from its increased range and better armour-piercing capability, the main difference between the two is that this grenade is fitted with a rocket motor in the tail boom.

On firing, the propellant is ignited by the launcher cartridge and burns for about 50 msec. This increases the grenade's velocity by about 30 m/sec over that of the HEAT-RFL-73N. The Jet HP version is aimed and launched in the same manner as its counterpart and with no more danger to the firer.

ARP-RFL-40N anti-tank rifle grenade

Manufacturer: **MECAR SA (Belgium)**

Dimensions	Length 257 mm
Weight	250 gm
Body material	Metal
Charge	Shaped HE
Arming distance	6 m
Sight	Graduated grid
Calibre	40 mm
Method of discharge	Any rifle
Propellant	Ballistite round
Muzzle velocity	90 m/sec
Range	Operational 150 m–200 m Maximum 500 m
Fuse	Impact
Effect	Penetrates 100 mm of armour or 300 mm of concrete
Environment	−32 C to +52 C

ARP-RFL-40N rifle grenade.

ARP-RFL-40BT 5·56 mm anti-tank rifle grenade

Manufacturer: **MECAR SA (Belgium)**

Dimensions	Length 257 mm
Weight	290 gm
Body material	Metal
Charge	Shaped HE
Arming distance	6 m
Sight	Graduated grid

Calibre 40 mm
Method of discharge Any 5·56 mm rifle
Propellant Ball ammunition
Muzzle velocity 63 m/sec
Range Operational 100 m
Maximum 275 m
Fuse Impact
Effect Penetrates 100 mm of armour or 300 mm of concrete
Environment – 32 C to + 52 C

The conventional method of launching rifle grenades is to use a special ballistite (or ballistite-type) cartridge. The disadvantage of this system is that the rifle usually has to be unloaded before the launch can take place. At the expense of a small increase in weight, and about 40% reduction in range, Mecar have successfully designed a launch method which enables a grenade to be projected using normal ball ammunition.

Thus the Mecar range of 40 mm grenades has two versions. One employs the conventional launch method, the other incorporates a bullet trap in the tail boom. Briefly, in the latter case, a bullet is caught in the trap and its kinetic energy is passed to, and overcomes, the inertia of the grenade. However, the dissipation of energy on impact with the bullet trap causes a reduction of range. The two grenades, types N and BT, have the same effects despite the shorter range of the latter.

ARP-RFL-40BT 7·62 mm anti-tank rifle grenade

Manufacturer: **MECAR SA (Belgium)**

Dimensions Length 340 mm
Weight 350 gm
Body material Metal
Charge Shaped HE
Arming distance 10 m
Sight Graduated grid
Calibre 40 mm
Method of discharge Any 7·62 mm rifle
Propellant Ball ammunition
Muzzle velocity 70 m/sec
Range Operational 200 m
Maximum 300 m
Fuse Impact
Effect Penetrates 100 mm of armour or 300 mm of concrete
Environment – 32C to + 52C

This grenade uses the Mecar bullet-trap system of launch already described above (ARP-RFL-40BT 5·56) and its effects are much the same. The configuration, however, is different. The standard safe arming distance is 10 m, but this can be altered.

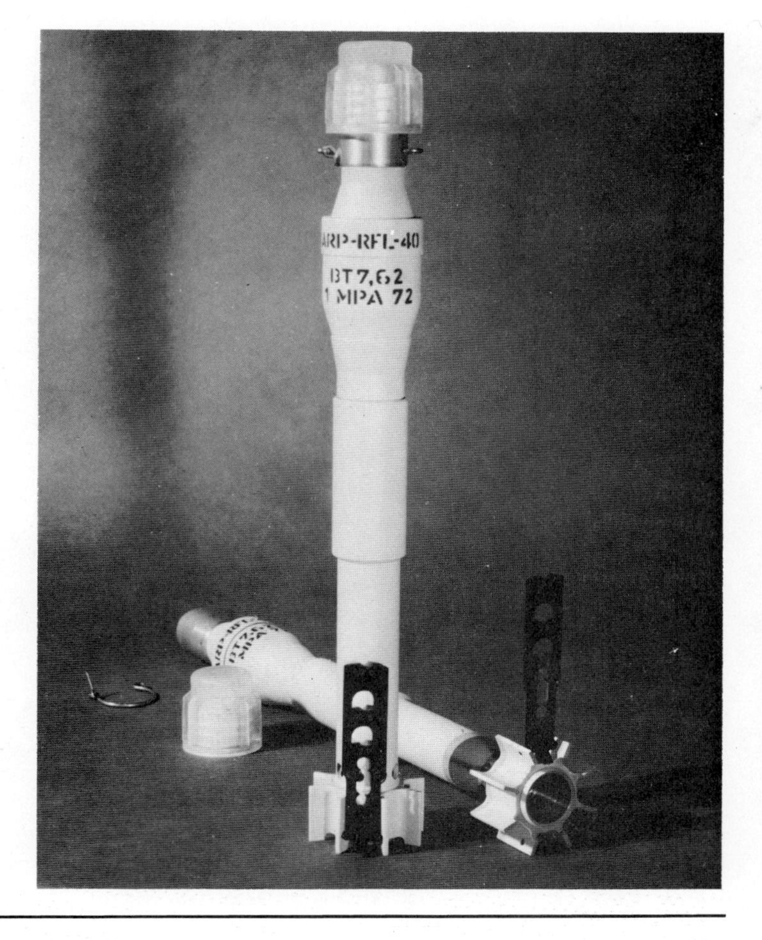

ARP-RFL-40BT 7·62 mm rifle grenade.

FRG-RFL-40N anti-personnel rifle grenade

Manufacturer: **MECAR SA (Belgium)**

Dimensions Length 197 mm
Weight 220 gm
Body material Metal
Charge HE
Arming distance 6 m
Sight Graduated grid
Calibre 40 mm
Method of discharge Any rifle
Propellant Ballistite round
Muzzle velocity 92 m/sec
Range 500 m
Fuse Impact
Effect 300 fragments out to 30 m
Environment – 32 C to + 52 C

FRG-FRL-40BT 5·56 mm anti-personnel rifle grenade

Manufacturer: **MECAR SA (Belgium)**

Dimensions	Length 197 mm
Weight	255 gm
Body material	Metal
Charge	HE
Arming distance	6 m
Sight	Graduated grid
Calibre	40 mm
Method of discharge	Any 5·56 mm rifle
Propellant	Ball ammunition
Muzzle velocity	65 m/sec
Range	300 m
Fuse	Impact
Effect	300 fragments out to 30 m
Environment	−32 C to +52 C

These two grenades produce the same effect on impact and are useful against targets in the open as well as those behind cover. However, as described above, there are differences between the N and BT types. The standard safe arming distance for both is 6 m, but this can be varied if required.

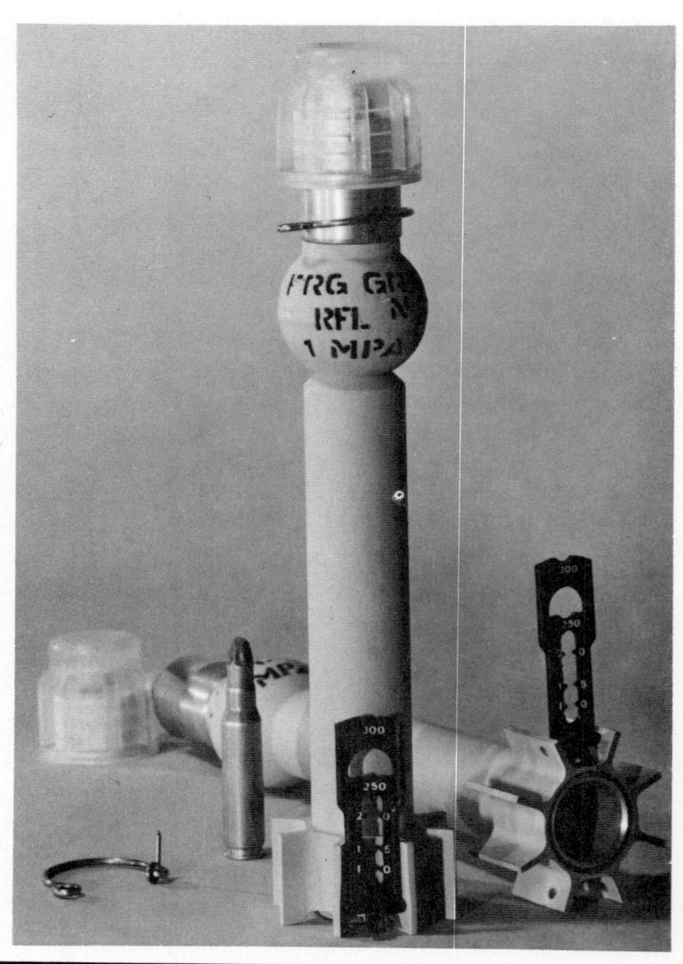

FRG-RFL-40N rifle grenade.

FRG-RFL-40BT 7·62 mm anti-personnel rifle grenade

Manufacturer: **MECAR SA (Belgium)**

Dimensions	Length 285 mm
Weight	325 gm
Body material	Metal
Charge	HE
Arming distance	10 m
Sight	Graduated grid
Calibre	40 mm
Method of discharge	Any 7·62 mm rifle with a 22 mm diameter muzzle
Propellant	Ball ammunition
Muzzle velocity	78 m/sec
Range	350 m
Fuse	Impact
Effect	300 fragments out to 30 m
Safety	Manual pin
Environment	−32C to +52C

This grenade has a different configuration to its 5·56 mm counterpart, although its effects are the same. It can be launched from any 7·62 mm calibre rifle with a muzzle diameter of 22 mm. The necessary aiming grid is provided with each grenade. The grenade is a useful area weapon which can also reach targets behind cover.

In service with the Belgium and Dutch forces

FRG-RFL-40BT 7·62 mm rifle grenade.

SMK-RFL-40N smoke rifle grenade

Manufacturer: **MECAR SA (Belgium)**

Dimensions	Length 163 mm
Weight	170 gm
Body material	Metal
Charge	White or orange smoke composition
Arming distance	5 sec ignition delay
Sight	None
Calibre	40 mm
Method of discharge	Any rifle
Propellant	Ballistite round
Range	315 m
Duration of screen	Orange 120 sec or white 150 sec
Effect	Signal or screen
Environment	−32 C to +52 C

SMK-RFL-40BT 5·56 mm smoke rifle grenade

Manufacturer: **MECAR SA (Belgium)**

Dimensions	222 mm
Weight	390 gm
Body material	Metal
Charge	White or orange smoke composition
Arming distance	5 sec ignition delay
Sight	None
Calibre	40 mm
Method of discharge	Any 5·56 mm rifle
Propellant	Ball ammunition
Range	150 m
Duration of screen	Orange 120 sec or white 150 sec
Effect	Signal or screen
Environment	−32 C to +52 C

Designed to produce an intensive white or orange smoke for 150 sec or 120 sec respectively, these grenades can be used both for screening and signalling purposes. They are launched either by the conventional ballistite round or by the Mecar bullet-trap method. The latter is designed for 5·56 mm rifles except where stated otherwise.

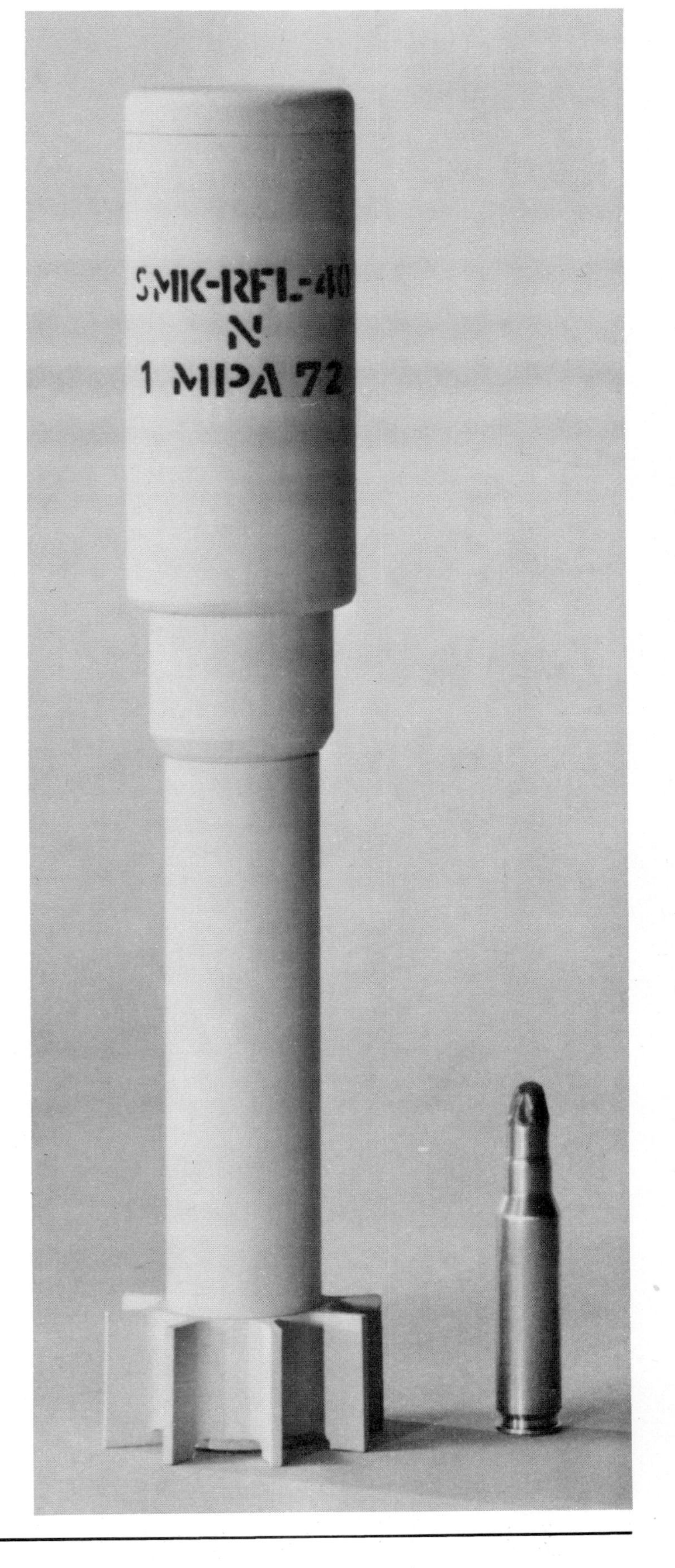

SMK-RFL-40N rifle grenade.

SMK-RFL-40BT 7·62 mm smoke rifle grenade

Manufacturer: **MECAR SA (Belgium)**

The SMK-RFL-40BT 7·62 mm grenade is, apart from being a bit longer and a bit heavier, the same as its 5·56 mm smoke rifle grenade counterpart.

In service with the Belgian and Dutch forces.

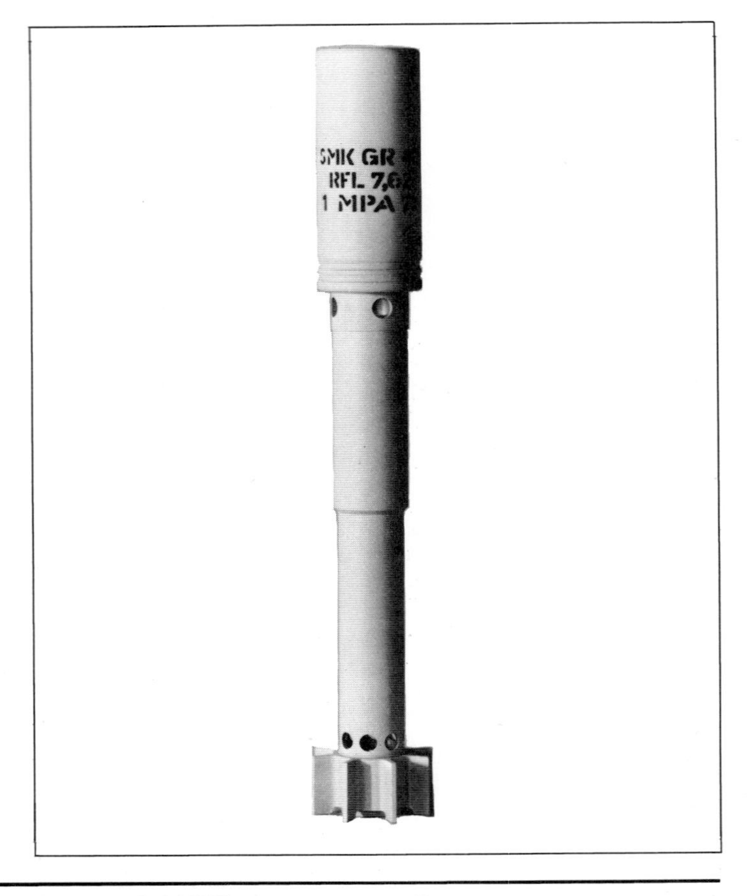

SMK-RFL-40BT 7·62 mm rifle grenade.

PSS-RFL-40N parachute smoke signal rifle grenade

Manufacturer: **MECAR SA (Belgium)**

Dimensions	Length 294 mm
Weight	290 gm
Body material	Metal
Charge	Red, green or yellow smoke composition
Arming	On discharge
Sight	None
Calibre	40 mm
Method of discharge	Any rifle
Propellant	Ballistite round
Release delay	5 sec
Height of release	120 m
Duration of signal	34 sec
Environment	−32 C to +52 C

PSS-RFL-40BT 5·56 mm parachute smoke signal rifle grenade

Manufacturer: **MECAR SA (Belgium)**

Dimensions	294 mm
Weight	335 gm
Body material	Metal
Charge	Red, green or yellow smoke composition
Arming	On discharge
Sight	None
Calibre	40 mm
Method of discharge	Any 5·56 mm rifle
Propellant	Ball ammunition
Release delay	3 sec
Height of release	65 m
Duration of signal	34 sec
Environment	−32 C to +52 C

These signal grenades emit red, green or yellow smoke as required and descend controlled by parachute. Like the rest of the 40 mm series by Mecar, they can be launched with a ballistite round or by the Mecar bullet-trap system, explained above (ARP-RFL-40BT 5·56), which restricts the flight performance a little.

In service with the Belgian and Dutch forces.

SIG-RFL-40N signal rifle grenade

Manufacturer: **MECAR SA (Belgium)**

Dimensions	Length 202 mm
Weight	185 gm
Body material	Metal
Charge	Red, green, yellow or white flare composition
Arming	Ignited after launch
Sight	None
Calibre	40 mm
Method of discharge	Any rifle
Propellant	Ballistite round
Height of signal	375 m maximum
Duration of signal	13 sec
Effect	Point source light
Environment	−32C to +52C

So far as is known, a bullet-trap version is not yet available. Designed as a signal grenade, it is available in four colours—red, green, yellow and white—and burns for about 15 sec at a maximum height of 375 m. The signal is clearly visible in daylight.

In service with the Belgian and Dutch forces.

PFL-RFL-40N parachute illuminating rifle grenade

Manufacturer: **MECAR SA (Belgium)**

Dimensions	Length 294 mm
Weight	290 gm
Body material	Metal
Charge	White, red or green flare composition
Sight	None
Calibre	40 mm
Method of discharge	Any rifle
Propellant	Ballastite round
Range	250 m
Height of release	120 m (approx)
Duration of signal	30 sec
Effect	Area illumination—25,000 cp (white–60,000 cp also)—and signal
Environment	−32C to +52C

PFL-RFL-40BT 5·56 mm parachute illuminating rifle grenade

Manufacturer: **MECAR SA (Belgium)**

Dimensions	Length 294 mm
Weight	335 gm
Body material	Metal
Charge	White, red or green flare composition
Sight	None
Calibre	40 mm
Method of discharge	Any 5·56 mm rifle
Propellant	Ball ammunition
Range	110 m
Height of release	65 m (approx)
Duration of signal	30 sec
Effect	Area illumination—25,000 cp (white–60,000 cp also)—and signal
Environment	−32C to +52C

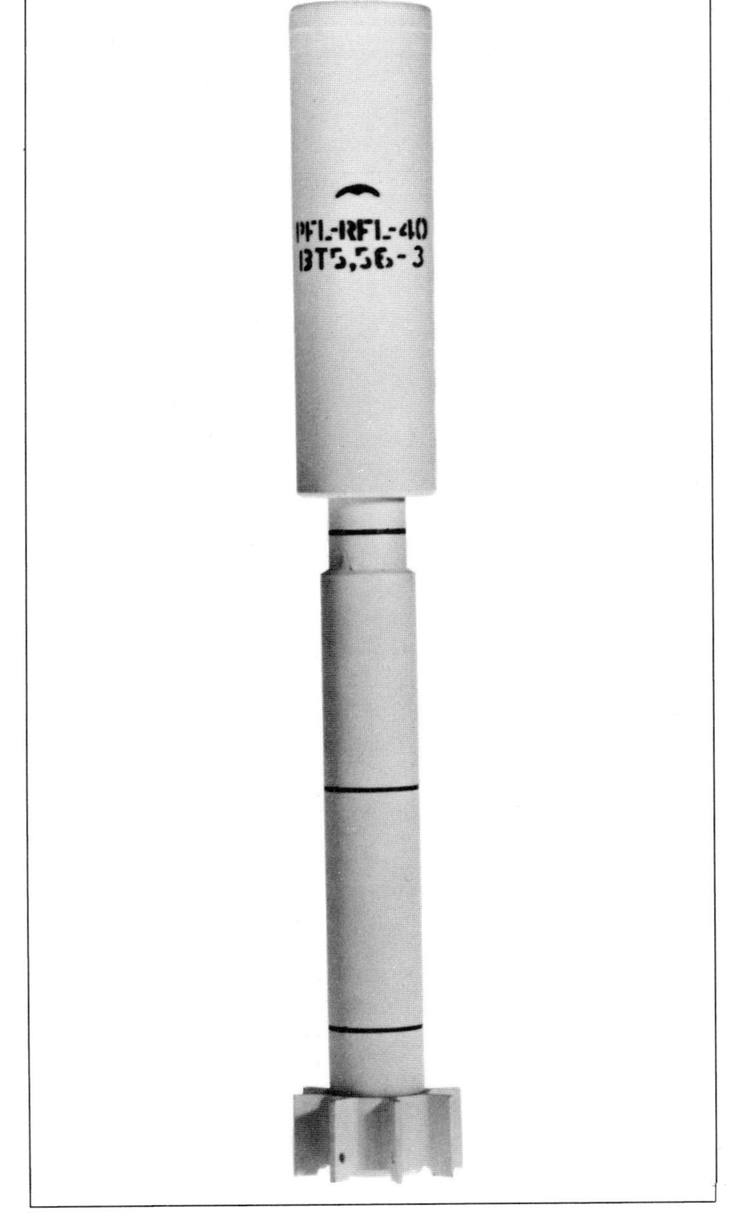

PFL-RFL-40 5·56 mm rifle grenade.

These parachute illuminating grenades are intended for both signalling and illumination. Each coloured flare burns for 30 sec at 25,000 cp as it descends on its parachute. Three different colours are available—red, green or white. In addition, the white can be supplied to burn for 60 sec at 60,000 cp or 25,000 cp. The bullet-trap version is launched by the method already described under grenade ARP-RFL-40BT 5·56 mm above.

In service with the Belgian and Dutch forces.

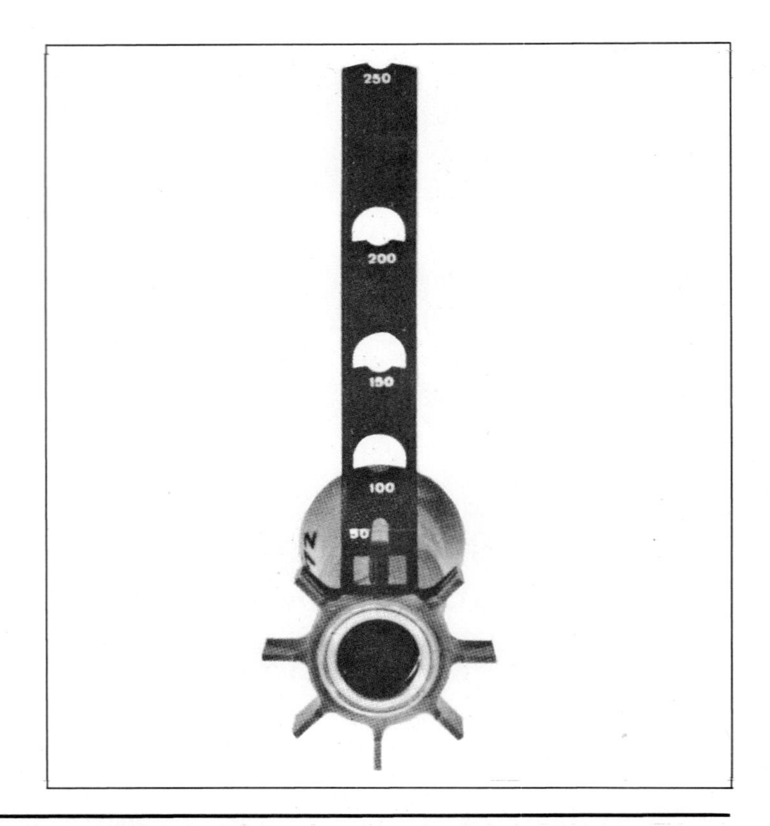

The Mecar grenade sight.

PFL-RFL-40BT 7·62 mm parachute illuminating rifle grenade

Manufacturer: **MECAR SA (Belgium)**

This parachute illuminating rifle grenade has the same capabilities as the PFL-RFL-40BT 5·56 mm parachute illuminating rifle grenade, except that it is a little longer and a little heavier. As with the other bullet-trap grenades, it can be fired accurately using regular ball ammunition. The white flare burns at 25,000 cp or 60,000 cp, while the red and green flares burn at 25,000 cp. The brighter of the two white flares is also produced in a 60 sec version.

In service with the Belgian and Dutch forces.

AP 32 Z anti-personnel/anti-vehicle rifle grenade

Manufacturer: **Fabrique Nationale Herstal (Belgium)**

Dimensions	Length 315 m
Weight	515 gm
Body material	Metal
Charge	Shaped HE
Arming	On firing
Sight	Graduated grid
Calibre	40 mm
Method of discharge	Rifle with 22 mm diameter muzzle
Propellant	Ballistite round
Muzzle velocity	69 m/sec
Range	Anti-personnel 380 m Anti-vehicle 150 m
Fuse	Impact
Effect	Penetrates 100 mm of armour Fragments out to 20 m
Safety	Manual pin
Environment	Pan climatic

AP 32 Z rifle grenade.

The AP32Z, like all the AP32Z series, is produced by FN under licence from Luchaire SA. It is similar to the STRIM F1, being both anti-personnel and anti-vehicle due to its shaped charge. It can penetrate over 100 mm of armour plate and explodes fragments out to 20 m or more.

In service with the Belgian and Dutch forces.

AP 32 ZA anti-personnel/anti-vehicle rifle grenade

Manufacturer: **Fabrique Nationale Herstal (Belgium)**

Dimensions	Length 350 mm
Weight	495 gm
Body material	Metal
Charge	Shaped HE
Arming	On firing
Sight	Graduated grid
Calibre	40 mm
Method of discharge	Rifle with 22 mm diameter muzzle
Propellant	Ballistite round
Muzzle velocity	72 m/sec or 90 m/sec depending on launch cartridge
Range	Anti-personnel 600 m Anti-vehicle 150 m
Fuse	Impact
Effect	Penetrates 80 mm of armour Fragments out to 20 m
Safety	Manual pin
Environment	Pan climatic

The AP 32 ZA is basically an anti-personnel grenade, but with an improved capability over the AP 32 Z on two counts. First, the fragmentation of the body is controlled, and over a thousand spherical projectiles of equal size (about 3·2 mm in diameter) are dispersed at high speed over 20 m from the point of detonation. Secondly, two propelling cartridges are supplied for this grenade. One for direct fire to 150 m and the other for ranges out to 600 m. In addition, the AP 32 ZA is capable of penetrating 80 mm of armour plate.

In service with the Belgian and Dutch forces.

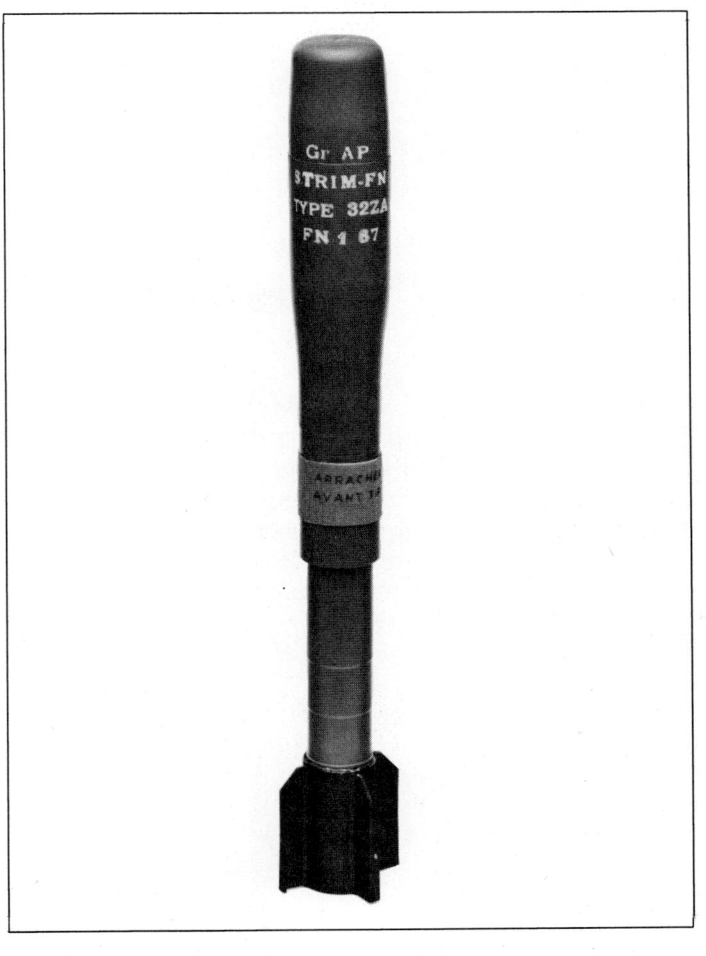

AP 32 ZA or AP 32 ZB rifle grenade (see below).

AP 32 ZB fragmentation rifle grenade

Manufacturer: **Fabrique Nationale Herstal (Belgium)**

Dimensions	Length 350 mm
Weight	495 gm
Body material	Metal
Charge	Shaped HE
Arming	5 m
Sight	Graduated grid
Calibre	40 mm
Method of discharge	Rifle with 22 mm diameter muzzle
Propellant	Ballistite round
Muzzle velocity	90 m/sec
Range	600 m
Fuse	Impact
Effect	1250 fragments out to 20 m
Safety	Manual pin
Environment	Pan climatic

The AP 32 ZB is an anti-personnel grenade similar to the AP 32 ZA, but has a greater anti-personnel effect. It has no anti-vehicle capability, however. The improved effect is due to the larger number of projectiles contained in the body. It is launched by the long-range cartridge (see AP32ZA) from any rifle with a 22 mm diameter muzzle.

In service with the Belgian and Dutch forces.

65 AC 28 R2 anti-tank rifle grenade

Manufacturer: **Fabrique Nationale Herstal (Belgium)**

Dimensions	Length 420 mm
Weight	735 gm
Body material	Metal
Charge	Shaped HE
Arming distance	5 m
Sight	Graduated grid
Calibre	65 mm
Method of discharge	Rifle with 22 mm diameter muzzle
Propellant	Ballistite round
Muzzle velocity	59 m/sec
Range	Effective 120 m
Fuse	Impact
Effect	Penetrates 300 mm of armour
Safety	Manual pin
Environment	Pan climatic

This grenade is an impact-initiated anti-tank weapon capable of penetrating 300 mm of armour. The maximum effective range with a flat trajectory is 120 m using any rifle with a 22 mm diameter launcher.

Inert practice grenades are available with the same ballistite characteristics and launching techniques.

In service with the Belgian forces.

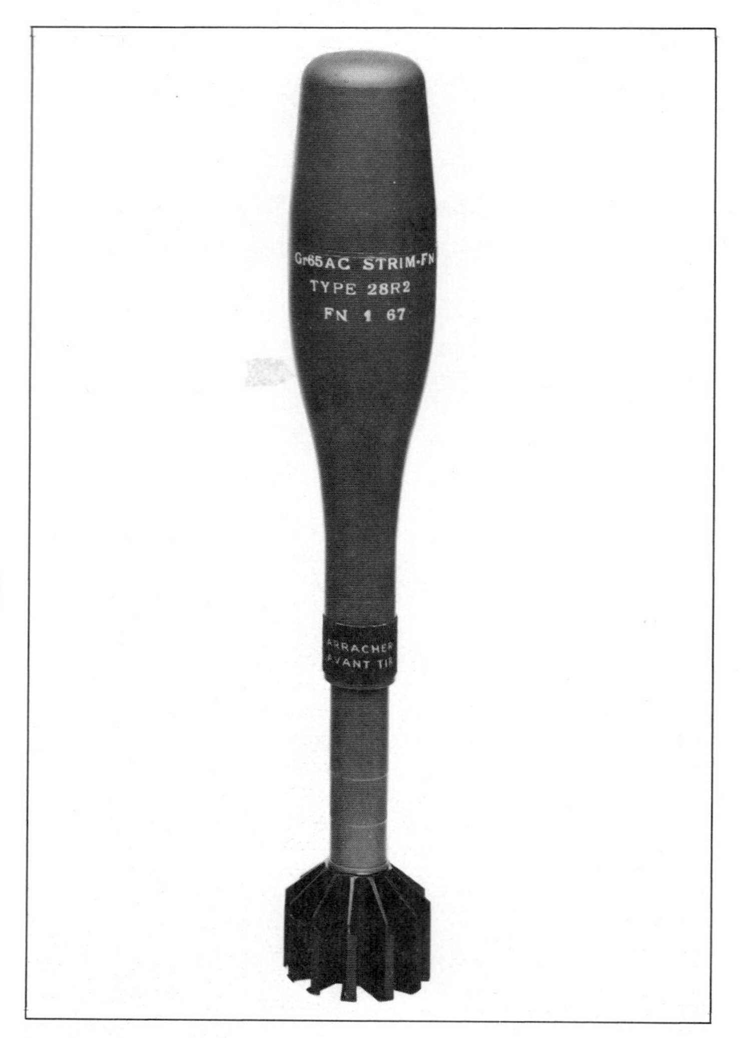

65 AC 28 R2 rifle grenade.

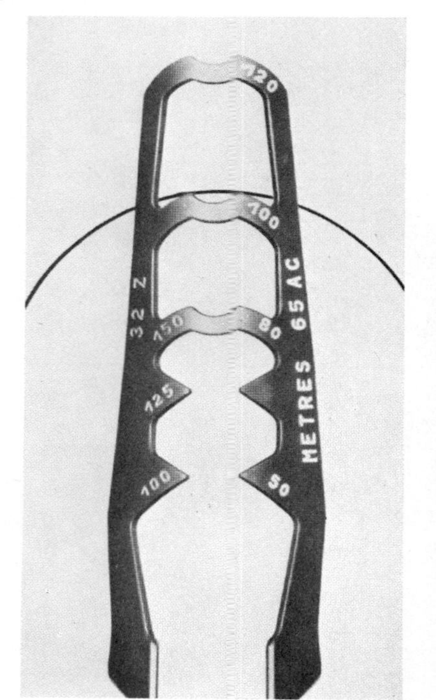

The sight graduated for the different grenades.

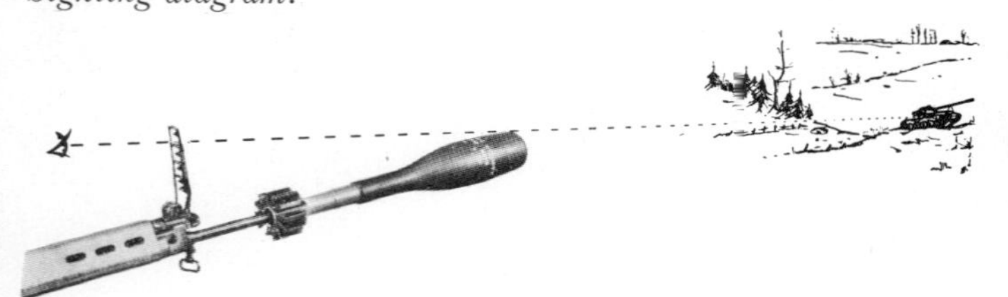

Sighting diagram.

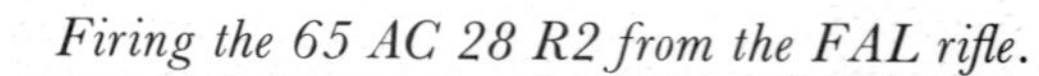

Firing the 65 AC 28 R2 from the FAL rifle.

M32 defensive hand grenade

Manufacturer: **State factories (People's Republic of China)**

See the RGD 5.

In service with the communist Chinese forces.

RG34 offensive hand grenade

Manufacturer: **State factories (Czechoslovakia)**

Dimensions	Height 7·4 cm Diameter 6·5 cm
Weight	0·3 kg
Body material	Sheet steel
Charge	HE (100 gm)
Arming	Pin, spring and striker
Activation	Impact
Effect	Fragments out to 15 m or 25 m
Safety	Manual pin

The Czech RG34 hand grenade is an offensive anti-personnel weapon which can, when necessary for defensive purposes, be fitted with a pre-fragmented cast-iron jacket over the sheet steel body. In the latter case the grenade is lethal out to a radius of 25 m, but this is reduced to 15 m without the jacket. This grenade is not fitted with a delayed-action fuse, and after the safety-pin and tape are removed the percussion-detonating mechanism (the spring-loaded striker) is activated only by impact on the grenade body. This grenade is being superseded by the RG4 from which it differs by having flatter ends, no corrugated grip, and a more primitive type of safety clip.

In service with the Czechoslovak forces.

RG4 offensive/defensive hand grenade

Manufacturer: **State factories (Czechoslovakia)**

Dimensions	Height 8·4 cm Diameter 5·3 cm
Weight	0·3 kg
Body material	Sheet steel
Charge	HE (105 gm)
Arming	Clip, tape and spring-loaded striker
Activation	Impact
Effect	Fragments out to 15 m or 25 m
Safety	Clip and tape

The Czech RG4 hand grenade, an offensive anti-personnel weapon, is an up-dated version of the RG34, which it is intended to supersede. Like the RG34, this grenade can, when required for defensive purposes, be quickly fitted with a cast iron pre-fragmented jacket over the sheet-steel body so as to increase its effective range from 15 m to 25 m. The grenade has been redesigned to produce a more streamlined shape with a corrugated grip to increase throwing range, whilst at the same time slightly reducing overall weight, yet increasing the HE charge. The design of the safety-clip has been simplified and made more secure, but the activation principles remain the same. Explosion on impact is by means of a spring-loaded striker, after the latter is freed by release of the safety-clip and tape.

In service with the Czechoslovak forces.

Mk F1 smoke rifle grenade

Manufacturer: **Etablissements Ruggieri (France)**

Dimensions Length 275 mm
Weight 0·6 kg
Body material Plastic
Charge Smoke composition
Sight Graduated grid
Calibre 54 mm
Method of discharge Rifle
Propellant Ballistite round
Range 80 m–300 m
Fuse Impact
Effect Thick smoke for 40 sec
Safety Manual
Packing Partitioned wooden box containing 24 grenades in individual containers, grouped by fours

The Mk F1 50 mm smoke grenade is designed to produce a thick cloud of smoke for more than 40 sec. Its initiation is by an instantaneous impact percussive fuse. Using an appropriate blank cartridge, it can be launched from any rifle with a muzzle diameter of 22 mm to a maximum range in excess of 300 m.

In service with the French forces.

Alsetex OF offensive hand grenade

Manufacturer: **Société Alsacienne d'Études et d'Exploitation (France)**

Types A and B (see text)
Dimensions Diameter (A 50 mm; B 55 mm) Height (A 100 mm; B 120 mm)
Weight (A 220 gm; B 300 gm)
Body material Plastic
Filling Tolite (A 150 gm; B 225 gm)
Arming Pin, lever, striker
Fuse Alsetex Mk 67 5 sec pyrotechnic train
Effect High blast
Safety Manual pin
Environment Pan climatic

Alsetex produce two plastic-bodied pot-type grenades. They are both offensive grenades filled with compressed tolite, but of different size. For convenience they are called 'A' and 'B' as no official designation is available at the time of writing. The smaller of the two (A) has a diameter of 50 mm, an overall height of 100 mm and contains 150 gm of explosives. B contains 250 gm of explosive in a casing that measures 55 mm by 120 mm. Both grenades are armed, using the Alsetex Mk 67 ignition device, a pin, lever, striker system with a 5 sec delay train. The actuation block is made of plastic whilst the safety pin, striker and retaining lever are of metal.

In service with the French, and other, forces.

63 mm Grafac anti-tank rifle grenade

Manufacturer: **Société d'Études de Réalisations et d'Applications Techniques (France)**

Dimensions Length 350 mm
Weight 500 gm
Body material Metal
Charge Shaped HE
Arming 6 m muzzle safety
Sight Graduated grid
Calibre 63 mm
Method of discharge Rifle
Propellant Ballistite round
Muzzle velocity 65 m/sec
Range 350 m (effective 100 m)
Fuse Electro-magnetic impact
Effect Penetrates 300 mm of armour plate
Environment Pan climatic

Little information has been released on this grenade, but it has been specially designed for the light FA 5·56 mm MAS rifle (see Rifles), and is soon to be issued to the French armed forces.

The Grafac is launched with an appropriate cartridge, and different calibre cartridges are available. It can also be launched from any service rifle having a 22 mm muzzle launcher, and the muzzle safety exceeds 6 m. In appearance the Grafac is slightly bulbous and the tail boom assembly looks longer than that of other comparable grenades. The hollow charge is said to be capable of piercing more than 300 mm of armour at a zero angle of incidence.

The impact fuse is believed to incorporate an electromagnetic generator.

Under development for the French forces.

MDF polyvalent hand and rifle grenade

Manufacturer: **Losfeld Industries (France)**

Dimensions	Diameter 48 mm Length 270 mm (MD and M – 150 mm)
Weight	490 gm (MD – 414 gm; M – 262 gm)
Body material	Plastic with metal sheet (M – plastic only)
Charge	HE (87 gm)
Arming	By removal of fuse cover
Sight	None
Calibre	48 mm
Method of discharge	Rifle with 22 mm diameter muzzle (MD and M – manual)
Propellant	Ballistite round } not applicable to MD and M
Muzzle velocity	70 m/sec
Range	370 m
Fuse	Multi-purpose (see text)
Effect	1000 fragments out to 20 m (M – blast only)
Safety	Manual pin
Environment	–32 C to +51 C

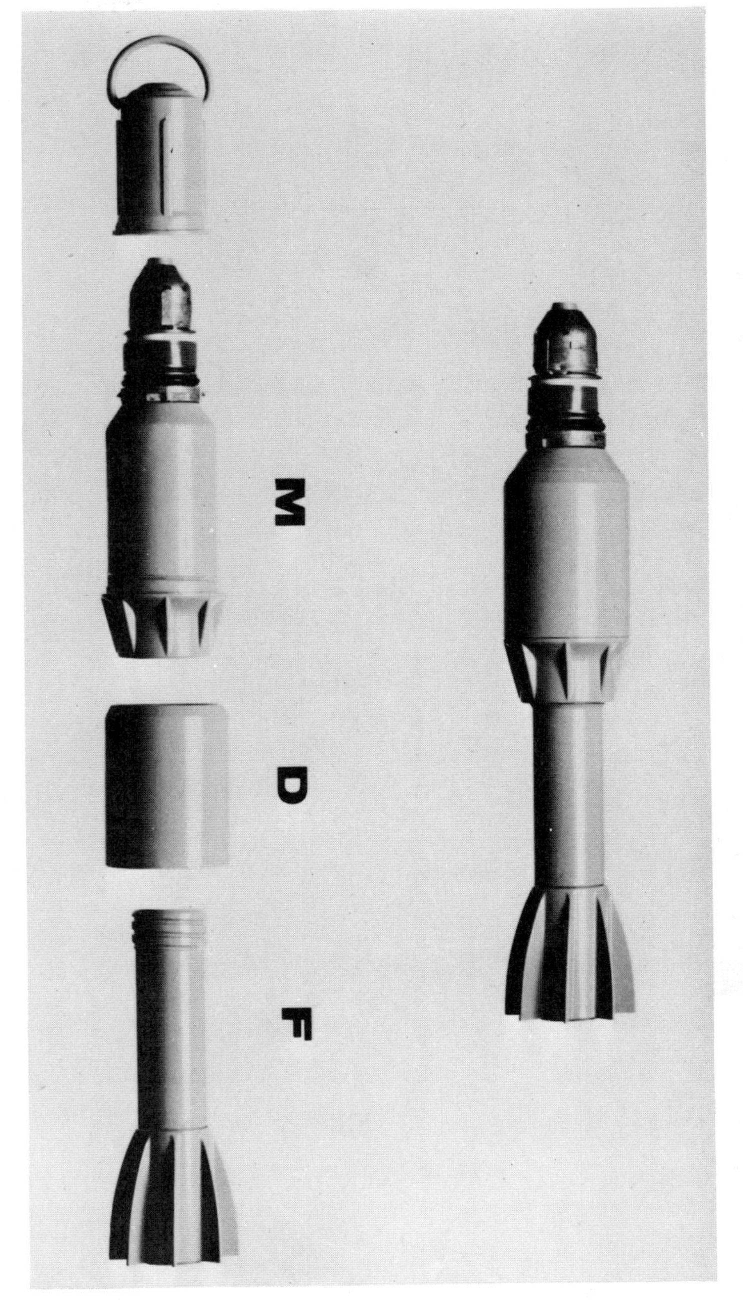

Losfield MDF grenade.

In the weapons context the term 'polyvalent' is relatively new and means that a weapon is designed to be modified by the user in order to fulfil certain functions. In the case of the MDF grenade, the functions are rifle anti-personnel, offensive hand and defensive hand.

In order to carry out all three tasks, the MDF is made up of detachable components, named M, D and F, which can make up the three configurations: M, MD and MDF (see illustration). M is the main body of the grenade and is filled with 87 gm of explosive. D is the pre-fragmented defensive sleeve and F is the tail assembly. In order to use this grenade in the offensive role, D and F are removed. For defensive operations only, F is removed. As an anti-personnel rifle grenade, all three components, M, D and F, are used.

Thus, in the M configuration, the soldier has a high-explosive hand grenade which creates a shock wave of 5·1 lb/sq in at 3 m. In the MD configuration it becomes a defensive hand grenade producing about 1000 fragments (280 weigh about 0·4 gm) with an effective radius of 20 m.

Finally, in the MDF configuration, a soldier can launch an anti-personnel rifle grenade with the same fragmentation effects as the MD version out to 400 m. In this configuration the grenade can be launched from any rifle with a muzzle diameter of 22 mm using the cartridge provided.

The fuse for the MDF grenades has three settings: 'Impact and Delay' for explosion on impact with a guarantee of self-destruction by the delay if the grenade lands on very soft ground; 'Delay only', which ensures that the grenade will not be detonated by accidental contact in flight; 'Impact only' when long trajectories are contemplated.

When firing the grenade from a rifle only the first or last of the above settings are used. Launched at an angle of 16 degrees, the 'Impact and Delay' setting will result in the grenade exploding some 2 m above the ground at a range of 210 m. Should the angle of fire be lower, the grenade will function on impact.

There is an inert version (Mx) which is capable of being used in all three modes by adding the other components as required.

In service with the French forces.

M1937 offensive hand grenade

Manufacturer: **Luchaire SA (France)**

Dimensions	Height 95 cm Diameter 60 mm
Weight	140 gm
Body material	Aluminium
Filling	90 gm TNT or compressed tolite
Arming	Pin, lever, striker
Fuse	5 sec pyrotechnic train
Effect	High blast
Safety	Manual pin
Environment	Pan climatic

This is a two-piece aluminium-bodied grenade filled with 90 gm of piled tolite or TNT. Actuation is achieved with a Mk 35 lead igniter which, from the limited information available, appears to be of the pin, lever and striker type, and has an approximate 5 sec delay. A heavily fragmented pattern is avoided despite its metal construction as the casing is sufficiently thin not to fragment on detonation. Identification of the grenade in poor-light conditions is assisted by a definite ridge round the centre of the body.

In service with the French forces.

DM46 defensive hand grenade

Manufacturer: **Luchaire SA (France)**

Dimensions	Height 100 mm Diameter 55 mm
Weight	540 gm
Body material	Cast iron
Filling	90 gm TNT or piled tolite
Arming	Pin, lever, striker
Fuse	5 sec pyrotechnic train, Mk 35 lead igniter
Effect	Fragments out to 20 m plus
Safety	Manual pin
Environment	Pan climatic

The DM46 has a similar configuration to the M1937 grenade and is armed in the same way. Unlike the M1937, however, there is no ridge round the centre of the casing.

The body is made of cast-iron and is filled with tolite or TNT, and, on detonation, a heavy fragmentation pattern is developed over a considerable radius. However, at the time of writing no precise information has been received on the grenade's performance and capabilities.

In service with the French forces.

Mk 61 65 mm anti-tank rifle grenade

Manufacturer: **Luchaire SA (France)**

Dimensions	Length 420 mm
Weight	725 gm
Body material	Metal
Charge	Shaped
Sight	Graduated grid
Calibre	65 mm
Method of discharge	From any rifle with a 22 mm launcher
Propellant	Ballistite round
Muzzle velocity	60 m/sec
Range	320 m (100 m flat trajectory)
Fuse	Impact
Effect	Penetrates 300 mm of armour plate
Safety	5 m from launch
Environment	Pan climatic

This is a shaped-charge rifle grenade designed for close action against armour. It is capable of penetrating the heaviest armour and can be launched from any rifle with a 22 mm muzzle diameter, using a special blank cartridge.

The Mk 61 is equipped with an instantaneous impact fuse that is automatically armed 5 m from the muzzle of the launch weapon. It meets NATO safety requirements for transport and handling and can be air dropped in its packaging.

In service with the French forces.

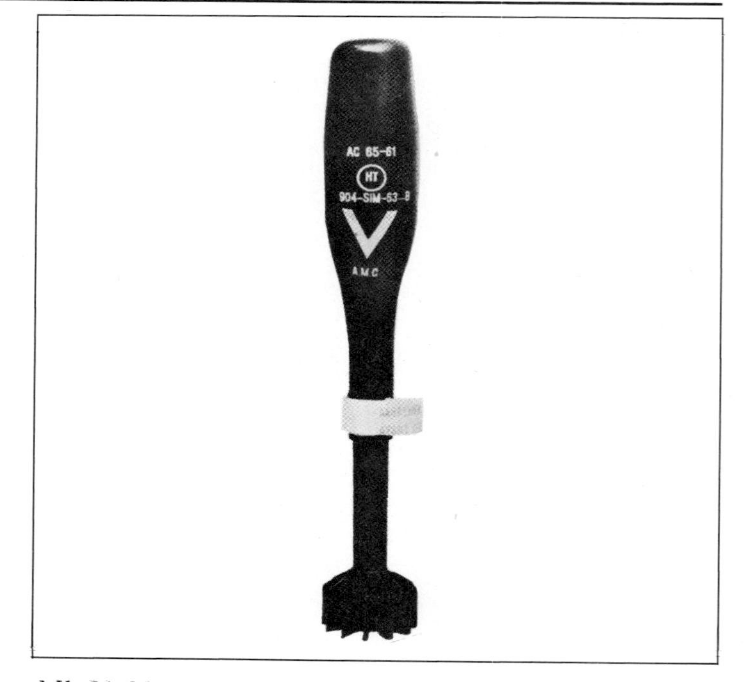

Mk 61 65 mm anti-tank rifle grenade.

40 mm STRIM F1 anti-personnel/anti-vehicle rifle grenade

Manufacturer: **Luchaire SA (France)**

Dimensions	Length 305 mm
Weight	510 gm
Body material	Metal
Charge	Shaped HE (80 gm)
Arming distance	5 m
Sight	Graduated grid
Calibre	40 mm
Method of discharge	Rifle with 22 mm diameter muzzle
Propellant	Ballistite round
Muzzle velocity	70 m/sec
Range	Anti-personnel 400 m Anti-vehicle 100 m
Fuse	Impact
Effect	Penetrates 100 mm of armour or 360 mm of concrete Fragments out to 100 m
Safety	Manual pin
Environment	−32C to +55C

The 40 mm type AP/AV is an explosive rifle grenade and can be launched from any rifle with a 22 mm diameter muzzle launcher.

The body of stamped steel contains 80 gm of explosive, and fragments on detonation. The fragments are effective out to 30 m and remain dangerous out to 100 m. Since the charge is of the hollow type the F1 can be used against vehicles, provided the trajectory is flat. The charge is capable of penetrating up to 120 mm of armour or 360 mm of concrete. The fuse is an impact type armed by the gas pressure of the launch cartridge. The safety pin is held in place by an adhesive band, which must be removed before launching.

The sighting system is designed to give a curved trajectory when the anti-personnel role is contemplated and flat trajectory against vehicles. Ranges out to 400 m are practical for anti-personnel requirements, but 100 m is the maximum practical range in the anti-vehicle role.

In service with the French forces, and others.

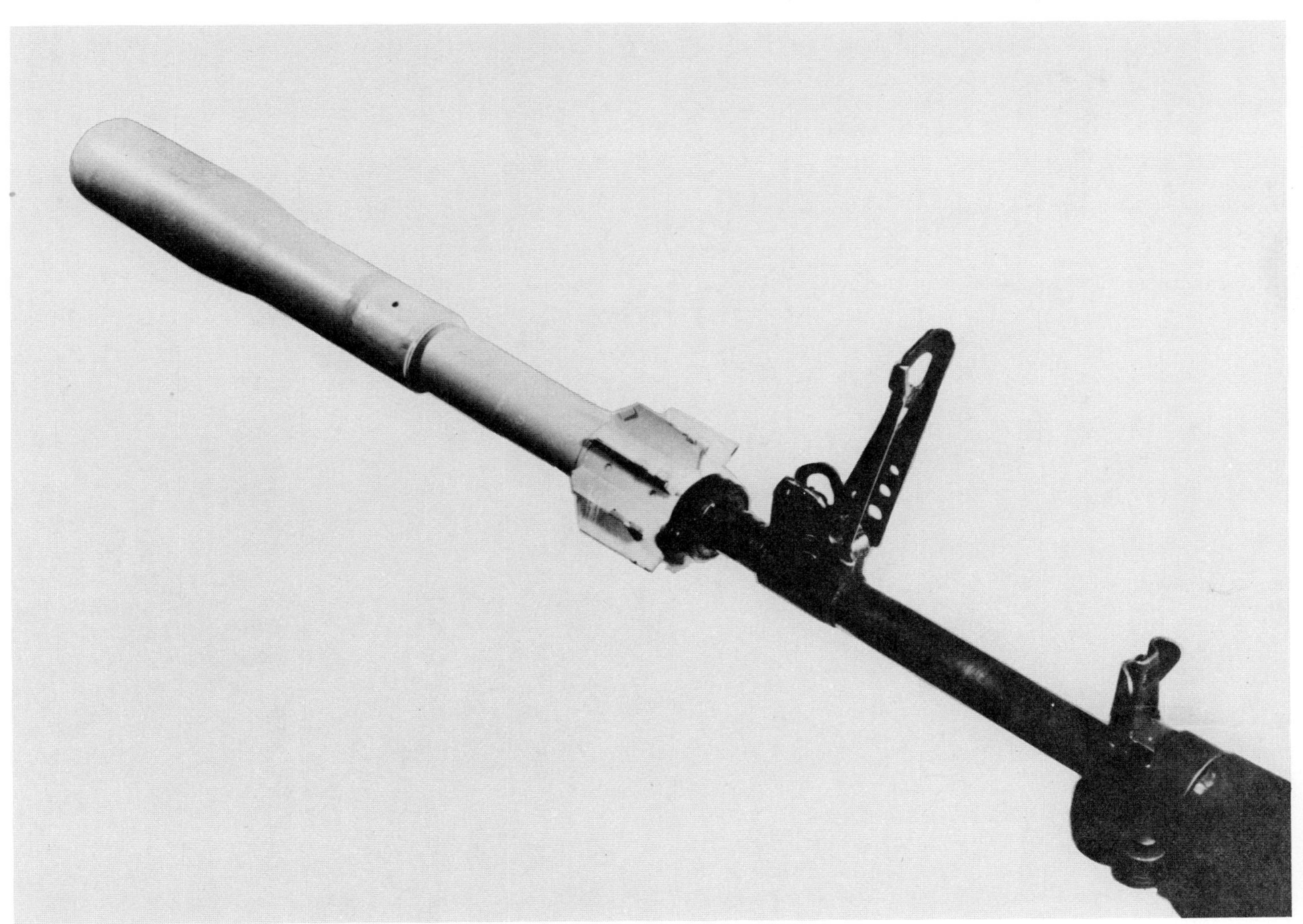

40 mm STRIM F1 AP/AV ready to be fired.

47 mm STRIM type F3 instant smoke rifle grenade

Manufacturer: **Luchaire SA (France)**

Dimensions	Length 324 mm
Weight	517 gm
Body material	Metal
Charge	Smoke composition (170 gm)
Arming	On firing
Sight	Graduated grid
Calibre	47 mm
Method of discharge	Rifle with 22 mm diameter muzzle
Propellant	Ballistite round
Muzzle velocity	70 m/sec
Range	400 m
Fuse	Instantaneous percussion
Effect	Smoke for about 55 sec
Safety	Manual pin
Environment	−32C to +55C

Luchaire SA are advocates of the theory that if infiltrating enemy tanks are not destroyed by first-round strikes from anti-tank weapons, it is vital to blind the crews with instantaneous smoke. They market the 47 mm STRIM F3 to meet this requirement.

This grenade releases an effective smoke screen within 2 sec of impact for 40–60 sec, thus hampering possible return fire and enabling anti-tank crews to fire again if necessary. The structure of the F3 is similar to that of the 47 mm coloured smoke grenade.

In service with the French forces.

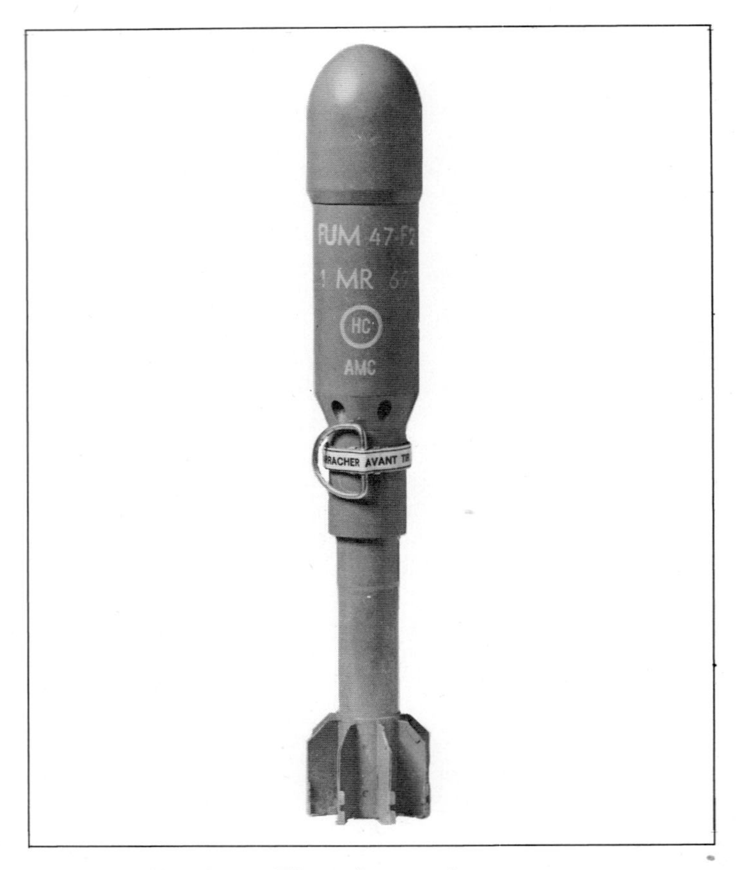

47 mm STRIM type F3 smoke grenade.

47 mm STRIM type 60 smoke and incendiary rifle grenade

Manufacturer: **Luchaire SA (France)**

Dimensions	Length 320 mm
Weight	0·5 kg
Body material	Metal
Charge	Phosphorous composition (140 gm)
Arming	On firing
Sight	Graduated grid
Calibre	47 mm
Method of discharge	Rifle with 22 mm diameter muzzle
Propellant	Ballistite round
Muzzle velocity	70 m/sec
Range	400 m
Fuse	Impact
Effect	Smoke for 10–15 min
Safety	Manual pin
Environment	Pan climatic

This grenade has a similar configuration to the other 47 mm STRIM grenades. However, instead of a smoke compound, it is filled with phosphorus and is able to fulfil several functions.

Impact on any type of ground results in an immediate

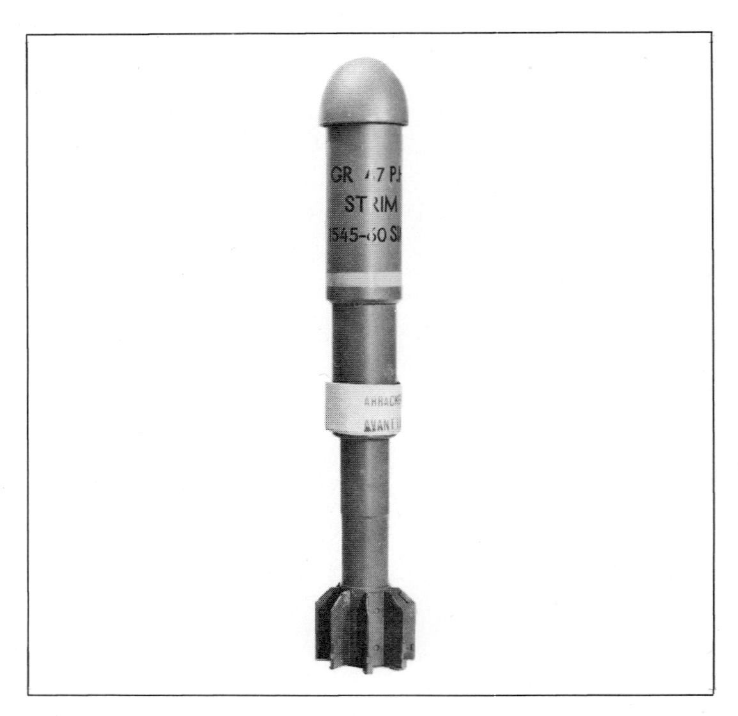

47 mm STRIM type 60 smoke and incendiary grenade.

emission of thick smoke which lasts for about 2 min. Subsequently, more smoke is generated to maintain the initial screen. This secondary generation lasts from 8 to 13 min, thus supplying a sustained screen for up to about 15 min.

The type 60 grenade, with the thermal qualities of its phosphorous filling, can be used as an incendiary to damage or destroy weapons, equipment and stores.

In service with the French forces.

47 mm STRIM coloured smoke rifle grenade

Manufacturer: **Luchaire SA (France)**

Dimensions	Length 320 mm
Weight	517 gm
Body material	Metal
Charge	Yellow or white smoke composition (145 gm)
Arming	On firing
Sight	Graduated grid
Calibre	47 mm
Method of discharge	Rifle with 22 mm diameter muzzle
Propellant	Ballistite round
Muzzle velocity	70 m/sec
Range	400 m
Fuse	Impact
Effect	Smoke for up to 1 min
Safety	Manual pin
Environment	−32C to +55C

This grenade is available with two different fillings which generate white or yellow smoke accordingly. The loaded body is made from light alloy and contains 145 gm of smoke composition. The tail assembly consists of a tail boom of 22 mm interior diameter with eight stabilising fins. Two ballistite rounds are supplied with each grenade.

The fuse, which screws into the base of the body, is the integrated primer type. A safety pin is held in place by an adhesive band which can be replaced if the grenade is not used. On impact there is a percussion effect and initiation follows.

This grenade fulfils the dual role of signalling and the provision of an instant smoke screen.

In service with the French forces.

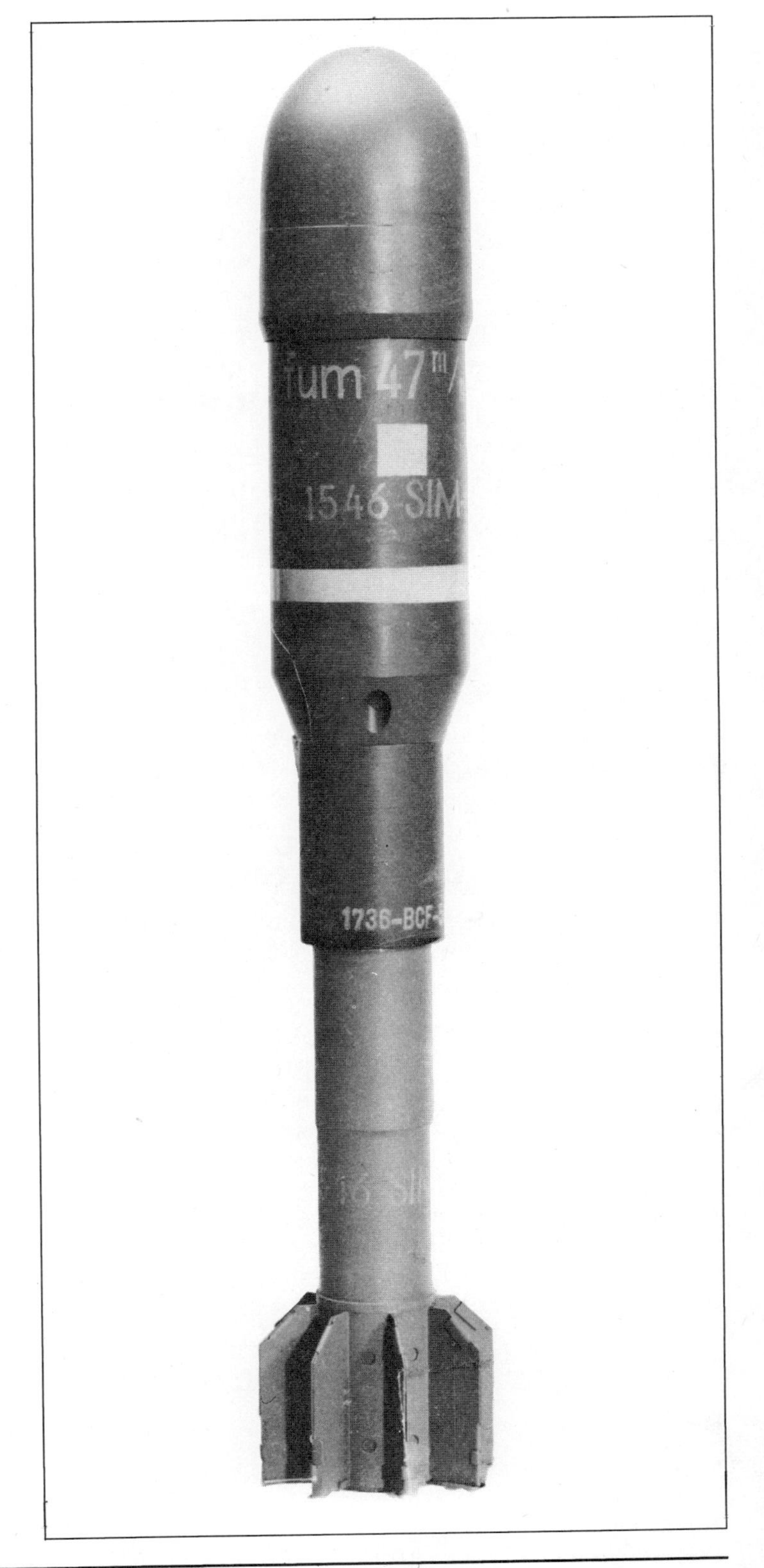

47 mm STRIM coloured smoke grenade.

A45 anti-personnel and anti-vehicle rifle grenade

Manufacturer: **Luchaire SA (France)**

Dimensions	Length 365 mm
Weight	556 gm
Body material	Steel
Charge	85 gm of shaped HE
Arming	Manual, with 1·75 m muzzle safety
Sight	Graduated grid
Calibre	45 mm
Method of discharge	Rifle
Propellant	Ballistite round
Muzzle velocity	80 m/sec
Range	460 m (effective 150 m)
Fuse	Impact
Effect	Penetrates 200 mm of armour plate or 540 mm of concrete, with additional fragmentation effect
Safety	Manual pin
Environment	Pan climatic

The A45 is a dual-purpose rifle grenade capable of being launched from any rifle with a 22 mm muzzle diameter. The body of this grenade is made from pressed steel and contains a shaped charge which can penetrate 540 mm of concrete or 200 mm of armour plate. Actuation is by an instantaneous impact fuse which is armed after 1·75 m of flight. On detonation the body fragments and, as an anti-personnel weapon, it is said to be comparable to a light mortar.

As far as is known the A45 is still under development, but is intended as a replacement for some of the older grenades now in service with the French forces.

Under development.

S32 smoke hand grenade

Manufacturer: **State factories (German Democratic Republic)**

Weight	250 gm
Body material	Cardboard
Charge	Composition
Arming	Friction cap
Activation	7 sec delay ignition fuse
Effect	Black smoke up to 2 min
Safety	Cap protects ignition pellet

The S32 East German smoke hand grenade is the older and smaller of two grenades of similar construction used in the Nationale Volksarmee. The contents of the light cardboard container are easily and quickly activated by twisting the small cap on the top of the grenade—a small abrasive pad inside the cap ignites an ignition pellet, which in turn ignites the delayed-action fuse. Care should be taken to throw the grenade without delay, as the 7 sec fuse is not always accurately measured. Instructions for use are printed on the side of the body, under the designation Rauchkorper (smoke body).

In service with the DDR forces.

S53 smoke hand grenade

Manufacturer: **State factories (German Democratic Republic)**

Weight	300 gm
Body material	Cardboard
Charge	Composition
Arming	Friction cap
Activation	7 sec delay ignition fuse
Effect	White smoke for 30 sec
Safety	Cap protects ignition pellet

The S53 East German stick smoke grenade is, apart from its handle, of similar construction to the S32 smoke grenade. The grenade is activated in a similar fashion by twisting the protective cap to ignite the ignition pellet and thus the delayed-action fuse. The filling, however, is of a completely different faster burning material producing white smoke, but has the advantage of being able to continue producing smoke, even submerged in water. As with the S32, instructions for use are printed on the side of the cardboard cylinder beneath (in this case) the designation Nebelhandgranate (fog hand grenade). This grenade, too, should be thrown straight after igniting as, once again, the 7 sec fuse is not wholly reliable.

In service with the DDR forces.

V40 fragmentation hand grenade

Manufacturer: **NWM de Kruithoorn (Holland)**

Dimensions	Diameter 45 mm; height 57 mm
Weight	100 gm
Body material	Pre-fragmented metal
Charge	Composition B
Arming	Pin, lever and striker
Fuse	4 sec pyrotechnic train
Effect	400 fragments out to 25 m
Safety	Manual pin

Environment	Pan climatic
Packing	5 grenades in a bandolier. 32 bandoliers in a steel box (32 kg) of the US M548 re-usable pattern

The V40 is the smallest grenade of current known manufacture, yet it is highly lethal at close proximity, and in an enclosed space. The size and weight of this grenade are roughly half that of most current fragmentation grenades available today. Nevertheless, it produces 400–500 fragments with a lethal radius of 5 m and a maximum effective zone of 25 m from the point of detonation. It should be noted, however, that the fragments lose velocity after about 5 m. The small size of the V40 permits it to be chucked rather than lobbed, and its weight allows it to be thrown about 50% further than the conventionally sized grenade.

The grenade consists of a pre-fragmented body filled with composition B and a percussion-firing mechanism of the pin, lever and striker type, with a 4 sec delay.

The active V40 grenades are olive drab and marked HE, whilst the inert ones are blue and marked INERT.

In service with the Dutch forces.

V40 hand grenade.

M42 offensive hand grenade

Manufacturer: **State factories (Hungary)**

Dimensions	Height 19·4 cm Diameter 4·8 cm
Weight	0·3 kg
Body material	Sheet steel
Charge	HE (134 gm)
Arming	Pin, spring and striker
Activation	3–5 sec delay pyrotechnic train
Effect	Blast to 25 m
Safety	Manual pin

The main reason for the retention in service of the Hungarian World War II stick grenade is probably the interesting design feature of threading at both ends of the grenade body which allows several grenades, after removal of the handle, to be screwed together to form a demolition charge. Otherwise the weapon is a normal offensive anti-personnel grenade designed for clearing bunkers and trenches, with a dangerous and unreliable delayed-action fuse of the percussion-operated type, activated simply by extraction of the safety-pin releasing the striker spring.

In service with the Hungarian forces.

M26 fragmentation hand grenade

Manufacturer: **Israel Military Industries (Israel)**

Dimensions	Diameter 62 mm Height 107 mm
Weight	425 gm
Body material	Metal
Charge	Composition B (150 gm)
Arming	Pin, lever and striker
Fuse	4·3 sec pyrotechnic train
Effect	1000 fragments out to 10 m
Safety	Manual pin
Environment	Pan climatic

The M26 is the defensive counterpart to the No 14 grenade manufactured by Israel Military Industries. It must therefore be thrown from behind cover.

The M26 is egg-shaped and consists of two main parts:

M26 hand grenade.

the body and the actuation block. The body is made of sheet steel enclosing a spirally wound steel coil and a charge of cast composition B. The actuation block is of the pin, lever and striker type and is equipped with a 4 sec delay.

IMI claim that the M26 has a 50% hit probability on men standing at 10 m from the point of detonation. The maximum effective zone is not known.

In service with the Israeli forces.

No 14 offensive hand grenade

Manufacturer: **Israel Military Industries (Israel)**

Dimensions	Diameter 64 mm Height 115 mm
Weight	325 gm
Body material	Laminated paper with sheet metal ends
Charge	TNT flakes (200 gm)
Arming	Pin, lever and striker
Fuse	4·5 sec pyrotechnic train
Effect	Blast
Safety	Manual pin
Environment	Pan climatic
Packing	Wooden box containing 500 grenades in plastic bags. Wooden box containing 200 fuses in cartons.

The Israeli No 14 grenade is a pot-type grenade made from laminated paper with sheet-metal ends and filled with TNT flakes. It is equipped with a 4·5 sec pyrotechnic delay fuse, initiated by a spring-loaded striker. This striker is held by a lever which is itself locked by a split pin. Being an offensive grenade, it has the shock killing and stunning effects without the lethal fragments, and so the thrower need not take cover.

In service with the Israeli forces.

No. 14 hand grenade.

F1/N60 defensive rifle grenade

Manufacturer: **State factories (Poland)**

Dimensions	Diameter 55 mm Height 270 mm
Weight	630 gm
Body material	Cast iron
Charge	HE (45 gm)
Fuse	Impact
Effect	Fragments out to 20 m

The Polish Army uses two rifle grenades—the F1/N60 anti-personnel fragmentation grenade and the PGN-60 anti-tank grenade—a type of weapon employed by no other communist country except Yugoslavia. These grenades are fired from the PMK-DGN—an AK-47 modified with a shoulder pad strapped to the butt, a large tangent leaf rearsight graduated 100–240 m, and

F1/N60 rifle grenade.

a spigot-type muzzle attachment. The grenade is also a Polish modification of a Soviet weapon—in this case the F1 fragmentation hand grenade, which it largely resembles, but is fitted with a simple stabilising boom, has no safety-pin ring, and uses an impact fuse in place of the F1's delay fuse. The pre-fragmentated body enables defending troops to increase the effectiveness of their fire against an attacker by launching anti-personnel grenades very accurately and rapidly to a distance far exceeding the normal grenade hand throw. A special small magazine can hold ten launching cartridges, and is made with the forward side blocked so that normal cartridges cannot be loaded in error.

In service with the Polish forces.

PGN-60 HEAT rifle grenade

Manufacturer: **State factories (Poland)**

Dimensions	Diameter 67·5 mm Height 405 mm
Weight	580 gm
Body material	Steel
Charge	HEAT (218 gm)
Range	90 m
Fuse	Impact
Effect	Concentrated blast and penetrates up to 100 mm of armour plate

The PGN-60 HEAT rifle grenade is of wholly Polish design, unlike the other of the two Polish rifle grenades, the F1/N60 anti-personnel grenade. Of all communist countries, only Poland and Yugoslavia employ this type of grenade. Like the F1/N60, the PGN-60 is launched using the Polish modification of the Soviet AK-47—the PMK-DGN, fitted with shoulder pad, tangent leaf rear-sight graduated 100 m–240 m, a spigot-type muzzle attachment, and 10 round magazine. The sights, however, appear to have been designed basically for the personnel F1/N60 grenade, as the effective anti-tank range of the PGN-60 is only about 90 m, maximum penetration capability of the shaped-charge warhead being in the region of 100 mm. Stabilisation in flight is ensured by an extended tail-boom fitted with narrow fixed fins.

In service with the Polish forces.

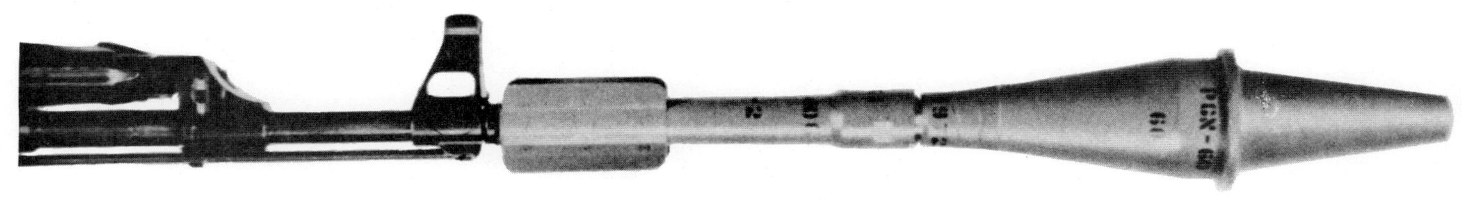

PGN-60 rifle grenade.

RDG-2 (and RDG-1) smoke hand grenade

Manufacturer: **State factories (USSR)**

Dimensions	Diameter 4·5 cm Height 25 cm
Weight	500 gm
Body material	Waxed cardboard
Charge	Smooth composition
Arming	Friction cap
Fuse	5 sec delay pyrotechnic train
Effect	White smoke for 100 sec

The Soviet RDG-2 is a long, narrow cylinder of waxed cardboard, activated by the normal friction cap and delay-fuse principle. The white smoke cloud produced covers an area of about 20 m by 10 m after burning for some 1½ minutes.

RDG-1 is a similar grenade of waxed cardboard, but has a wooden handle to facilitate throwing and two slightly different models produce either white or black smoke. The activation principle is the same as that of RDG-2, but this grenade has one further advantage. Owing to its wooden handle, it does not sink, and will continue to burn and produce smoke in water.

In service with the Soviet and other Warsaw Pact forces.

RGD5 defensive hand grenade

Manufacturer: **State factories (USSR and People's Republic of China)**

Dimensions	Diameter 5·6 cm Height 11·4 cm
Weight	310 gm
Body material	Sheet steel
Charge	TNT (110 gm)
Arming	Pin, lever and striker

Fuse	3–4 sec delay pyrotechnic train
Effect	Fragments out to 25 m
Safety	Manual pin

The latest development in Soviet anti-personnel fragmentation grenades is the defensive RGD5, which is only just over half the weight of the older F1 but retains a similar effective range and can naturally be thrown much further. The sheet body is smooth, oval and stamped in two pieces with a raised lip round the centre, with, however, little change in the method of arming and activation. The 3–4 sec delay fuse is activated by the striker being released when the safety lever is allowed to to pivot on the end of the long fuse body. The fragmentation jacket is fitted inside the grenade body, being serrated in the case of the Soviet model and smooth-surfaced in the Chinese version, which is called the M32. This grenade, like most Soviet hand grenades, uses the UZRG time fuse.

In service with the Soviet, other Warsaw Pact, North Vietnamese, communist Chinese forces and the Vietcong.

RGD5 hand grenade.

RKG3/3M/3T anti-tank hand grenade

Manufacturers: **State factories (USSR)**

Dimensions	Diameter 5·5 cm Height 36·2 cm
Weight	1070 gm
Body material	Sheet steel
Charge	HEAT (565 gm)
Arming	Pin, inertial striker
Fuse	Impact
Effect	Shaped charge concentrated blast
Safety	Manual pin
Packing	Body, fuse and handle separate

Most Warsaw Pact countries now use the RKG3 or its modernised version, the RKG3M, as the standard infantry anti-tank hand grenade to supplement the RPG7V anti-tank grenade launcher, and both systems have been sent to North Vietnam. The RKG3 series grenades are much heavier and longer than the Soviet anti-personnel grenades and are transported in the three separate parts—the cylindrical body containing 567 gm of HE shaped-charge filler, the handle containing the safety-pin and a drogue parachute assembly, and the small detonator. After assembly, the grenade is operated as follows: the handle is held in one hand while the other hand removes the safety ring and pin—this action frees both the detonator and the handle cap retaining the parachute. The grenade is now thrown and the parachute retaining cap releases the parachute which ensures that the shaped-charge warhead strikes the target at the correct impact angle, whereupon the firing pin, located in the handle, is forced down to strike the detonator. Owing to its weight, the RKG3 can only be thrown about 20 m, but it can penetrate up to 120 mm of armour plate. The only difference between RKG3 and RKG3M is that the latter has a copper charge-lining. The Chinese copy is called RKG3T and is of exactly the same design as the Soviet model.

In service with the Soviet, other Warsaw Pact, North Vietnamese forces and the Vietcong.

RG42 defensive hand grenade

Manufacturers: **State factories (USSR)**

Dimensions	Diameter 5·4 cm Height 12·7 cm
Weight	420 gm
Body material	Sheet steel
Charge	TNT (118 gm)
Arming	Pin, lever and striker
Fuse	3–4 sec pyrotechnic train
Effect	Fragments out to 20 m
Safety	Manual pin

The RG42 anti-personnel stick grenade dates back to World War II, but can still be found in many communist countries. Although its outward appearance is that of an offensive blast grenade, inside the sheet-metal cylinder body is a light serrated metal liner, which is fragmented on detonation. The weapon is not thrown by its handle, but is operated in a similar fashion to the British Mills grenade. When the grenade is thrown, the lever is released and it springs from the cylinder, allowing the detonator, housed in the handle, to strike and activate the 3–4 sec delay fuse, the UZRG standard fuse employed in most Soviet hand grenades. The grenade can be thrown about 40 m.

In service with the Soviet, other Warsaw Pact, North Vietnamese and communist Chinese forces.

RG42 hand grenade.

F1 defensive hand grenade

Manufacturers: **State factories (USSR and People's Republic of China)**

Dimensions	Diameter 5·5 cm Height 12·4 cm
Weight	690 gm
Body material	Cast iron
Charge	TNT (60 gm)
Arming	Pin, lever and striker
Fuse	3–4 sec delay pyrotechnic train
Effect	Fragments out to 20 m
Safety	Manual pin

Like the RG42, the F1 anti-personnel fragmentation defensive grenade was first produced in World War II and has since been used (and still is) by most communist countries. Although somewhat similar in operation and appearance to the British Mills grenade, having an oval heavily-serrated body and a long side-mounted safety lever, the F1 is, however, loaded by inserting the detonator into the top after unscrewing the elongated fuse body, which is then replaced. As with the RG42, the spring-loaded striker activates the fuse when released by the safety lever being now allowed to pivot when the grenade leaves the throwing hand. Whilst the danger zone is given as 20 m radius, it is not unknown for fragments to cause injury at 100 m. Poland uses a modification of the F1 (with an impact fuse) as the F1/N60 anti-

F1 hand grenade.

personnel rifle grenade. The Chinese model is called the Type 1/M33, and is an exact copy, apart from markings. The grenades can be thrown about 45 m.

The fuse of the F1 can be either the standard UZRG or the F1, the latter burning $\frac{1}{5}$ sec longer. Owing to the large fragmentation area, the grenade should be thrown from behind cover.

In service with the Soviet, other Warsaw Pact, North Vietnamese, communist Chinese forces and Vietcong.

83 smoke hand grenade

Manufacturer: **Royal ordnance factories (United Kingdom)**

Dimensions	Height 14·5 cm Diameter 6·1 cm
Weight	0·4 kg
Body material	Tin-plate
Charge	Coloured smoke mixture
Arming	Pin, lever and striker
Actuation	4 sec pyrotechnic train
Effect	Smoke emission 25—45 sec
Safety	Manual pin
Environment	Pan climatic
Packing	Issued ready for use in cardboard cylinders, 24 per box

This grenade is similar in appearance to the 80 grenade except for the markings and absence of the twisted cone-shaped base. Also sea-green in colour, the 83 coloured smoke grenade resembles a small soft drink can but with the addition of twin lugs on top to hold the safety pin retaining the flat safety lever. No preparation is necessary to use this grenade, as it is issued already primed. All that is required is to hold the grenade in the throwing hand with the safety lever securely in the palm, withdraw the safety pin and throw. Although there is almost no explosion, the smoke being emitted via apertures in the casing, the 83 grenade should always be thrown and not placed in position. When released, the safety lever pivots up and over, allowing the spring-loaded striker to descend and hit the fuse which, after the requisite 4 sec delay, ignites the detonator. The grenade may be used either to produce a smoke screen or as a signalling device.

In service with the United Kingdom forces.

83 smoke grenade.

36 defensive hand grenade

Manufacturer: **Royal ordnance factories (United Kingdom)**

Dimensions	Height 8·9 cm Diameter 5·7 cm
Weight	0·7 kg
Body material	Cast iron
Charge	HE
Arming	Pin, lever and striker
Actuation	4 or 7 sec pyrotechnic train
Effect	Fragments out to 230 m (maximum)
Safety	Manual pin
Environment	Pan climatic
Packing	Separate fuse and detonator, 12 per box with 4 boxes each of 3 igniters

The 36 grenade has been the standard British defensive anti-personnel grenade for many years and is still regarded as an excellent weapon. The egg-shaped cast-iron casing is completely grooved to provide rectangular fragments on detonation. The range of the fragmentation effect can vary from 23 m on soft ground to 230 m on a hard surface, and the thrower must, throwing range being only about 9 m, seek cover immediately on throwing. However, the grenade can be rifle-projected 180 m using a grenade cartridge and discharger cup. Two ignition sets are available—the 4 sec delay for throwing and the 7 sec delay for use with the rifle. The 36 grenade consists of the oval cast-iron body fitted with twin lugs to retain the safety pin, the filler-plug and in the base, the detonator access plug. The spring-loaded striker is inserted through an aperture on top and the safety lever held down by the safety pin, whilst the detonator is inserted through the base aperture. When thrown, the striker spring will force the safety lever to pivot upwards, allowing the striker to descend and hit the igniter which inites the detonator after the requisite delay. An HE-filled grenade carries a line of red crosses around the top.

In service with the United Kingdom forces, but obsolescent.

Open section of 36 grenade with baseplate fitted for firing by rifle.

36 hand grenade.

80 smoke hand grenade

Manufacturer: **Royal ordnance factories (United Kingdom)**

Dimensions	Height 14·5 cm Diameter 6·1 cm
Weight	0·5 kg
Body material	Tin-plate
Charge	Phosphorus
Arming	Pin, lever and striker
Actuation	4 sec pyrotechnic train
Effect	Smoke for 20–40 sec, incendiary blast out to 15 m
Safety	Manual pin
Environment	Pan climatic
Packing	Separate fuse and detonator, 24 of each per box

Although the main purpose of the 80 grenade is to produce a smokescreen, the white phosphorous filling has an additional incendiary effect and can cause casualties out to a radius of 15 m. The grenade consists of a tin-plate cylindrical body (sea-green in colour) with a twisted

80 smoke grenade.

cone-shaped base and twin lugs on the flask-like top holding the safety pin which secures the flat safety lever. Unlike the 36 grenade, the complete striker, detonator and fuse are inserted as a pre-set assembly through the screw-on top, although the fuse is similar to that of the 36 grenade. When the grenade is thrown, the safety lever is forced up by the striker spring, which at the same time allows the striker to descend and hit the fuse, putting into operation the delayed-action train to ignite the detonator. Because of the similarity in shape and size of this grenade to the 83 (and 91) grenades, and the dangerous nature of its filling, the tapered base was fitted to ease recognition in darkness.

In service with the United Kingdom forces.

L2A1 offensive hand grenade

Manufacturer: **Royal ordnance factories (United Kingdom)**

Dimensions	Height 10·9 cm Diameter 6 cm
Weight	0·51 kg
Body material	Steel
Charge	RDX/TNT
Arming	Pin, lever and striker
Actuation	4·3 sec pyrotechnic train
Effect	Fragments lethal to 10 m
Safety	Manual pin
Environment	All climates

L2A1 offensive hand grenade.

The L2A1 grenade, with its L25A4 fuse, is in production for the British forces. It replaces the long obsolescent 36 grenade, and is derived from the US M48, which it closely resembles. It is an effective and robust modern design, and is well proven. Although originally intended to be a dual-purpose grenade with the option of launching from the muzzle of a rifle, using a tail adaptor, this has now been abandoned and hand-throwing is the only means of projecting.

The body is a thin, sheet-steel case containing a coil of notched wire which breaks up into fragments of predictable size. In this it differs sharply from the 36 type whose cast-iron body often broke in a random manner giving only a few large fragments. The fuse is entirely conventional and screws into the top of the body, giving a 4·3 sec delay and a degree of safety.

In service with the United Kingdom forces.

M18 coloured smoke hand grenade

Manufacturer: **Department of the United States Army**

Weight	538 gm
Body material	Sheet steel
Filling	326 gm of red, green, yellow or violet smoke composition
Arming	Pin, lever, striker
Fuse	1–2 sec pyrotechnic train
Effect	Emits smoke for 50–90 sec
Environment	Pan climatic

This grenade is available in four colours—red, green, yellow and violet and is used for signalling, or as a short-duration screen. The sheet-metal body has four emission holes, one in the base and three round the top allowing escape of the smoke on ignition of the 326 gm of smoke composition. The ignition system is of the pin, lever, striker type but does not have a detonator. Instead there is a high-heat pyrotechnic starter, which ignites the smoke composition which then burns for 50–90 sec. Should the pyrotechnic starter not fire the composition, the grenade may still be actuated by punching a hole in its base and applying a naked flame to the exposed composition.

In service with the United States forces.

M26 and M26A1 defensive hand and rifle grenade

Manufacturer: **Department of the United States Army**

Weight	455 gm
Body material	Sheet metal with steel liner
Filling	155 gm composition B
Arming	Pin, lever, striker
Fuse	4–5 sec pyrotechnic train
Effect	Fragments out to 15 m
Safety	Manual pin
Environment	Pan climatic

The M26 has been in service with the United States forces since the Korean war. The original M26 was slightly modified to improve fragmentation and was designated M26A1. Both are in use and look alike. The body is made of thin metal sheeting lined with a pre-fragmented spirally wound steel coil and filled with 155 gm of composition B. An actuation block of the pin, lever, striker type containing a 4–5 sec delay train is screwed into the top. On detonation, the M26 and M26A1 create a casualty zone with a radius of 15 m. Both grenades can be launched from a rifle with an adapter and a blank cartridge, the maximum range being about 160 m.

In service with the United States forces.

M26 grenade ready for launch from the Armalite rifle.

M33 defensive hand grenade

Manufacturer: **Department of the United States Army**

Weight	390 gm
Body material	Steel
Filling	184 gm composition B
Arming	Pin, lever, striker
Fuse	4–5 sec pyrotechnic train
Effect	Fragments out to 15 m
Safety	Manual pin
Environment	Pan climatic

The M33 has an oblate spheroid steel body filled with 184 gm of composition B and is armed in a similar manner to the M56, though the actuation block has a different configuration due to the shape of the body. No provision has been made for launching this grenade from a rifle.

In service with the United States forces.

M34 incendiary/fragmentation hand grenade

Manufacturer: **Department of the United States Army**

Weight	765 gm
Body material	Rolled steel
Filling	425 gm white phosphorus
Arming	Pin, lever, striker
Fuse	4–5 sec pyrotechnic train with small tetryl burster charge
Effect	Blast, fragments and WP particles out to 35 m, smoke
Safety	Manual pin
Environment	Pan climatic

This grenade can be used as an incendiary, for signalling and screening, and in the anti-personnel role. The body of rolled steel is serrated to help fragmentation, and the 425 gm white phosphorous filler will burn at 2700°C on contact with air for about 60 sec. The fuse is basically a 4–5 sec delay device of the pin, lever, striker and pyrotechnic train type. The detonator's explosion is insufficient, however, to burst the grenade's casing, so a small tetryl burster charge is incorporated to do so. Detonation of the burster results in the rupture of the main body, and white phosphorous particles, capable of causing casualties, are scattered over a 35 m area. The smoke from this and other white phosphorus grenades has limited screening value due to the updraught caused by the intense heat.

In service with the United States forces.

Mk 38A defensive hand grenade

Manufacturer: **Department of the United States Army**

Weight	442 gm
Body material	Fibre
Filling	225 gm TNT
Arming	Pin, lever, striker
Fuse	4–5 sec delay pyrotechnic train
Effect	Blast
Safety	Manual pin
Environment	Pan climatic

This is a blast-effect grenade consisting of a fibre body containing 225 gm of TNT. The fuse system is the same as the M34 white phosphorus grenade. Though it is an offensive grenade, and its main effect is concussive, fragments from the actuation block can be projected out to 200 m.

In service with the United States forces.

M56 defensive hand and rifle grenade

Manufacturer: **Department of the United States Army**

Weight	430 gm
Body material	Sheet metal with steel liner
Filling	180 gm composition B
Arming	Pin, lever, striker
Fuse	4–5 sec pyrotechnic train
Effect	Fragments out to 15 m
Safety	Manual pin
Environment	Pan climatic

The M56 is basically the same as the M26A1 except that it has a larger quantity of filler, 180 gm as opposed to 155 gm, and uses a different fuse assembly that has a larger thread on the actuation block. The effects of the M56 are also similar to those of the M26 series.

In service with the United States forces.

M57 defensive hand grenade

Manufacturer: **Department of the United States Army**

Weight	430 gm
Body material	Sheet metal
Filling	190 gm composition B
Fuse	Impact with 1 sec delay
Effect	Fragments out to 15 m
Safety	Manual pin
Environment	Pan climatic

The M57 differs from the M56 only in that it utilises an impact detonating fuse and contains a little more explosive. This fuse is electrical and functions either on impact or after a 4 sec delay. A 1 sec arming delay is built in, which means that the grenade will detonate on impact 1 sec after the safety lever has been released. Should the grenade fail to explode on impact, a 4 sec self-destruct system operates. Unlike the M26 and M56 grenades, the M57 cannot be launched from a rifle since the impact detonator may be initiated by the gas pressures. In addition, when thrown, a minimum trajectory height of 4·5 m must be achieved if the impact detonator is to work.

In service with the United States forces.

M59 offensive hand grenade

Manufacturer: **Department of the United States Army**

Weight	390 gm
Body material	Steel
Filling	184 gm or composition B
Fuse	Impact
Effect	Fragments out to 15 m
Safety	Manual pin and special clip
Environment	Pan climatic

The M59 has the characteristics of the M33, but is equipped with the same impact fuse as the M57.

In service with the United States forces.

AN-MB HC smoke hand grenade

Manufacturer: **Department of the United States Army**

Weight	680 gm
Body material	Sheet steel
Filling	538 gm of type C HC smoke composition
Arming	Pin, lever, striker
Fuse	1–2 sec pyrotechnic train
Effect	Dense smoke for 105–150 sec
Safety	Manual pin
Environment	Pan climatic

This grenade produces a thick white screen, which can also be used for signalling. The sheet steel body is filled with 538 gm of type C HC smoke mixture which burns for 105–150 sec. The ignition system is the same as for the M18.

In service with the United States forces.

AM-M14 TH3 incendiary hand and rifle grenade

Manufacturer: **Department of the United States Army**

Dimensions	Height 14·5 cm Diameter 6·3 cm
Weight	0·9 kg
Body material	Sheet metal
Filling	750 gm of TH3 (thermate) composition
Arming	Pin, lever, striker
Fuse	0·7 sec–2 sec pyrotechnic train
Effect	Burns at 2150°C for 30–45 sec
Safety	Manual pin
Environment	Pan climatic

The AN-M14 TH3 was developed by the Chemical Warfare Service of the United States Government to meet a requirement for a hand-delivered incendiary device that enables an individual soldier to destroy equipment. Its sheet-steel body is filled with 750 gm of thermate (TH3) mixture. Thermate is an improved form of the thermate composition used during World War II. In the AN-M14 TH3 it burns for 40 sec at 2150°C, and will burn through a ½ in homogeneous armour plate. In addition, it produces its own oxygen and can therefore be used under water. Though normally delivered by hand, this grenade can be launched from a service rifle using an adaptor and special blank round. The ignition system is the same as for the M18 and AN-M8 HC.

In service with the United States forces.

Mk1 illuminating hand grenade

Manufacturer: **Department of the United States Army**

Weight	283 gm
Body material	Sheet steel
Filling	99 gm illuminating composition
Arming	Pin, lever, striker
Fuse	Quick match train with 7 sec delay
Effect	Illuminated area of 200 m for 25 sec at 55,000 cp
Safety	Manual pin
Environment	Pan climatic

The Mk1 grenade is used for signalling, point illumination and, occasionally, as an incendiary as it burns fiercely. The body is made of sheet steel, and the filler is ignited by a 7 sec quick match system that is actuated by the pin, lever, striker method. Once lit, the illuminating compound burns at 55,000 cp for about 25 sec with an effective radius of illumination of 100 m.

In service with the United States forces.

Mk2 defensive hand and rifle grenade

Manufacturer: **Department of the United States Army**

Weight	595 gm
Body material	Cast iron
Filling	57 gm flaked TNT
Arming	Pin, lever, striker
Fuse	4–5 sec pyrotechnic train
Effect	Fragments out to 10 m
Safety	Manual pin
Environment	Pan climatic

This is the renowned 'pineapple' grenade that has been in service with the United States forces and some of her allies for many years. It is now being phased out as stocks are expended.

The Mk2 consists of a serrated cast-iron body filled with 57 gm of flaked TNT and an actuation block of the pin, lever, striker type containing a 4–5 sec pyrotechnic train. An average man should be able to throw the Mk2 about 30 m, and it is therefore a defensive rather than an offensive weapon. However, it can be projected out to 140 m with a service rifle equipped with a suitable adapter and blank cartridge. The Mk2 has an effective casualty radius of more than 10 m.

In service with the United States, South Vietnamese and Taiwan forces, but is being phased out.

M52R (and M69) offensive hand grenade

Manufacturer: **State factories (Yugoslavia)**

Weight	60 gm
Body material	Stamped steel
Charge	HE
Fuse	4–5 sec delay pyrotechnic train (M69) Impact (M52R)
Effect	Blast out to 20 m

The Yugoslav M52R and M69 anti-personnel offensive hand grenades closely resemble each other, the only real difference being that the older M52R is fitted with an impact fuse and the M69 has been given a safer delay fuse. Both are of an oval shape with a large fuse body extending from one end which is unscrewed to allow insertion of the detonator. Of similar size, these two grenades are very small for their actual weight (almost twice that of most other hand grenades used by communist countries).

In service with the Yugoslav forces.

M60 HEAT rifle grenade

Manufacturer: **State factories (Yugoslavia)**

Dimensions	Diameter 6 cm Height 39 cm
Weight	600 gm
Body material	Sheet steel (stamped)
Charge	HEAT (235 gm)
Range	150 m
Fuse	Impact
Effect	Concentrated blast

This anti-tank rifle grenade is one of the four rifle grenades (the others being anti-personnel, smoke and illuminating devices) now being manufactured in Yugoslavia after years of being dependent on Belgium for such weapons. All of these grenades have a slim streamlined outline, with this, the anti-tank missile, being the largest. All employ the same rounded stabilising fin system, but the round-nosed body of the anti-tank grenade is slightly enlarged over its front half. The spring-loaded detonator is mounted level with the junction of the cylindrical tail section and the body swelling. With a maximum effective range of 150 m, this grenade is very much superior to the PGN-60, as used by the only other communist country to employ such weapons—Poland. Launching is effected from the spigot-type fitting of the M59/66 adaptation of the Soviet SKS carbine, or from the older M48 rifle, as with all three other Yugoslav rifle grenades.

In service with the Yugoslav forces.

M60 fragmentation rifle grenade

Manufacturer: **State factories (Yugoslavia)**

Dimensions	Diameter 3 cm Height 31 cm
Weight	520 gm
Body material	Sheet steel
Charge	HE (67 gm)
Range	400 m
Fuse	Impact
Effect	Fragments out to 50 m

The Yugoslavs and the Poles are the only communist nations to employ rifle grenades. Until a short time ago Yugoslavia imported rifle grenades from Belgium, but is now producing her own anti-personnel and anti-tank rifle grenades, both of which have a very slim, streamlined shape. The anti-personnel fragmentation grenade has an excellent range of up to 400 m, being fired by the spigot-type launcher of the M59/66 Yugoslav modification of the SKS carbine, or from the older M48 rifle. Although fitted with rounded-tail stabilising fins similar to those on the anti-tank rifle grenade, this missile is smaller, lighter and of almost equal diameter for nearly the whole of its length. It is cylindrical and has a flat, slightly tapered nose, containing the impact fuse, whilst the HE filling occupies the central third of the grenade.

In service with the Yugoslav forces.

M62 smoke rifle grenade

Manufacturer: **State factories (Yugoslavia)**

Dimensions	Diameter 4 cm Height 33 cm
Weight	480 gm
Range	465 m with 7·9 mm rifle
Fuse	Base detonating with 7–8 sec time delay

M62 illuminating rifle grenade

Manufacturer: **State factories (Yugoslavia)**

Dimensions	Diameter 4 cm Height 33 cm
Weight	450 gm
Range	240 m with 7·9 mm rifle
Fuse	Burning time 30 sec

The illuminating and the smoke rifle grenades, together with the anti-personnel and the anti-tank rifle grenades are very recent developments in Yugoslavia. All are long, streamlined missiles, using similar rounded tailfin assemblies, differing in appearance only slightly. Both the smoke and illuminating grenades are torpedo-shaped, the front half slightly thicker than the rear half, and have the safety-pin, with a ring attached, inserted just below half-way. Whilst the nose of the smoke grenade is smooth and rounded, that of the illuminating grenade is semi-elliptical and is encircled by a milled band. As with the anti-personnel and anti-tank grenades, these other two missiles can be fired from the spigot-type launcher of the M48 rifle and the M59/66 Yugoslav modification of the Soviet SKS carbine.

In service with the Yugoslav forces.

Grenade Launchers

As can be seen from the examples that follow in this section and the section on grenades, grenade launchers are basically of two types. The first is a weapon resembling a large single barrel shot gun which can be fired by itself or attached to a rifle. The second type of launcher is made by so designing the muzzle of a rifle (or by attaching a tube-like extension to it) that a grenade can be propelled off the end of a rifle by a small blank (or ballistite) cartridge or, in some cases, a conventional bullet.

In all cases, there is recoil, sometimes quite considerable and it is this that basically differentiates between a grenade launcher and a rocket launcher, even though the effect at the receiving end might be the same. Another difference is, of course, the range. It is mainly because of the relatively short range of the grenade discharger that rocket launchers were developed.

The range of grenades that can be fired by a launcher is quite phenomenal and some are even multi-purpose or polyvalent which, while wasteful of material in some respects, does have the merit of reducing the load the soldier has to carry.

Two interesting developments are worthy of note: one is the Jet Shot by sa PRB described in this section. This is clearly a weapon of considerable promise and potential though it might be prone to damage in transit and thus liable to variations of range when fired.

The other development is that of the bullet-trap grenades by Mecar SA. It will be recalled that these grenades are fired, as is inferred, by a conventional bullet being 'trapped' in the tail of the grenade and the energy so produced, launching the grenade. This method has penalities of range, but offers considerable potential to the user. It is to be hoped that the rifle barrel does not suffer in the process of firing.

Lastly, there is no doubt that the grenade launch attachment should be discarded in favour of a rifle designed to launch a grenade from the muzzle without any adaptation. Some rifles are so designed, all others should be as soon as possible.

JOHN OWEN

HK69 grenade launcher

Manufacturer: **Heckler & Koch GMBH (Germany)**

Calibre	40 mm
Dimensions	Length 390 mm
Weight	1·6 kg
Range	350 m
Sight	Swivelling-rail type with notch and barleycorn
Propellant	Grenade cartridge

The HK69 is a manually cocked, single-round, 40 mm grenade launcher. It is designed to fire explosive grenades (like the M118) out to 350 m.

The HK69 consists of two basic assemblies, the barrel and the receiver. The barrel assembly is composed of the barrel itself, a retaining sleeve which almost surrounds the barrel and the pistol-grip which houses the mechanical trigger and thumb-operated safety lever. The barrel is made of a specially treated aluminium alloy with 1152 mm of right-hand twist in its 320 mm length. The grooving is designed to stabilise the projectile.

The receiver is also made of aluminium alloy and serves as a guide for the barrel-retaining sleeve. The extractor is mounted in the receiver and engages in the breech when the weapon is locked. The cocking-lever is connected to the spring-loaded firing pin located at the rear of the receiver. When cocked, the pin is held by a catch and released by a connecting rod from the trigger mechanism. The opening of the weapon results in the automatic extraction of the case.

The sight is designed to be attached to either side of the weapon and is adjustable for elevation and windage. This sight is of the rail type with notch and barleycorn which swivels so that a marker on the rail corresponds to ranges marked on the receiver.

The HK69 can be attached to any of the Heckler and Koch assault rifles or carbines, without using tools, but each weapon can function independently. It is rumoured that the manufacturer is contemplating the production of adapters so that the HK69 can be fitted to a wider range of weapons, but so far no information has been made available.

Not yet in service.

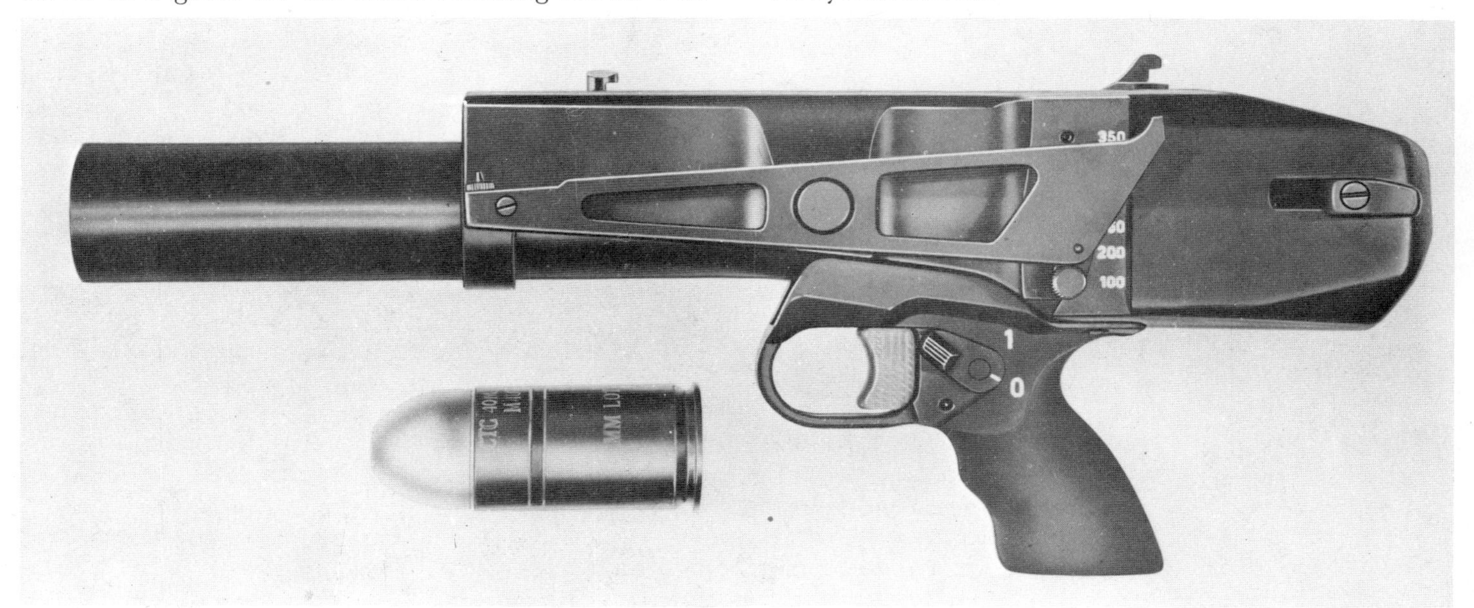

HK69 and grenade

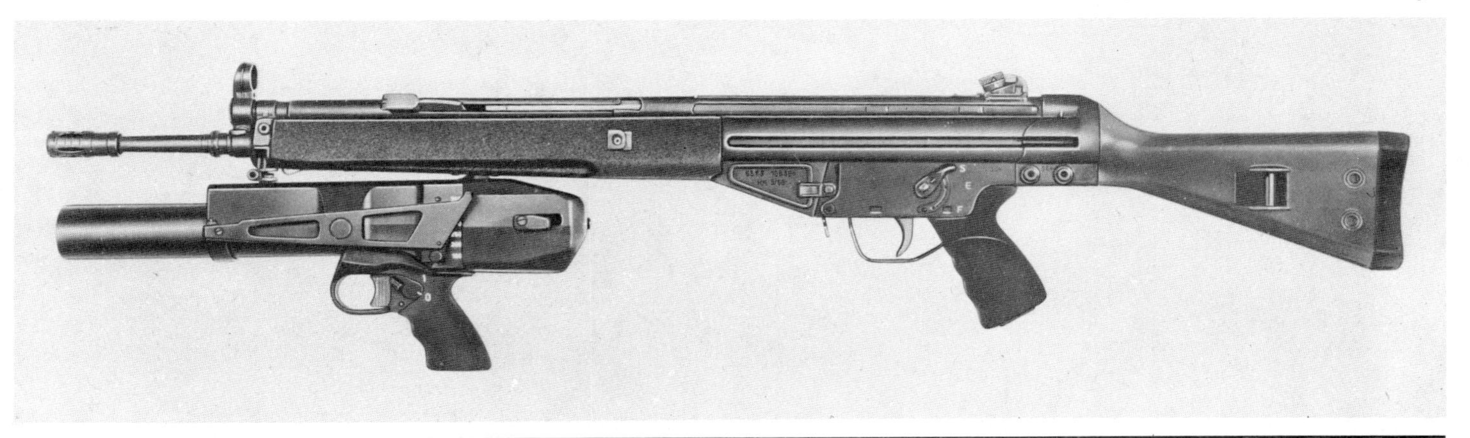

HK69 attached to the G3 rifle

M7 grenade launcher

Manufacturer: **Department of the United States Army**

Rifle	·30 in automatic rifle M1
Length	19 cm (M7, M7A1, M7A2) 23 cm (M7A3)
Weight	340 gm
Projectiles (with ranges)	Anti-tank rifle grenade M11A4 (180 m) HEAT rifle grenade M31 (120 m) Smoke rifle grenade M19A1 (190 m) Fragmentation hand grenade Mk 2 (160 m) Chemical hand grenade (140 m) Signal flares (210 m)

The M7 series of grenade launchers can be used for a wide variety of missiles. The different sub-marks improve the accuracy progressively but do not affect the range, which varies only with the different projectiles, as shown above. In order to project the two hand grenades, however, it is necessary to use an additional grenade-launching adaptor, the M1A2 for the fragmentation grenade and the M2A1 for the chemical hand grenade. The ranges quoted above can be varied by positioning the projectile against the appropriate ring on the cylinder.

The launcher is locked on to the rifle muzzle by the bayonet lug. When firing, the rifle should be unloaded, then loaded with one grenade cartridge after applying the safety catch. The rifle bolt is closed and the grenade slid on to the tube. When required to be fired, the grenade safety pin and the rifle safety catch should be released.

In service with the United States reserve forces.

M8 grenade launcher

Manufacturer: **Department of the United States Army**

Rifles	·30 in carbines M1, M1A1 and M2
Length	15 cm
Weight	340 gm
Projectiles	Anti-tank rifle grenade Smoke rifle grenade M19A1 Streamer smoke rifle grenade Fragmentation hand grenade Mk2 Chemical hand grenade Practice hand grenade

As in the case of the M7 series of grenade launchers, the M8 requires the additional use of a grenade-launching adaptor to protect the hand grenades, the M2 chemical grenade-launching adaptor being used for the corresponding missile and the M1 and M1A1 adaptors for the other hand grenades.

This launcher is attached to the carbine by the screw clamp, which is secured behind the foresight. Loading and operation are similar to the operation of the M7 launcher.

In service with the United States and some South-East Asian forces.

M76 grenade launcher

Manufacturer: **Department of the United States Army**

Rifle	7·62 mm automatic rifle M14
Length	21 cm
Weight	200 gm
Projectiles	Anti-tank rifle grenade Fragmentation hand grenade

The M76 grenade-launching attachment is made for the M14 automatic rifle, formerly standard issue to United States troops serving in NATO.

To effect projection a 7·62 mm rifle grenade cartridge, the M64, is used. This launcher is secured to the rifle by locking the clip over the bayonet lug. Loading and operation are similar to the operation of the M7 launcher.

In service with some United States forces, including the United States National Guard.

MX148 40 mm grenade launcher

Manufacturer: **Department of the United States Army**

Calibre	40 mm
Dimensions	Length 41·9 cm Barrel length 25·4 cm
Weight	1·4 kg
Range	400 m
Sight	Articulated arm with adjustable rear aperture and post foresight
Operation	Breech loaded, manual
Muzzle velocity	74·5 m/sec
Ammunition	Cased projectiles

This is a low-weight, 40 mm grenade launcher for use in conjunction with the M16 and M16A1 rifles. It is manually loaded by pushing the pistol-grip and barrel assembly forward, and inserting a round into the exposed chamber. The weapon is then closed and manually cocked by pulling back on a cocking handle. The trigger extends back on the right-hand side to a position just forward and below the rifle trigger. The sight is an articulated adjustable rear aperture and post foresight combination, graduated for ranges out to 450 m. Though this weapon was used in small numbers during the Vietnam war it was never fully adopted and was subsequently superseded by the M203.

In service in small numbers, but obsolescent.

40 mm MX148 launcher

M203 40 mm grenade launcher

Manufacturer: **Colt Industries (United States)**

Calibre	40 mm
Dimensions	Length 38·8 cm Barrel length 30·5 cm
Weight	1·4 kg
Range	350 m
Sight	Primary—quadrant Secondary—leaf and post
Operation	Breech-loaded, manual
Muzzle velocity	71 m/sec
Ammunition	Cased projectiles

The M203 is the successor to the M79 grenade launcher and was developed by the AAI Corporation at the direction of the United States Army Weapons Command.

The M203 is a single-shot, breech-loading, pump-action weapon for direct attachment to the M16 and the M16A1 rifles and, as such, fulfils the need for a rifle/grenade launcher package which will enable infantrymen to engage targets at ranges from 30 m to 375 m.

To load the M203, the barrel release is depressed and the barrel pushed forward. A round is then inserted. An automatic safety sear ensures against accidental discharge since the weapon is automatically cocked when opened.

Two sighting systems are used with the M203. The primary sight is located on the left side of the carrying handle and consists of an aperture and post system mounted on a swivelling arm. Ranges are marked on a quadrant scale and set by moving the sight latch rearwards, and swivelling the arm until the desired range appears in a window. Small adjustments in windage can be made by moving the rear aperture sight. The secondary sight is a folding, graduated leaf sight mounted on the forestock. This is used for rapid target engagement out to 250 m and can be adjusted for elevation and azimuth. The leaf is of the open ladder type graduated in 50 m increments. This sight uses the post foresight of the rifle as a front aiming reference.

The M203 is capable of firing a variety of 40 mm projectiles of both United States and overseas manufacture.

In service with the United States forces.

M79 grenade launcher

Manufacturer: **Department of the United States Army**

Calibre	40 mm
Dimensions	Length of launcher 730 mm Length of barrel 356 mm
Weight	2·93 kg (loaded)
Sight	Protected blade foresight with adjustable leaf rearsight
Propellant	Grenade cartridge

The M79 fires high-explosive grenades with considerable accuracy. Operating it is akin to using a squat shotgun, since it works in a similar manner to a break-open double.

In order to load the M79, the locking latch, which is situated on top behind the face, must be pushed fully to the right. The barrel is then pressed down, thus breaking the weapon, which also makes the weapon safe. The safety catch is of the slide type found on most side-by-side shotguns, and is located in the same area. Once open, a grenade cartridge is inserted until the rim of the case contacts the extractor, and the weapon is then closed. Only minimal stripping of the weapon is necessary for cleaning in the field.

The sights on the M79 are of the protected blade-type foresight, with a leaf rearsight which is adjustable for windage. The rearsight is also graduated for ranges from 100 m to 400 m.

The increased development of integral grenade launchers for many combat rifles has led to the near obsolescence of the M79. Nevertheless, it is an effective and simple weapon for which the development of a canister round has been suggested. This would make it a deadly short-range weapon for use in ambush and against mass attack.

In service with the United States, South Vietnamese and Cambodian forces.

M79

Jet Shot silent weapon system

Manufacturer: **sa PRB (Belgium)**

There has long been a requirement for silent, flashless and smokeless weapons. The Jet Shot system is a development by PRB to provide one answer. Jet Shot is basically a cartridge designed around the principle of the dynamic resistance of metals, used for an explosion chamber, under high pressure. As the Jet Shot system is manual, it is covered here in some depth. The grenades used with the system are dealt with in the section on grenades.

The Jet Shot cartridge, which is fitted into the tail boom of the (PRB) grenades, consists of a thin-walled metal tube, one end of which is closed by either a percussion or an electric ignition device. The other end of the tube is closed by a sliding piston which is stopped at the end of its stroke by a threaded collar screwed into the tube. This collar is drilled so that a push-rod can be inserted to rest on top of the piston, which has below it a small, extremely high pressure charge. This charge is designed to combust in about 1 msec (ie almost instantaneously), so that the transformation of thermal energy into kinetic energy takes place before the metal of the tube has time to react. The kinetic energy thus created, forces the piston up the tube to the collar. When it hits the collar, it seals the tube. This accounts for the virtual lack of noise, flash and smoke. The push-rod, which was resting on the piston, continues to move, taking the grenade with it.

PRB have designed two grenade launchers for the Jet Shot cartridge as well as two disposable mortars (see mortars. One, their single-hand launcher, comes in two configurations: for percussion and for electric operation. Both versions consist of a lightweight cylindrical body with a spigot mounted on one end containing either a floating striker or an isolated contact ring. On the other end there is a simple baseplate. Between the spigot and the plate there is a fixed link marked so that, when the firer's foot is placed in the sling, the angle of fire will be

45 degrees.

The percussion version has a sliding handle on the cylinder which, when pushed forward, engages a hammer. On being pulled back, it stretches a spring which releases the hammer by fixed tension. The electrical version is equipped with a 1·5 volt battery and firing switch. All the necessary connections are contained in the body.

The other launcher is of the multi-spigot variety which is intended to launch 12 grenades, in pairs, in series. The manufacturer maintains that the launcher is capable of launching the 12 grenades quickly enough for the last pair to be fired before the first pair have reached their target.

So far there is no special ground mounting for the multi-spigot launcher. It can, however, be fitted on to any stable platform. The launcher consists of a baseplate attached to a device which allows adjustment for elevation and azimuth, whilst the fixed spigots are angled to allow for dispersion on the ground. Twelve grenades can, it is claimed, cover an area 10 m × 50 m. An electric sequential ignition device is used which is also capable of remote operation.

So far as is known the Jet Shot system is not yet in service. Nevertheless, it is a most interesting idea which has considerable potential and promise.

Jet Shot multi-spigot launcher (PRB 426)

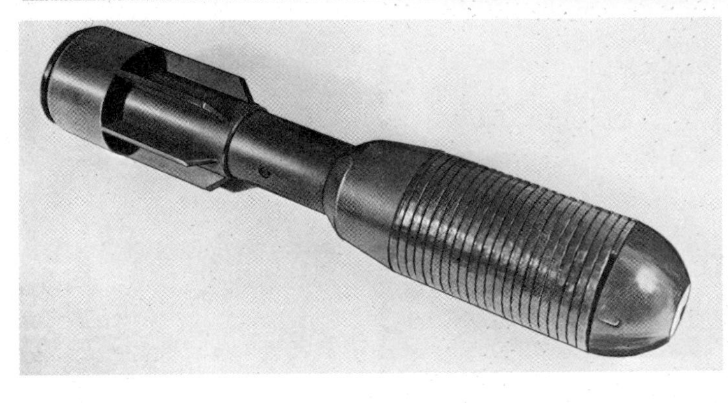

Jet Shot anti-personnel grenade (PRB 404)

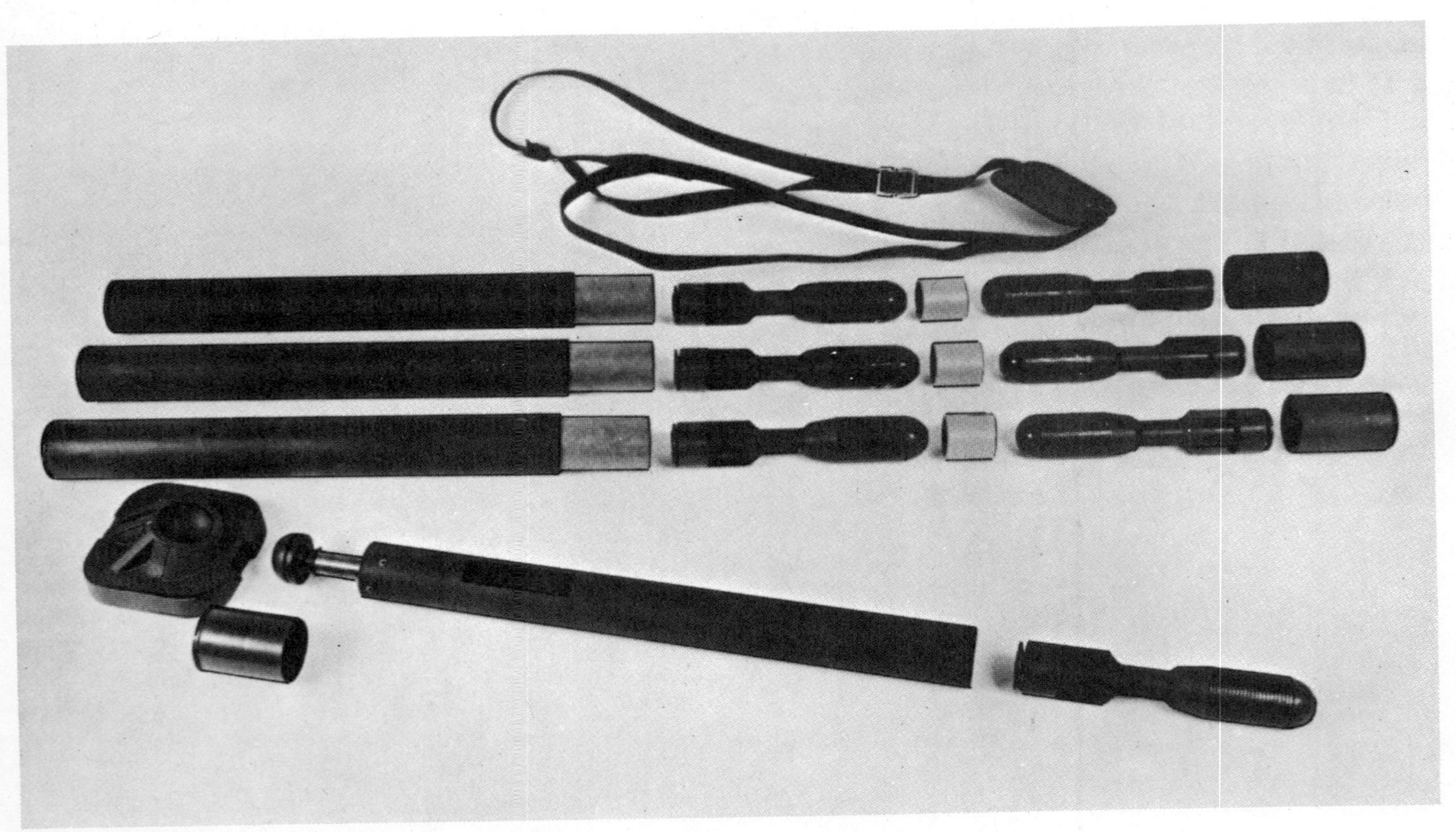

Jet Shot disposable mortars (PRB 424 and 425)

Jet Shot single-hand launcher in action

1 pushing rod
2 piston
3 powder
4 ignition device

electric

percussion

Diagram showing principles of Jet Shot

Flamethrowers

Fire has been employed as an instrument of warfare for hundreds of years, but the modern flamethrower was Richard Fiedler's conception. In 1901, this Berlin engineer offered two models for the German army to try. The smaller *flammenwerfer* was sufficiently light to be carried by one man and used gas pressure to eject a stream of flaming oil for a distance of about 20 m; while the bigger version had a range of 40 m and held enough fuel for 40 sec continuous firing and needed a team to handle it.

The principle on which the *flammenwerfer* worked was simple; a valve released gas in the lower chamber which pushed liquid in the upper chamber into a rubber pipe. The fluid was held in check by two other valves before reaching the ignition device. This device comprised a small tube containing a spring, a detonator, gun cotton and a paraffin wick. At a point when the gas forced the liquid against the spring, the wick ignited and a jet of flame projected for 20 m, or more. The duration of the flame was approximately two minutes.

The equipment was subsequently issued to the 23, 24, 25 Pioneer Battalions and in 1912, the first *Flammenwerfer* regiment was formed consisting of 12 flamethrower companies and named the 3rd Guard Pioneer Regiment. The German flamethrowers were a success at the Battle of Hooge in 1915 because the British and German trenches were very close together. Tactically, flamethrowers were worth deploying only if the forward lines of the opposing forces were no further apart than the maximum range of the equipment—and herein lay its weakness and the cause of frustration for the operators of the equipment.

In the 1939–45 War, with the onset of mechanisation and mobility, it was inevitable that the flamethrower would be substantially modernised. The small man-portable infantry flamethrower was still used, but some larger equipments were now fitted to tanks. The most effective and imaginative of all the flamethrowers was the British Crocodile mounted on the Mark VII Churchill tank. The flamethrower could only project its hot shot up to 110 m and usually did not open fire until about 75 m. A 6 ton trailer towed behind the tank carried 1800 l of napalm and the tow-bar carried the linkage that supplied the fuel to the gunner's position. Impetus was applied by nitrogen gas from five cylinders at an initial pressure of 210 kg/sq cm reduced to a working pressure of 20 kg/sq cm. The flame fuel could be shot at 181 m/sec in a solid 'rod' ignited by a spark and petrol vapour system. It was possible for a good gunner to despatch this 'rod' through the slit in a pill box at extreme range.

In future wars, on terrain suitable for mobile warfare, the use of flamethrowers is likely to be limited, for tanks towing such clumsy equipment will be very vulnerable. On the other hand, in urban areas, smaller flamethrowers will be extremely valuable to attacker and defender alike. They will remain useful weapons for some time to come and it is a pity that development of them in the forces of the Western World has been so reduced.

ROGER SIBLEY

ROKS-2 manpack flamethrower

Manufacturer: **State factories (USSR)**

Capacity	10·9 kg (10·4 l)
Range	35 m

The ROKS–2 manpack flamethrower is the oldest of the three weapons of this portable type used by Warsaw Pact countries. It is not likely to be met with in the Soviet Army, but will be in some Warsaw Pact forces and it is possible that communist China and North Vietnam may still retain the ROKS–2 in service. Cunningly designed as a surprise weapon, the ROKS–2 assembly looks very much like a rifle and haversack.

The assembly consists of the rifle-like launcher, connected by a flexible hose from the base of the 'breech' to the bottom of the pack containing the flat, box-like, sheet-steel fuel tank, with a thin flexible air-pipe feeding the fuel-pipe from the compressed air bottle, secured also to the base of the fuel tank. In order to effect minor adjustments and repairs to the fuel and air supply system, a small set of tools is also provided, contained in a small rectangular canvas pocket attached to the front of the fuel tank. The tank is filled through an inlet with a one-way valve on top of the tank. For carriage, a double sling is fitted to the launcher and shoulder-straps to the fuel container. The ignition cartridges, activated by the trigger, are to be found in the cylindrical muzzle attachment.

In service with some Warsaw Pact forces.

ROKS-3 manpack flamethrower

Manufacturer: **State factories (USSR)**

Weight	24 kg (filled)
Capacity	8·8 kg (8·2 l)
Range	35 m

The Soviet-made ROKS-3 portable flamethrower is a slightly more modern version of the ROKS–2, but is likewise being phased out and is being replaced by the manpack LPO–50. In this case, however, there is little attempt to deceive the enemy as, although the launcher still resembles a rifle, the fuel tank is completely undisguised. The ROKS–3 comprises a rifle-like launcher equipped with a cylindrical 10 round ignition cartridge drum fitted round the muzzle, a flexible hose connecting the launcher 'breech' to the base of the cylindrical fuel tank, and a compressed air cylinder secured to the side of the fuel tank. The fuel tank inlet is located centrally on top of the tank. With a full tank, the whole assembly weighs 23·3 kg and, as with ROKS–2, is carried by shoulder-straps on the back of the operator. To operate, one pull on the trigger opens the fuel hose valve and a second pull activates one of the 10 ignition cartridges. It is claimed that sufficient fuel is carried to permit a 5 sec burst with each cartridge. The maximum range of 35 m can only be attained by using thickened fuel—otherwise, the range is reduced to 15 m. A burst is completed when the trigger is released, automatically closing the spring-loaded hose valve. As with the ROKS–2, the launcher is provided with a rifle-type sling for carriage when not in use.

In service with some Warsaw Pact, communist Chinese and North Vietnamese forces.

Sketch of ROKS-3 manpack flamethrower.

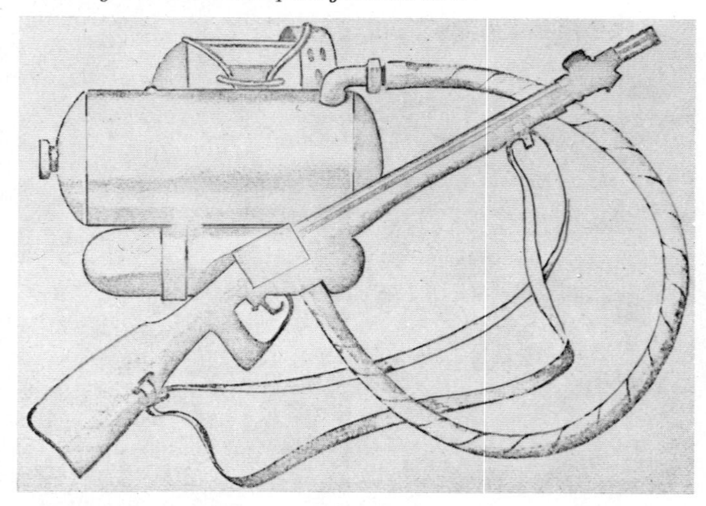

LPO-50 manpack flamethrower

Manufacturer: **State factories (USSR)**

Weight	25 kg (filled)
Capacity	10·6 kg (10 l)
Range	70 m

The LPO–50 is replacing the old ROKS–2 and ROKS–3 portable flamethrowers in the Soviet Army and most Warsaw Pact forces. Compared to its predecessors, the LPO–50, with a similar weight, carries more fuel and boasts over twice the range. This weapon consists also of a rifle-like launcher fitted with a folding bipod, a pistol-grip and carrying-sling, a flexible hose connecting the metal butt casing to the triple tank assembly, and the tank assembly itself. The three tanks are fixed side by side on a manifold tubular base which feeds fuel directly into the fuel hose, one-way valves being located in the base of each tank to prevent any return flow. No compressed air bottle is required, as each tank carries on top next to the safety valve a pressurising charge mounted in the cap of the fuel inlet. Shoulder-straps are fitted to allow it to be carried on the back of the operator, who is also issued with a protective face-mask. The whole assembly weighs 23 kg, but the tank-assembly can be reduced to two tanks, or one, if damaged or if some other reason makes this necessary. Normal trigger operation releases the fuel and activates the electrical ignition system contained in the nozzle. In addition, however, the trigger action electrically activates the pressurising charge in the filler cap. The maximum range of 70 m can only be attained if thickened fuel is used—otherwise 20 m is the maximum range.

In service with the Soviet, most Warsaw Pact and North Vietnamese forces and the Vietcong.

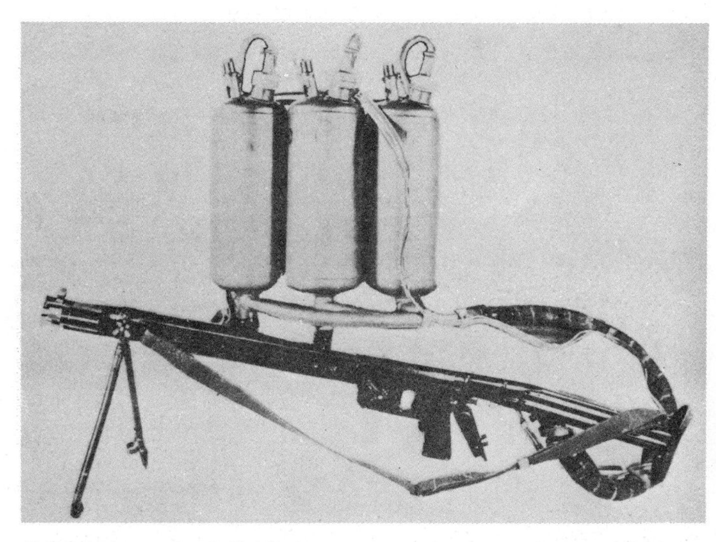

LPO-50 manpack flamethrower.

The U.S. army's now obsolete M-7 portable flamethrower in action.

Mines

Mining in the true military sense began soon after gunpowder ceased to be regarded as a combat aid, in the sense that Chinese crackers and Greek fire were combat aids, and it became in the 14th century a weapon of war. The destructive effects of explosives were soon recognised, and it was not long before the tacticians of the Middle Ages realised the potential, given them by explosives, for breaching fortifications. The research establishments in those days soon discovered that the most effective way to destroy a target was to place charges beneath it. It was assumed, rightly, that this method would be quicker and surer than laying siege, or marching round and round a city blowing trumpets waiting for the walls to fall, like Joshua. It was also likely in theory at any rate to be less harmful to the attackers than storming the walls or exposing themselves to boiling oil by operating battering rams to achieve this aim, as the Crusaders and others quickly found. However, the same problems of approach, concealment and the correct placing of the charges remained. All this called for special skills, intelligence and some luck, so units of sappers and miners were raised and trained for the purpose.

Gunpowder remained the only explosive available for such operations until late into the 19th century and even then little technical advance was achieved. However, considerable research and development effort was put into the manufacture of new explosives during the 1914–18 war. The static warfare on the Western Front was such that ground could only be won by disastrous frontal assault. Despite intensive artillery bombardments and heavy machine gun support, casualties were shatteringly high and, in an effort to reduce these, other means of gaining ground had to be resorted to. One such means was mining, which culminated, towards the end of the war, in the detonation of colossal quantities of explosives. This resulted in the displacement of hundreds of tons of earth and the formation of gigantic craters which literally obliterated salient features in the front lines. The explosive favoured by many mining engineers was ammonal. This was a grey powder with a power three times greater than that of gunpowder. There were, of course, complications in that ammonal was hygroscopic which made it unsuitable for any lengthy storage underground. It was also corrosive to copper, so aluminium-sheathed detonators had to be devised. Amatol was an alternative explosive without the faults of ammonal, but less efficient.

Examples of mining during World War I ranged from relatively modest charges of gunpowder (130 lb–900 lb) in 1915 in the Ypres area to an impressive charge of 1,000,000 lb made up of 23 separate charges and fired together on a single morning in 1917 to herald the British offensive into Flanders. It was during this period, due to the hygroscopic effect mentioned, and the shortage of gunpowder as well, that ammonal was packed experimentally into water-tight tins and used very successfully to set off charges.

During the 1930s, the increasing use of wheeled and tracked vehicles led to an early realisation by some, and confirmation of their views by others, such as the Generals Fuller and de Gaulle, that armoured warfare would play a more and more important part in any future war. Clearly, some form of countermeasure to combat armoured fighting vehicles was necessary. Thus, there began in earnest the escalating struggle between the anti-tank gun on the one hand and the tank's offensive capability of its gun, its armour and its speed and manœuvrability on the other. An equally effective, but much cheaper means of defence against the tank was the use of land minefields, whereby powerful explosive devices could be deployed defensively across the front, as at sea, to stem the advance of attacking tanks by blowing off their tracks. All that was needed was a tin packed with explosive and coupled to a fusing device which could be set off by a heavy weight. The first real anti-tank mine was brought into British service in September 1935.

This new and devilish device consisted of a round steel body some 18 cm in diameter and 5 cm high and was filled with baratol 10/90. The central chamber accommodated a firing pistol which consisted of a body containing a spring-loaded striker restrained by a sheer-wire. Beneath the striker, there was a cap placed alongside a cavity in the central chamber which housed four perforated CE pellets surrounding a detonator. The mine was surmounted by a circular domed steel cover, which was held off the mine by a strong spider/spring and designed to give under a pressure of some 165 kg. The mine was buried about 7½ cm below ground level. When a heavy weight passed across it the cover was depressed until the sheer-wire parted. This allowed the spring to force the spider downwards to fire the cap. The flash from the cap fired the detonator which set off the exploder and the main filling, and up, it was hoped, went the target.

Mines of various descriptions and complexities followed from this, the first of its kind. They came in various sizes and with various devices including anti-lift devices and booby-traps. It is only latterly, perhaps, that new shapes have materialised, mainly because of the need to either accommodate new devices, reduce their chances of detection, or to enable them to be laid mechanically. Latterly, too, developments have included the use of new materials which cannot be detected electro-magnetically, and materials which have greater heat or cold, and water resistance.

In addition to these charges which would be predictable in an age of quick technological advance, mine development has taken a turn outside the conventional hole-in-the-ground concept. The French (DTAT) have developed the MAH F1 mine which, in simple terms, is a sort of missile launcher set at waist height and triggered off either by a tripwire or by a remote control. There is Astrolite, a liquid explosive, developed by the United States which can be sprayed on to the ground and is difficult to detect. Gaining favour too in some countries is the use of standard charges which can be built up sequentially as necessary into a mine of any size but not, one imagines, to the size of the mountain of ammonal set off by General Plumer at 0310 on 7 June 1917. That sort of cratering can be more practically carried out by nuclear mines, although not so simply politically.

In this section of the book, we concern ourselves mainly with the more conventional mines and not with demolition charges, although the borderline in some cases is difficult to determine. We also deal briefly with detection but make no mention of mine laying —a skill carried out usually by infantry, though with engineer support and advice. Mining is a complicatedly wasteful form of warfare but one which, as the Services' manpower becomes scarcer, will become more necessary.

No mention has been made of anti-personnel mines, many examples of which are to be found in this section. In general terms, the mines themselves are manufactured to a limited number of basic mechanical or material configurations. It is in their application, siting, triggering and effect that there are infinite variations and where human ingenuity knows few bounds, but the reader can discover some of this for himself in the pages that follow.

JOHN OWEN

SOME EXAMPLES OF MINES

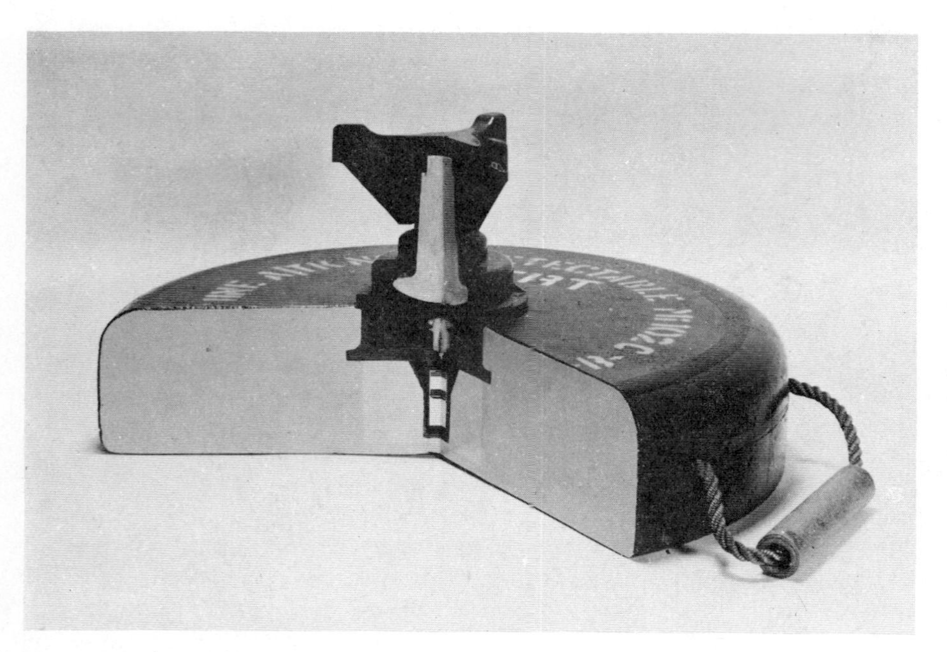

Anti-tank mine (buried)
(Bofors AT102C)

Anti-personnel mine
(Eurometaal AP23)

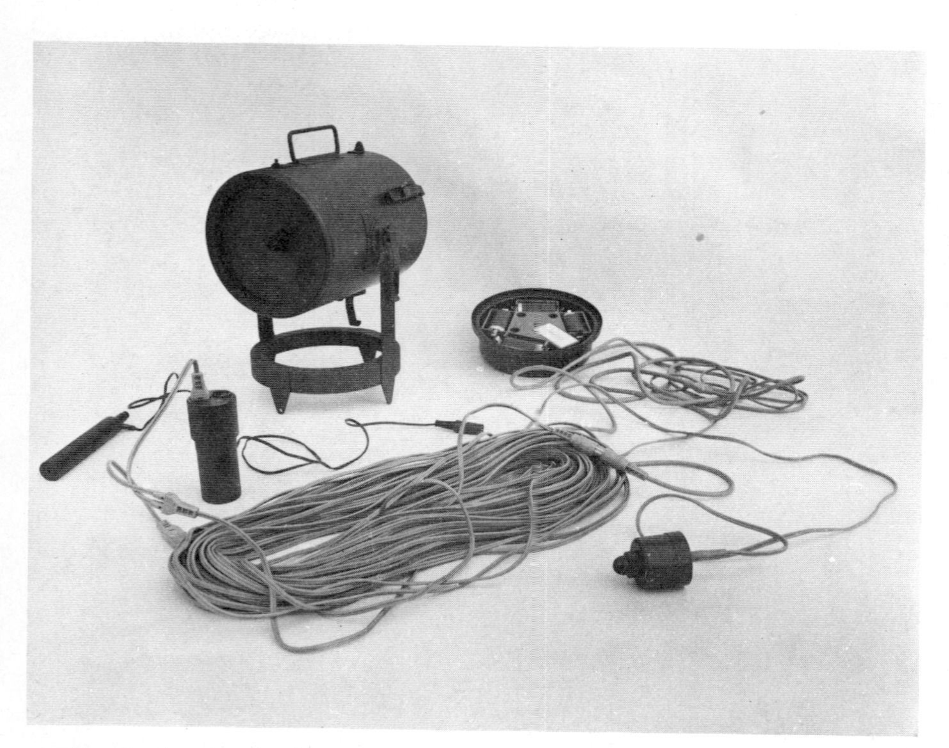

Anti-tank mine (surface)
(DTAT MAHF1)

PRB-M35 anti-personnel mine

Manufacturer: **Pouderies Réunies de Belgique SA (Belgium)**

Dimensions	Height 6 cm Diameter 6·5 cm
Weight	158 gm
Body material	Plastic
Charge	100 gm TNT–KN03
Method of laying	Manual
Actuation	Pressure
Effect	Blast
Safety	Manual pin
Environment	−40°C to +60°C
Detection	By prodding
Packing	8 mines in fibre containers and 8 containers in a zinc-lined wooden box; 8 fuses in cartons and 16 cartons in a second zinc-lined wooden box. Or 64 fuses and 64 mines in one box

M35 anti-personnel mine.

This anti-personnel mine is designed to be laid in large quantities alone or in mixed fields. Detection is extremely difficult as only 1 gm of metal is used in its construction, and all other parts are of plastic. The plastic pot-body, with its threaded fuse, contains 100 gm of TNT–KN03 composition which is extremely stable, and mines can be laid very close to each other without risk of sympathetic detonation.

The fuse is of the double-percussion type. Two sprung-steel strikers are held apart by a hollow bolt that has two apertures. The bolt is connected to the pressure membrane and freely moves in a slide containing two percussion caps. The fuse is actuated by the application of weight on the pressure plate. This displaces the fuse membrane and the bolt moves in the slide. This bolt movement uncovers the percussion caps and releases the strikers through the apertures. Impact of the strikers on the cap activates the detonator and the mine explodes.

Laying the mine is very simple—a small shallow hole is dug and the fuse assembly is screwed into the mine body—and it is armed by removing the safety pin.

In service with the Belgian forces.

M35 mine body, M5 fuse and safety pin.

PRB-M409 anti-personnel mine

Manufacturer: **Pouderies Réunies de Belgique SA (Belgium)**

Dimensions	Height 2·8 cm Diameter 8·2 cm
Weight	183 gm
Body material	Plastic
Charge	80 gm cast trialene
Method of laying	Manual
Actuation	Pressure
Effect	Blast
Safety	Manual pin and protective plate
Environment	−32°C to +52°C
Detection	Visual or by prodding
Packing	5 mines in a fibre container and 30 containers in a 'No-nail' wooden box

This ia a 'pancake'-type mine made almost entirely from plastic. Its function in principle is similar to that of the PRB–M35, being of the pressure-plate type. However, the dimensions of the M409 enable it to be laid on the ground and camouflaged, rather than dug in. The M409 is a direct-contact, high-blast mine containing 80 gm of cast trialene (70% TNT, 15% hexogen, and 15% atomised aluminium powder). This composition is extremely stable and sympathetic detonation is extremely rare. The effect of 80 gm of trialene is equivalent to 130 gm of TNT. Detection of the M409 is extremely difficult since it contains only 1 gm of metal. Even when detected, the clearance of this mine presents serious problems since only about 1·5–3 mm displacement of the pressure membrane will trigger an explosion. Apart from its anti-personnel role, the M409 can be used as a primer charge for making up anti-tank mines by laying it on top of a quantity of explosive. The mine is equipped with a protective plate held in place by a steel pin for safety in transit. Removal of the pin and plate automatically arms the mine.

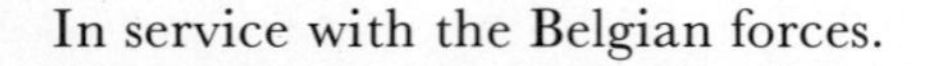

In service with the Belgian forces.

M409 anti-personnel mine.

PRB 413 anti-personnel mine

Manufacturer: **Pouderies Réunies de Belgique SA (Belgium)**

Dimensions	Height 105 mm Diameter 46 mm
Weight	640 gm
Body material	Plastic with steel-wire fragmentation sleeve
Charge	90 gm composition B
Method of laying	Manual
Actuation	Tripwire
Effect	Lethal to 14 m, safe at 30 m
Safety	Replaceable safety clip
Environment	−32°C to +52°C
Detection	Visual or electronic

This is a trip-initiated mine consisting of three main parts, the picket, the mine body and the firing device. The mine is designed to throw fragments outwards to a radius in excess of 21 m, and the manufacturers consider it to be lethal at 14 m, but safe at 30 m. The mine can be used in a variety of ways other than in the normal perimeter security role. For example, since it is tripwire initiated, it can be used to booby-trap doors, windows and vehicles.

The mine body is made from a thermo-plastic case filled with 95 cm of cast composition B. A spirally wound steel wire sleeve which surrounds the body is pre-fragmented to ensure the scattering of 600 regular fragments. The body is screwed on to a metal cross-picket which can be pushed into the ground or knocked into a tree or wall.

The tripwire-initiated firing device, PRB 410, is not attached to the mine, but is screwed on when required. Wires are attached to the four rings on the outside of the device and secured to convenient anchors. Once the wires are set out and the safety on the device is removed, a 2–5 kg traction force on any of the wires will lift both the striker and the slide in the body of the firing device, thus compressing the spring around the striker. At a given

413 anti-personnel mine.

moment the locking balls on the slider are attracted sideways and the released striker is forced down by the spring on to the primer, which ignites the detonator, and the mine explodes before the pressure on the wire displaces the position of the mine.

In service with the Belgian forces

413 mine—method of operation.

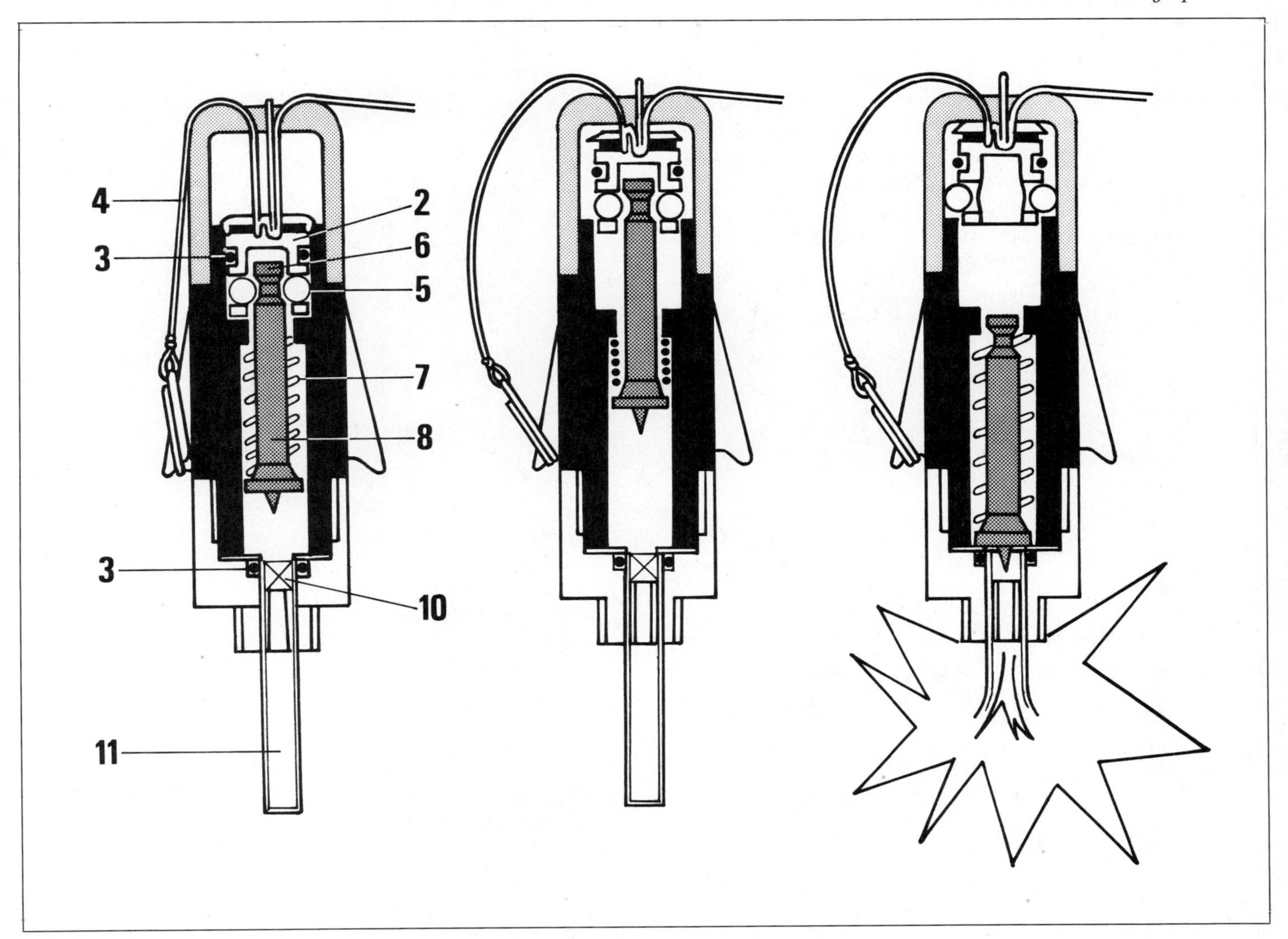

PRB 410

2. slider
3. o ring
4. wire
5. steel ball
6. striker head
7. striker spring
8. striker
10. cap
11. detonator

☐ When the enemy pulls one of the trip wires, the antenna lifts up both the slider and the striker thus compressing the spring.
☐ The two balls of the slider are ejected laterally thus releasing the striker head.
☐ The striker is then pushed downward by the spring causing the firing pin to strike the primer.
☐ The primer ignites the detonator and the mine explodes before the traction made on the wire causes the mine to tilt and to fall down from its support.

C3A1 and M25 (Elsie) anti-personnel mines

Manufacturer: **Canadian Arsenals Limited (Canada)**

Dimensions	Height 7·6 cm Diameter 5 cm (top) and 2·7 cm (trunk)
Weight	86 gm
Body material	Plastic
Charge	9·5 gm HE
Method of laying	Manual
Actuation	6–8 kg pressure
Effect	Blast
Safety	Special spring-steel clip
Environment	Pan climatic
Detection	Not susceptible to electro-magnetic detectors unless detector ring is fitted

This mine was developed by the Canadian Army and has been accepted as standard by the ABC countries. The C3A1 contains an aluminium-cased 6 grain detonator integral with the charge, while the M25 contains a gilded metal-cased detonator. The mines are otherwise identical and will be described as one.

It is a ground-burst mine made almost completely of plastic, and supplied in two parts—the body assembly and the charge assembly. When issued, the body contains a transit plug which is removed and replaced by the charge assembly which contains a 9·5 gm of explosive and is equipped with a safety clip. Removal of this clip arms the mine which is detonated under a pressure load of 6–8 kg. Though the mine is normally undetectable using electro-magnetic devices, it can be made detectable by the attachment of a metal ring.

In service with the forces of the ABC countries.

A version of the C3A1 anti-personnel mine.

NA-Mi-Ba anti-personnel mine

Manufacturer; **State factories (Czechoslovakia)**

Dimensions	Height 24·7 cm Diameter 19·6 cm
Weight	2·4 kg
Body material	Plastic
Charge	TNT

The Czech Na-Mi-Ba mine is a tripwire-operated booby trap. It consists of a TNT charge activated by a chemical fuse, spring stiker and detonator housed in a corrugated-plastic cylinder. On top of the cylinder, a lever is hinged in the centre in such a manner that, if it is moved by the wire attached to its outer end, the lever depresses a knob. Depression of this knob will fracture the two phials of chemicals in the fuse and their interaction will release the striker. Other methods of employing this mine are as an initiating charge for larger engineer demolition charges when normal electrical ignition is not available and again using the tripwire to activate anti-tank mines not detonated by a tank's tracks. As detonation results merely from depression of the knob on top of the mine, it is obvious that the opportunities for using alternate means of depressing this switch are many and varied.

In service with the Czechoslovak forces.

PP-Mi-Sr anti-personnel mine

Manufacturer: **State factories (Czechoslovakia)**

Dimensions	Height of casing 12·5 cm Diameter 10 cm
Weight	3·2 kg
Body material	Sheet steel
Charge	TNT

The Czech PP-Mi-Sr bounding mine is a short, thick steel cylinder with a rounded top rim. In the centre on top is the plastic cap on the propellant charge cylinder and, on either side of that, the two smaller screw-head caps of the filler-cap and the detonator well-plug. The explosive filler (325 gm of TNT), propellant charge and ignition mechanism are housed in an inner casing surrounded by a mass of steel-rod pieces inside the outer casing. Initial activation may be by RO-1 pull-fuse using a tripwire, or by an RO-8 pressure-fuse—these fuses operate the propellant charge which, after a 3 sec delay, causes the mine to leap upwards. Attached to the propellant charge is a 1 m long securing wire. As this becomes taut, it releases the spring-loaded striker to hit the detonator, so that the mine explodes immediately—while still in the air. The advantage gained is that the explosion is activated at waist height without the mine having to be placed in view, as is the case with a stake mine such as the PP-Mi-Sb. Although the PP-Mi-Sr is much more powerful than the stake mine, it also needs quite a strong force to activate the fuse—3·5 kg, and so is less likely to be set off by small animals. Disarming is a slightly different process, depending on the fuse type. If the fuse is the RO-8 pressure type, a pin should be placed in the safety-pin aperture; if the RO-1 pull fuse is present, the tripwire (if loose) should be severed (a tight wire may be booby-trapped). The fuse can then be extracted.

In service with the Czechoslovak and some Near Eastern forces.

PP-Mi-Sb anti-personnel mine

Manufacturer: **State factories (Czechoslovakia)**

Dimensions	Diameter 7·5 cm
	Length 14 cm
Weight	2·1 kg
Body material	Steel and concrete
Charge	TNT

The Czech PP-Mi-Sb fragmentation mine consists of a short cylindrical casing made of concrete and small pieces of steel, normally erected on a wooden stake inserted into an aperture at one end, with the fuse projecting from the other. Usually an RO-1 pull fuse, attached to a tripwire, is used, but if required, the mine can be taken off its stake, placed in the ground, and an RO-2 pressure fuse substituted. In both cases a 1 kg force is needed to detonate the mine charge of 75 gm of TNT. If the tripwire is slack, the mine can be disarmed by severing the wire and extracting the fuse—a taut wire may be booby-trapped. The RO-2 fuse can be neutralised by inserting a pin in the safety-pin aperture and then extracting the fuse.

In service with the Czechoslovak forces.

PP-Mi-St anti-personnel mine

Manufacturer: **State factories (Czechoslovakia)**

See the POMZ-2 and POMZ-2M.

In service with the Czechoslovak forces.

PT-Mi-Ba anti-tank mine

Manufacturer: **State factories (Czechoslovakia)**

Dimensions	Height 10·2 cm
	Diameter 32·3 cm
Weight	7·6 kg
Body material	Plastic
Charge	TNT

The Czech PT-Mi-Ba anti-tank mine is of the plate-mine type, consisting of two round plastic mouldings welded together, with a smaller flattened dome in the centre on top (the pressure plate) and, on the base, a shallow fuse well in the centre, secured by a flat-threaded plate, flanked by two large flat bolt-heads to which a flexible plastic handle is attached. One of these bolt-heads is the filler plug, the other has no subsidiary purpose. A force of 200–400 kg applied to the pressure plate will cause the RO-7-11 fuse, located immediately below the plate and screwed into the rectangular booster charge, to shear and ignite the latter, which in turn detonates the main charge. This mine is not equipped with any integral booby trap and can, after clearing any external booby trap, be disarmed by unscrewing the threaded-plate from the base and removing the booster charge and shear-type fuse.

In service with the Czechoslovak and some Middle Eastern forces.

PT-Mi-D anti-tank mine

Manufacturer: **State factories (Czechoslovakia)**

Dimensions	Height 14 cm
	Length 32 cm
	Width 23 cm
Weight	9 kg
Body material	Wood
Charge	TNT

The Czech PT-Mi-D anti-tank mine consists of a rectangular wooden box with a rope handle on each of two sides. In the centre of the top can be seen a rectangular aperture almost filled by the wooden pressure-plate, bevelled on all sides. The pressure-plate is supported inside the box by wooden dowels which shear when pressure is applied to the plate—this pressure can be adjusted from 200–450 kg, depending on the target in mind. When the dowels shear off, they release the shear blocks which are thus forced down on to the top of the striker, the retaining pin of the striker being knocked free, allowing the RO-1 fuse to ignite the 400 gm of TNT booster-charge which detonates the main charge of 6·2 kg of TNT. A popular method of booby-trapping the mine is to attach a wire to the retaining pin of the striker and secure the other end of the wire to the ground.

In service with the Czechoslovak forces.

PT-Mi-K anti-tank mine

Manufacturer: **State factories (Czechoslovakia)**

Dimensions	Height 10·2 cm Diameter 30 cm
Weight	7·2 kg
Body material	Steel
Charge	TNT

The PT-Mi-K is the most modern Czech mine and is equipped with booby-trap wells, which to a certain extent counteract the disadvantage of the metallic casing. Although approximately the same size and shape as the earlier plastic PT-Mi-Ba, the pressure-plate assembly is of a more angular profile and the steel carrying handle is hinged to the side of the casing. The PT-Mi-K consists of a circular steel casing filled with the main charge of 5 kg TNT, the centre being occupied by the pressure-plate supported by shear pins inserted in the rim. Directly underneath is the vertically-mounted fuse (either RO-5 or RO-9), also held by shear pins in a channel in the centre of the booster-charge. The booby-trap well is located centrally in the base of the outer casing. The mine is activated by 330–450 kg pressure applied to the pressure-plate, breaking the shear pins to allow the fuse to initiate the detonator situated below it. The mine may be disarmed by removing the pressure-plate and then the fuse, but the detonator may well be booby-trapped and should be left in place. It is believed that this mine was developed with nuclear warfare in view, and provision has been made to prevent over-pressure from a nuclear burst activating the pressure-plate.

In service with the Czechoslovak and some Middle Eastern forces.

Mk 59 anti-personnel mine

Manufacturer: **Société Alsacienne d'Etudes et d'Exploitation (Alsetex) (France)**

Dimensions	Height 5·5 cm Diameter 6·2 cm
Weight	130 gm
Body material	Plastic
Charge	56 gm HE
Method of laying	Manual
Actuation	Pressure
Effect	Blast
Detection	Not susceptible to electro-magnetic detectors (except when fitted with the optional metal washer)

This is a pressure-initiated device made largely from a plastic material containing 56 gm of HE. It can be made impervious to electro-magnetic detection by the removal of a metal washer which, if required, can be left on to permit detection. The mine is armed by the removal of a protective cap over the ignition device, and pressure on the pressure plate results in detonation.

In service with the French forces.

MAH F1 anti-tank mine

Manufacturer: **Direction Technique des Armements Terrestres (France)**

Dimensions	Length 26·5 cm Diameter 19 cm
Weight	10 kg
Body material	Metal
Charge	6·5 kg shaped HE
Method of laying	Manual
Actuation	Remote or by breaking a trip-wire
Effect	Penetrates 70 mm of armour plate at 80 m
Safety	Electrical
Environment	Pan climatic
Detection	Visual
Packing	Two mines in a special moulded container

The MAH F1 owes its existence to some on-the-spot improvisations during World War II when allied troops made tank traps using rocket launchers. A loaded launcher was fixed in a hidden position across the axis of an enemy vehicle's advance and a line was attached to the firing mechanism. The operator then retired to a safe distance and waited. By pulling the line at the right moment he could kill the tank at relatively little risk to himself. Some troops became quite adept and devised a number of ingenious triggering devices from materials available to hand. The MAH F1 is a rationalisation of the idea, and was adopted by the French Army in 1968.

This mine consists of three basic assemblies—a pedestal-type mount equipped with lockable trunnion brackets on to which the mine is attached, the mine itself, which is composed of a spun-steel casing, with a sight, containing the electronic fuse and explosive charge and, lastly, the accessories which include the devices required for setting up, sighting and triggering the mine, either remotely or directly. The mine works by projecting a copper-plated hexalite hollow charge capable of penetrating 70 mm of armour plate or more.

The mine is triggered by the actuation of the electronic fuse which can be done in two ways. 60 m of tripwire with a breaking strain of only 0·4 kg is connected to a cable. When this wire has been broken by a vehicle, an electrical circuit is completed and the electronic fuse, which is powered by four conventional torch batteries, is actuated. The other method of triggering is by remote control. A control box with a 50 m separation cable is connected to the electronic fuse, and a soldier can trigger the mine by pressing a button. In addition, the control box can be used to check the mine, or to neutralise it, to allow passage of friendly troops. When the mine is to be trip-triggered a special jump lead is provided for the same purpose.

In service with the French forces.

The MAH F1 anti-tank mine showing the electronic fuse and control unit to the left rear.

The MAH F1 assembled (left) and two mines packed for transit (right).

Model 1953 anti-tank mine

Manufacturer: **Luchaire SA (France)**

Dimensions	Height 28 cm Diameter (of charge) 73 mm
Weight	1·9 kg (as a pair)
Body material	Metal alloy
Charge	0·6 kg shaped HE (as a pair)
Method of laying	Manual, using special borer
Actuation	By a third pressure-type mine via primacord
Effect	Penetrates 100 mm of armour plate (60 cm above ground)
Detection	Susceptible to mine detectors

The 1953 is a combination of two 73 mm shaped-charge mines connected to each other by a length of primacord. Laying is manual and follows the same system as the individual Model 1954 mines. However, the initiation method is different. Operationally, a pair of mines is laid in combination with a third pressure-sensitive device in the shape of a triangle. The primacord is laid so that its centre point forms the apex of the triangle and the pressure mine is laid at this point. The primacord, an instantaneous type of fuse, is ignited by the pressure mine and it, in turn, initiates the 0·5 sec delay trains of the two shaped-charge mines. The delay ensures that the target should have fully entered the pattern when the pair of mines explodes. The penetration capabilities are the same as those of the Model 1954 described below.

In service with the French forces.

Model 1954 anti-tank mine

Manufacturer: **Luchaire SA (France)**

Dimensions	Height 28 cm Diameter (of charge) 73 mm
Weight	900 gm
Body material	Metal alloy
Charge	300 gm shaped HE
Method of laying	Manual, using special borer
Actuation	By displacement of antenna
Effect	Penetrates 100 mm of armour plate (60 cm above ground)
Safety	Manual pin
Detection	Susceptible to mine detectors and observation

This is a shaped-charge mine made largely of light alloy components and is laid manually in a round hole 11 cm in diameter and 33 cm deep, with the actuation antenna left above ground. A special borer is used to make the hole and this takes an average of 90 sec. The antenna is a thin rod which, when moved by a passing vehicle, releases a striker in the primer housing. The action of the striker on a small primer results in the ignition of a 0·5 sec pyrotechnic train, and the shaped charge is then detonated. If the mine is correctly laid and covered with 5 cm of soil, it can pierce a 100 mm armour plate some 60 cm above the ground.

In service with the French forces.

K-2 anti-personnel bounding mine

Manufacturer: **State factories (German Democratic Republic)**

Dimensions	Diameter 10 cm
	Length 25 cm
Weight	5 kg
Body material	Plastic
Charge	Nitropenta

Although the East Germans use Soviet mines, both anti-personnel and anti-tank, to a great extent, they have developed one of each of their own. Along with Soviet stake mines, they have produced the K-2 as their bounding mine. In appearance it resembles at first sight a stick-grenade with its short cylindrical body and long fuse housing. It is set by attaching a tripwire to the fuse, placing the mine base down on the ground and extracting the safety-pin from the fuse-housing. A pull on the tripwire causes the fuse to activate the propellant charge making the mine bound about 1·5 m in the air, where it discharges its contents of ball-bearings and steel pieces. Disarming is simply a matter of inserting a pin in the safety-pin aperture after first severing the tripwire (provided that the wire is slack). K-1, the anti-tank mine, was developed simultaneously in 1958.

In service with the DDR forces.

K-1 anti-tank mine

Manufacturer: **State factories (German Democratic Republic)**

Dimensions	Height 15 cm
	Diameter 25 cm
Weight	11 kg
Body material	Plastic
Charge	TNT

Besides being constructed of plastic and thus difficult to detect, the East German K-1 anti-tank mine is equipped with a booby-trap fuse well. The K-1 is, with the K-2, a 1958 development to supplement the many Soviet mines used by the Nationale Volksarmee and has been retained in the inventory since then, with modifications only to fuse and detonator. Apart from the extra booby-trap fuse well, it is a conventional beehive-shaped mine, with the main pressure-plate on top in the centre and two small indentations on the side for the filler-plugs. In the base, the main fuse well is located centrally and the booby-trap fuse well to one side. This latter is a pull-fuse connected, when the mine is emplaced, to a short anchoring wire, and is very sensitive. It requires comparatively little pressure (150 kg) to detonate the charge of 7·5 kg of TNT.

In service with the DDR forces.

M49 anti-personnel mine

Manufacturer: **State factories (Hungary)**

Dimensions	Height 5·8 cm
	Length 18·5 cm
	Width 5 cm
Weight	0·3 kg
Body material	Wood or plastic
Charge	TNT

The small Hungarian M49 anti-personnel mine was originally produced with a wooden casing, but is now more often encountered in plastic. This mine is a narrow box, resembling the Soviet anti-personnel PMD-7 mine, but longer and is made in two halves, the top fitting over the lower half, with the fuse projecting through intersecting cut-away section at one end. The main charge of 75 gm of TNT is detonated by a pull-fuse and tripwire, taking a pull of only 1 kg.

In service with the Hungarian forces.

Bounding anti-personnel mine

Manufacturer: **State factories (Hungary)**

Dimensions	Height 30 cm
	Diameter 12 cm
Weight	3·6 kg
Body material	Steel
Charge	TRI-II

After the immediate post-war period, during which she depended to a great extent on the Soviet Union for her mines, Hungary developed three mines, two anti-tank and this one anti-personnel bounding mine. The mine differs considerably in concept from other Warsaw Pact weapons of this type in that it is tripwire-operated whilst being mounted on a short stake. It consists of a cylinder topped by a short lid in the centre of which is set the rather long fuse attached to the tripwire. The cylinder is lined with ball-bearings packed round the explosive charge of 800 gm of TRI-II, which in turn surrounds the propellant charge of black powder. A pull of 4½–9 kg (adjustable) on the tripwire will remove the safety pin from the fuse and release the two-pronged striker to activate the propellant charge which causes the mine to bound into the air and explode. Special provision is not made for booby-traps, but these may be present.

In service with the Hungarian forces.

Plate-charge anti-tank mine

Manufacturer: **State factories (Hungary)**

Dimensions	Height 8cm
	Diameter 38 cm
Body material	Aluminium
Charge	PETN
Effect	Penetrates 100 mm of armour plate

This is one of three mines developed by the Hungarians in recent years to supplement their holdings of Soviet mines. Like the other two, this weapon departs to a certain extent from the normal Warsaw Pact-type of mine design. The mine consists of a shallow aluminium bowl, three-quarters filled with PETN, capped with a broad aluminium ring, in the centre of which is bolted (with shear bolts) a circular steel disc 18 cm in diameter with a centrally-mounted steel spike. The electrically-operated fuse is located in the base of the bowl. Normal procedure is not to lay the mine in the ground, as with most other anti-tank mines, but to prop the mine up in a wooden triangular framework facing the direction of enemy advance. When a target reaches a range of about 20 m the mine is detonated by remote control—the projectile, consisting of the disc and spike, is said to be capable of piercing 100 mm of armour at that range. This mine would appear to be limited in scope except where traffic approaches are severely restricted and undergrowth (for camouflage) is plentiful.

In service with the Hungarian forces.

Shaped-charge anti-tank mine

Manufacturer: **State factories (Hungary)**

Dimensions	Height 14·2 cm
	Diameter 30 cm
Weight	5·7 kg
Body material	Cardboard, wood and canvas
Charge	TNT

This, the third of the Hungarian-developed post-war mines, must be one of the flimsiest anti-tank mines made in recent years; one of the cheapest to produce, but nonetheless effective. It consists of a round box, the side of cardboard, the top and bottom of thin wood and the whole encased in a camouflage-painted canvas cover. Set erect in the centre of the base is a pressure fuse, projecting into the TNT shaped charge which is encased in oiled paper and suspended from the underside of the circumference of the top. Although the fuse is normally set to be activated at about 450 kg (adjustable), it is surmised that it would need considerably less effort to crush this device and damage the fuse. Perhaps a more effective method would be to use the system, which apparently is practised, of attaching the mine to a loose projecting angle-iron. When a vehicle track or wheel strikes the angle-iron, the mine is thrown up violently against the vehicle body and detonates.

In service with the Hungarian forces.

No 10 anti-personnel mine

Manufacturer: **Israel Military Industries (Israel)**

Dimensions	Height 7·5 cm
	Diameter 7 cm
Weight	120 gm
Body material	Plastic
Charge	50 gm TNT
Method of laying	Manual
Actuation	15–35 kg pressure
Effect	Blast
Detection	Visual and prodding
Packing	40 detonators in 10 plastic boxes and 40 mines fitted into rigid-foam packing contained in wooden carrying box

This is a non-metallic anti-personnel mine of the 'shoe' type, which can be laid on the ground or easily buried. The mine is armed by the removal of a safety cap and the attachment of the pressure-fuse assembly. The body contains 50 gm of TNT, actuated by the pressure-firing device, which is initiated by a 15–35 kg load.

In service with the Israeli and Ugandan forces.

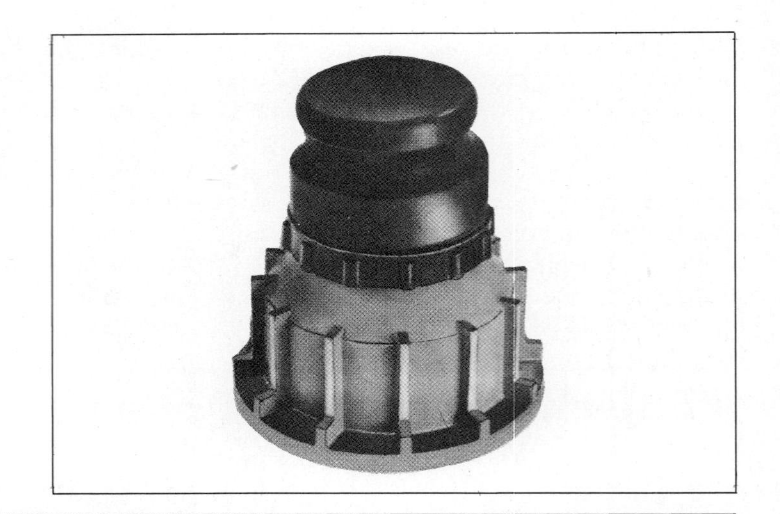

The no 10 anti-personnel mine.

No 12 anti-personnel mine

Manufacturer: **Israel Military Industries (Israel)**

Dimensions	Height 15·9 cm Diameter 10·2 cm
Weight	3·5 kg
Body material	Metal
Charge	250 gm TNT
Method of laying	Manual
Actuation	Tripwire
Effect	Steel balls out to 40 m
Safety	Manual pin
Detection	Visual
Packing	6 mines, complete with stakes and tripwire, in a wooden box

The no 12 mine is a picket-mounted, trip-actuated, air-burst device with an effective radius of approximately 40 m. Incorporated into the mine body is a small propellant charge which, when the mine is triggered, ejects the mine about 1 m into the air, where it explodes. The explosive charge is 250 gm of TNT, and a number of cast-steel balls cause a fragmentation effect. The ignition assembly is a three-anchor pull, pressure or push device with a 4·5 sec delay. Each mine is supplied with three pickets and three bobbins, each holding 10 m of tripwire as well as the fuse.

In service with the Israeli, Ugandan and Argentinian forces.

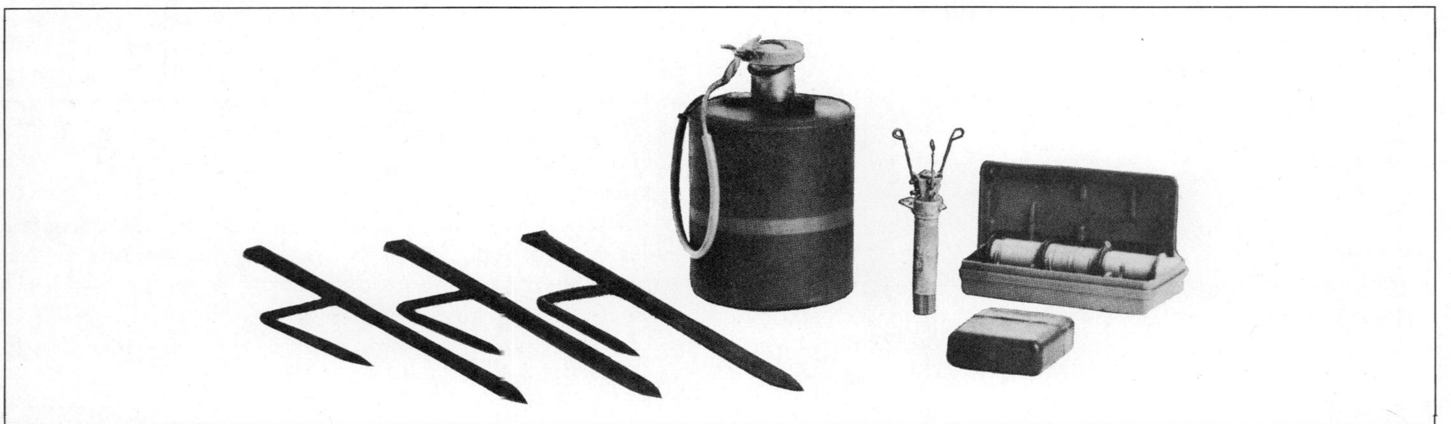

The no 12 anti-personnel mine with fuse, stakes and bobbins of wire.

Mi 101, 102, 103 anti-tank mines

Manufacturer: **Aktie Bulaget Bofors (Sweden)**

Weights	12·5 kg (101) 8 kg (102) 10 kg (103)
Body material	See text
Charge	TNT
Method of laying	Manual
Actuation	140–280 kg pressure
Effect	Running gear and crew destroyed
Environment	−40°C to +70°C
Detection	Not susceptible to electro-magnetic detectors
Packing	Two fuses in sealed canister and two mines in a case

These three mines are dealt with as one since they differ only in the quantity of explosive. The mine bodies have no casing, but have a hard, moulded outer surface of either TNT or hexatol reinforced with fibre glass. All three mines are pressure activated by a fuse of plastic construction. The fuse is screwed into a well in the mine and is initiated by either direct or incidental pressure being applied to its Y-shaped head. A direct pressure of 280 kg, or an incidental pressure of 140 kg, is transferred via a pestal-shaped plunger to an anvil which breaks on to the striker mechanisms and detonates the mine. Given that these mines are laid over 1 m apart, sympathetic detonation will not occur and an accidental drop of 5 m will not initiate them. Like most current anti-tank mines, the 101, 102 and 103 can be laid in water and left indefinitely.

In service with the Swedish forces.

The Mi 102 anti-tank mine.

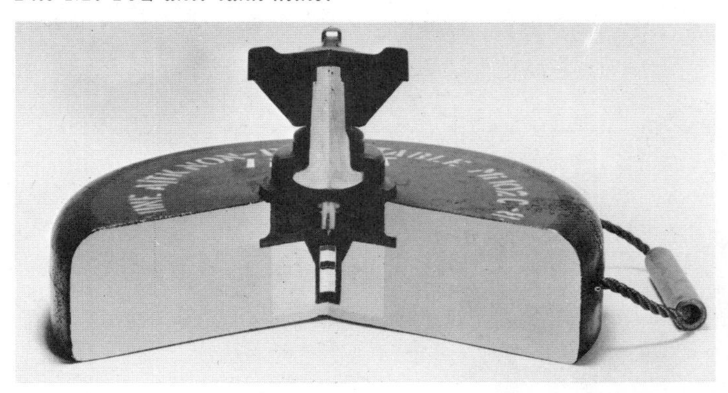

The Mi 102 cut away to reveal the fuse and Y-head.

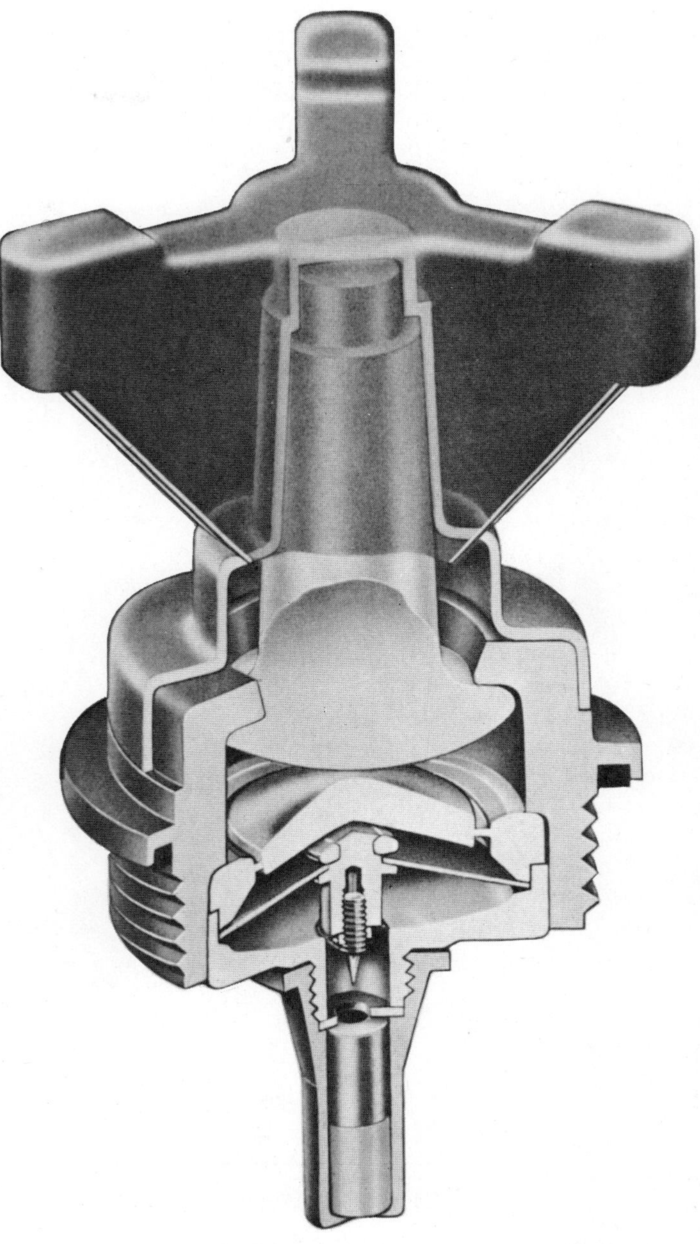

A diagram of the Y-head and fuse assembly.

AP12 anti-personnel mine

Manufacturer: **Aktie Bulaget Bofors (Sweden)**

Dimensions	Length 16 cm Height 9 cm
Weight	1·4 kg
Body material	Not known
Charge	Shaped HE
Method of laying	Manual
Actuation	Remote electric ignitor or trip-wire
Fuse	Pyrotechnic train-impact igniter
Effect	Steel balls out to 50 m in 45° arc
Safety	Manual pin
Environment	−40°C to +60°C
Detection	Visual
Packing	5 mines with all accessories in a compartmented wooden carrying box weighing 22 kg

The AP12 is a free-standing mine with a concave rectangular body containing a shaped charge and a large number of steel balls. Its shape results in the blast being directed forward over a range of more than 50 m through an arc of some 45°. Operationally the mine is either stood on the ground or (by using nails provided) attached to a convenient upright support. Once in position, the mine can be roughly aimed using its sight attachment, and then camouflaged, but only with grass, leaves or a light net.

Two forms of triggering device are supplied. One is electrical, the other is a trip-and-impact system. The electrical system is designed so that a soldier can set off the mine at a moment of his own choosing from a remote position. An electric detonator is fitted into the back of the mine and connected via a plug attachment to a 50 m cable which in turn is connected to a triggering device. Up to five mines can be triggered simultaneously using this system. The impact ignition method is actuated by pressure on the tripwire, which is attached to an igniter by a snap hook. A 1 m length of detonating cord connects the igniter to the detonator. The two systems can be combined so that they complement each other.

In service with the Swedish forces.

The AP12 anti-personnel mine, showing the bobbin of wire and the electric triggering device.

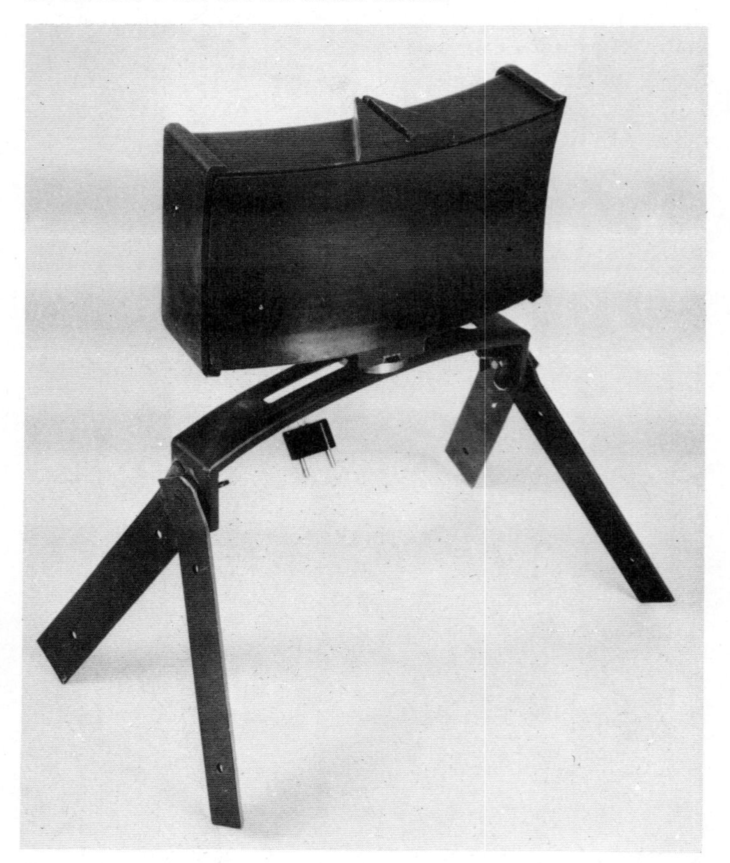

Front view of the AP12.

PMK-40 anti-personnel mine

Manufacturer: **State factories (USSR)**

Dimensions	Height 3·8 cm
	Diameter 7 cm
Weight	90 gm
Body material	Cardboard
Charge	TNT

This tiny nuisance-value mine contains only 50 gm of TNT and is intended to be left strewn around in abandoned locations to be stepped on. It consists of a little, round, waxed cardboard box with a bevelled top and a small round filler-plug on the side. In the box are the TNT and a pressure-operated lever fuse which, when subjected to about 9 kg of pressure, frees the spring-loaded striker to ignite a percussion-cap. The PMK-40 is hardly likely to kill, but can cause a nasty foot injury, and it is not easily noticed in grass or undergrowth. Furthermore, only the fuse assembly is of metal and the mine could easily elude a conventional metallic mine detector.

In service with Soviet and North Vietnamese forces and the Vietcong.

PMN anti-personnel mine

Manufacturer: **State factories (USSR)**

Dimensions	Height 5·6 cm
	Diameter 11·2 cm
Weight	0·6 gm
Body material	Plastic
Charge	TNT

The Soviet PMN anti-personnel mine is a little larger than the PMK-40 mini-mine, but performs the same function, using similar operating procedures. Indeed, it was developed as the successor to the PMK-40. The PMN consists of a 240 gm block of TNT, percussion-cap detonator and spring-loaded striker, encased in a small, round, flat duroplastic box. The top and bottom halves of the case are held together by a rubber band fastened by a small wire clip, and on the side of the bottom half there is a comparatively large cap, protecting the fuse and detonator, projecting through an aperture. As with the PMK-40, this mine is intended to be left strewn around in areas abandoned to the enemy, detonation occurring (with rather more severe results than with the PMK-40) when a soldier (or civilian) inadvertently treads on one. The resultant pressure forces the spring striker to ignite the percussion-cap. In the base of the PMN are four shallow wells formed by cruciform ribs, providing the opportunity for further booby-trapping.

In service with the Soviet forces.

The PMN anti-personnel mine.

OZM anti-personnel mine

Manufacturer: **State factories (USSR)**

Main constituent	120 mm mortar bomb or 122 mm/152 mm artillery shell
Charge	TNT

The OZM anti-personnel mine consists of a certain type of projectile, modified by the attachment of, in place of the nose-mounted impact fuse, a small box-shaped propellant charge (the UVK-1). This is connected by a thin metal tube to the fuse mounted at right-angles to the tail fins (or shell base). The fuse can be of either the pressure, pull or electrical type, and performs two tasks—activation of the propellant charge and of the delayed-action system of the detonator. The OZM is usually buried in the earth, nose down, with only the fuse lying above the mine and parallel to the ground. When the fuse is activated, the propellant projects the mine into the air between $1\frac{1}{2}$–$2\frac{1}{2}$ m, depending on the size of the bomb or shell used, and simultaneously ignites the delayed-action system incorporated in the propellant charge-box to detonate the mine at the top of its jump. The amount of explosive charge contained varies, with the type of projectile, the 120 mm mortar bomb carrying 1·8 kg of TNT, the 122 mm shell 3·4 kg and the 152 mm shell nearly 6·3 kg, while the complete mines weigh 18·6 kg, 24·5 kg and 45·4 kg respectively. It is therefore clear that such weapons can be a hazard to armoured vehicles as well as to infantry.

In service with the Soviet and North Vietnamese forces and the Vietcong.

PMD-6 anti-personnel mine

Manufacturer: **State factories (USSR)**

Dimensions	Height 6·5 cm Length 20 cm Width 9 cm
Weight	0·4 kg
Body material	Wood
Charge	TNT

The Soviet PMD-6, of similar design to the Czech plastic PT-Mi-D, is an anti-personnel blast mine consisting of a wooden two-piece casing, the top folding on to the bottom, containing a 200 gm block of TNT and a pull-type MUV fuse which projects through intersecting apertures cut in one end of both casing sections. Although it is possible to use this mine with a tripwire, it is more effective to set the lid so that a soldier can set off the mine by stepping on it (or placing something on top of it). In this way, the striker-retaining fin is pulled out by the downward movement of the edge of the cover. In a similar manner, it is possible to booby-trap the PMD-6 by attaching a cord or wire to the striker-retaining pin and anchoring the other end of the string to the ground. This mine is of such simple design that it is perfectly feasible to make one in the field and, consequently, although the explosive power will remain about the same, the dimensions may vary slightly. (See also PMD-7, PMD-7ts and PT-Mi-D.) Pressure required to detonate these mines varies from 1 kg to 5 kg.

In service with the Soviet, North Vietnamese and North Korean forces and the Vietcong.

The PMD-6 anti-personnel mine.

PMD-7, PMD-7ts anti-personnel mines

Manufacturer: **State factories (USSR)**

Dimensions	Height 5·1 cm
	Length 15·2 cm
	Width 7·6 cm
Weight	0·3 kg
Body material	Wood
Charge	TNT

The PMD-7 and PMD-7ts Soviet blast anti-personnel mines are identical except that the lower casing of the latter model is cut out of a single wooden block. The working principles and method of employment are the same as those of the PMD-6, which is larger and heavier and contains more TNT (200 gm as against only 75 gm). Again, the amount of pressure needed to detonate the mine can vary from 1 kg to 5 kg.

In service with the Soviet forces.

POMZ-2 and POMZ-2M anti-personnel mines

Manufacturer: **State factories (USSR and People's Republic of China)**

Dimensions	Diameter 6·7 cm
	Length 11·1 cm
Weight	1·7 kg
Body material	Cast iron
Charge	TNT

The POMZ-2 pre-fragmented anti-personnel mines rather resemble a Mills hand grenade planted on top of a wooden stake. Both models consist of a short, cylindrical, cast-iron segmented body with the pull-type MUV or MUV-2 fuse projecting from the top, and a charge of 75 gm of TNT. The usual system, as was practiced for years along the borders of Iron Curtain countries with Western countries, is to attach tripwires to the mines and to set them out in groups. The older POMZ-2 is heavier and longer in body than the modernised version, but contains the same amount of explosive and, in both cases, a pull of 1 kg is sufficient to cause detonation, severly injuring any person within 20 m range. Besides the Chinese communists, the Czechs also make this mine, calling it the PP-Mi-St.

In service with the Soviet, communist Chinese, North Vietnamese and most Warsaw Pact forces, and the Vietcong.

The POMZ-2 anti-personnel mine.

LMG anti-tank (grenade) mine

Manufacturer: **State factories (USSR)**

Weight	9·5 kg
Body material	Steel
Charge	TNT

The literal translation of the title LMG—'the Galitskii Flying Mine'—is a good description of its function. The LMG is really a tripwire-operated rocket, fired from a simple wooden anchored frame. The mine consists of a sheet-steel cylindrical body with a conical nose and base, which contains the 187 gm shaped charge of TNT, and a thin cylindrical tail section with four short delta-shaped fins, containing the MUV pull-type fuse and the black-powder propellant. Firing as it does only on a fixed line, this mine would appear to be only really effective if used in locations where traffic approaches are very restricted and sufficient camouflage is available. However, these mines were used quite effectively by the Red Army in World War II.

Probably held in reserve by the Soviet forces.

TMB-2 anti-tank mine

Manufacturer: **State factories (USSR)**

Dimensions	Height 13·3 cm
	Diameter 27·3 cm
Weight	7 kg
Body material	Tarred cardboard
Charge	Amatol (or TNT)

The TMB-2 (and also the similar, but slightly larger, TMSB) anti-tank mine resembles a large chocolate cake, being a round, dark-brown box with a black tape round the middle sealing the top and bottom together and a small, blue glass disc (the screw-plug of the fuse well) on top in the centre. Two-thirds of the mine contain the main charge, of about 6 kg HE, in the centre of which is placed vertically a 75 MD-2 detonating cartridge, and in the top part of that is inserted the MV-5 pressure-fuse, set to operate under a force of only 11·8 kg. Efforts have been made to combine the mine's non-detectability (through avoidance of metal parts) with resistance to detonation (through the use of tar, asphalt and tape) to such effect that this mine has for a while been accepted as standard issue in the Soviet Army, in spite of its apparently flimsy structure. The main charge can vary from 5 kg–605 kg and may be either TNT or amatol.

In service with the Soviet and North Vietnamese forces and the Vietcong.

TMSB anti-tank mine

Manufacturer: **State factories (USSR)**

Dimensions	Height 16·8 cm
	Diameter 28·7 cm
Weight	8 kg
Body material	Tarred cardboard
Charge	Amatol

The TMSB anti-tank mine is similar in appearance to the TMB-2 and is identical in its construction and function. It is, however, slightly larger, and the main charge is a standard 5·9 kg of amatol. Otherwise, characteristics are the same.

In service with the Soviet forces.

TMD-B anti-tank mine

Manufacturer: **State factories (USSR)**

Dimensions	Height 14 cm
	Length 32 cm
	Width 28 cm
Weight	7·7 kg (average)
Body material	Wood
Charge	Amatol, dynammon, ammonite, TNT, picric acid, or others

The well-tried TMD-B wooden anti-tank mine (very similar to the Czech PT-Mi-D and the Soviet TMD-44) is housed in an almost square box with a canvas handle on one side and a lid consisting of three short planks set side by side in the centre. These planks form the pressure-plate and the centre plank is hinged to allow the MV-5 pressure-fuse to be inserted in the MD-2 detonator. When this has been done, the centre plank is locked in place by a narrow slat pushed through a groove in the ends of all three planks. Inside the box the main charge can consist of 5 kg to 7 kg of any of the explosives mentioned above, but the booster-charge is usually a 200 gm block of TNT. All specifications of the TMD-B can vary, as the simple design allows this mine to be constructed in the field as well as industrially, but the force required to detonate the mine is usually about 200 kg. The TMD-B was employed by the Red Army in the latter stages of World War II and was one of several used by the North Koreans against United Nations troops, prior to its appearance in Indo-China.

In service with the Soviet, North Korean and North Vietnamese forces and the Vietcong.

TM46 and TMN46 anti-tank mines

Manufacturer: **State factories (USSR)**

Dimensions	Height 7·4 cm
	Diameter 31 cm
Weight	8·7 kg
Body material	Sheet steel
Charge	TNT

The only difference between the Soviet TM46 and TMN46 anti-tank mine is that the latter is equipped with a booby-trap fuse set well to one side in the base. Both mines should always be treated when found, therefore, as being of the TMN46 type and fitted with an anti-lift system. These mines are round, flattish, steel casings, painted green, with a slightly domed, ridged top,

The TM46 anti-tank mine.

containing, in the centre, a scalloped cap for the MV-5 pressure-fuse well. The filling-plug is located on the side beneath the light metal handle. The mine contains 5·3 kg of TNT, detonated by a centrally-placed 200 gm block booster-charge, also of TNT, which in turn is activated by a MD-2 detonator inserted in the booster-charge and connected directly to the fuse—a 180 kg force is sufficient to set off the mine. Although these mines were designed for use with the PMR-3 and PMR-60 mine-laying chutes, it is quite feasible to lay them by hand, either in groups or as a single weapon.

In service with the Soviet and North Vietnamese forces and the Vietcong.

YaM-5 anti-tank mine

Manufacturer: **State factories (USSR)**

Dimensions	Height 9 cm Length 47 cm Width 19 cm
Weight	7 kg (average)
Body material	Wood
Charge	Amatol (or TNT)

The Soviet YaM-5 anti-tank mine, like most wooden mines, is manufactured in several slightly different sizes but, unlike many of the others, is not sufficiently simple to be easily constructed in the field. Additionally, there is a rather larger version, the YaM-10. The case of this mine is a rectangular box with a hinged lid, which is provided with a flap-extension down the front of the box. The open-ended aperture in the centre of this flap serves to admit the end of the MUV pressure-fuse striker, which is held in position by a transverse fin between two staples affixed to the flap. A force of 136 kg on the box lid allows the staples to release the retaining fin and activate the fuse to detonate the main charge of 3·5 kg to 5 kg of HE (depending on the type of explosive and size of mine). There are no booby-trap fuse wells built into the YaM-5, but it is possible that an anti-lift anchoring wire could be attached to the striker retaining-pin.

In service with the Soviet forces.

YaM-10 anti-tank mine

Manufacturer: **State factories (USSR)**

Dimensions	Height 20 cm Length 62 cm Width 22 cm
Weight	11·8 kg
Body material	Wood
Charge	Amatol (or TNT)

The design and operating principles of the YaM-10 are the same as for the YaM-5, which it is replacing. The only differences between the two are a matter of size, the YaM-10 being virtually half as big again and containing a greatly increased main charge of 10 kg of HE.

In service with the Soviet forces.

Dog anti-tank mine

Manufacturer: **State factories (USSR)**

Weight	6·5 kg
Body material	Canvas
Charge	TNT

The Red Army learned to use these mines from the Japanese and the German armies in World War II. The system comprises two 3 kg TNT blocks housed in the two pouches of a canvas jacket, 200 kg of booster-charge, and a small metal box, located in the centre, containing the MUV pull-type fuse and operated by a trip-lever about 20 cm in length. The systems are mounted on the backs of dogs specially trained to run below the tank belly between the tracks when released by handlers. As a dog runs under the tank the trip-lever catches on the under side of the tank and releases the retaining-pin of the fuse to detonate booster and main charges. Even today there is still said to be a shortage of dogs in the USSR.

In service with the Soviet forces.

DM general purpose mine

Manufacturer: **State factories (USSR)**

Dimensions	Height 13 cm Length 15·5 cm Width 15·5 cm
Weight	1·8 kg
Body material	Wood
Charge	TNT

The DM is a small vibration mine normally used buried in a loose sand surface. Whilst not big enough in itself to be a danger to tanks, it can be used in the anti-tank role to trigger off a larger charge. In appearance, it is a square grey box of plywood with a sliding lid and two small holes in one side where wires project to connect with the battery of the electric detonator. The inside of the box is divided into halves, the bottom half containing the main charge of 1·2 kg of TNT, and the top half housing the large, circular, clockwork ChVZ vibration fuse and electric blasting-cap. This mine is a booby-trap in itself as, once armed, it cannot be neutralised and must be exploded from a safe distance. Direct pressure is not necessary to detonate the mine, which can be set off merely by the close passage of a motor vehicle or even an animal-drawn wagon.

In service with the Soviet and North Vietnamese forces and the Vietcong.

MZD general purpose mine

Manufacturer: **State factories (USSR)**

Dimensions	Various (rectangular)
Weight	Various
Body material	Wood
Charge	Amatol, TNT, ammonite, dynammon, picric acid, or others

The Soviet MZD mines are housed in plain rectangular wooden boxes with sliding tops. They vary in size, depending on the amount of explosive they contain—usually between 400 gm and 10 kg. Their purpose is equally varied, including anti-tank, anti-soft-skinned vehicles, for blowing up trains, or even as booby-traps in vacated buildings. Consequently, the fuses used will also vary in accordance with the purpose—VZ-1 (vibration), ChZ-35 or CRZ-10 (electric delay), EkRP (safety delay) or EKRV (electric) fuses can all be used. As the vibration and electric fuses are extremely sensitive, no attempt should be made to neutralise these mines by hand—the type of fuse cannot be discerned by visual inspection.

In service with the Soviet forces.

AKS general purpose mine

Manufacturer: **State factories (USSR)**

Dimensions	Height 12 cm Length 27 cm Width 23 cm
Weight	9 kg
Body material	Sheet steel
Charge	TNT

The Soviet AKS tilt-rod-operated mine has been proved to be more reliable than many other newer mines, and is effective against both men and vehicles. The main charge of 6·8 kg of TNT is contained in a square steel box, one side of which is a sliding panel, with, mounted centrally on top in a ball-joint, the tilt-rod. The latter is connected inside the case to the retaining-pin of the MUV pull-fuse, but is secured against inadvertent movement by a safety pin. Although the 63 cm long tilt-rod can be left in well-camouflaged cover to catch the underside of a vehicle on its own, a common practice is to bury the mine-casing and attach a large twig to disguise the rod. The amount of pressure and tilt required to detonate the mine can vary from 5 kg to 20 kg and 20°–50° respectively. Booby-trap wells are not provided, but an anti-lift device may be improvised.

In service with the Soviet and North Vietnamese forces and the Vietcong.

M16A1 anti-personnel mine

Manufacturer: **Department of the United States Army**

Dimensions	Height 14 cm Diameter 10·3 cm
Weight	3·6 kg
Body material	Cast iron and steel
Charge	0·5 kg TNT
Method of laying	Manual
Actuation	By tripwire or pressure of 3·7–9·2 kg
Effect	Fragments out to 27 m at a height of 1–2 m
Safety	Manual, two pin safeties
Detection	Visual

The M16 can be used either as a booby trap or as a conventional anti-personnel mine. It is actuated by a trip fuse that results in an iron fragmentation mine being thrown about 1 m into the air, and exploding. It has a casualty radius of about 27 m and is dangerous to 180 m.

In service with the United States forces.

M18A1 (Claymore) anti-personnel mine

Manufacturer: **Department of the United States Army**

Dimensions	Length 21·5 cm Width 3·8 cm Height 9 cm
Weight	1·6 kg
Body material	Polystyrene
Charge	0·7 kg composition C-4
Method of laying	Manual
Actuation	Remote or by tripwire to pyrotechnic train
Effect	Dispersion of 700 steel balls

Safety	Manual pin
Environment	Pan climatic
Detection	Visual

This mine was developed at Picatinny Arsenal to meet a requirement for an effective area defence against mass attacks and was used extensively in Vietnam.

The M18A1 has a curved rectangular case made from moulded polystyrene, reinforced with fibre glass. 700 steel balls are embedded in a plastic matrix at the front of the case. Behind this matrix is the explosive charge. The fragmentation case is horizontally convex, so that a full 60° pattern is achieved, and vertically concave to channel dispersion into one plane. Like the Bofors AP12, the M18A1 is sighted on a fixed axis by an incorporated sight and can be actuated remotely or by a trip-initiated pyrotechnic train. On detonation, the 700 steel balls are projected forward and are lethal to about 50 m.

In service with the United States, United Kingdom, South Vietnamese, West German and Israeli forces.

M7A2 anti-vehicle or anti-personnel mine

Manufacturer: **Department of the United States Army**

Dimensions	Length 17·8 cm Width 11·4 cm Height 6·4 cm
Weight	2·2 kg
Body material	Metal
Charge	1·6 kg tetrytol
Method of laying	Manual
Actuation	63–109 kg pressure
Effect	Blast
Safety	Removing fuse
Environment	Pan climatic
Detection	Susceptible to electro-magnetic detectors

The mine consists of HE charge in a rectangular metal body, and is intended for use against trucks and light tanks. It may also be used as a demolition charge or as an anti-personnel mine. As with the M6A2, the M603 pressure fuse is used and a secondary fuse enables it to be booby trapped easily, or fired remotely. Once armed, a sliding metal cover is placed over the fuse. The purpose of this plate is to ensure a larger pressure surface. A load of between 63 and 109 kg depresses the plate, which in turn depresses the pressure plate on the fuse. The fuse contains a spring-loaded striker which is thus released, and the detonator is initiated.

In service with the United States, South Vietnamese, Cambodian forces, and the Viet Cong.

M6A2 anti-tank mine

Manufacturer: **Department of the United States Army**

Dimensions	Diameter 33 cm Height 8·2 cm
Weight	9·2 kg
Body material	Metal
Charge	5·5 kg TNT
Method of laying	Manual
Actuation	138–184 kg pressure
Effect	Blast
Safety	Manual, arming plug
Detection	Susceptible to electro-magnetic detectors

This mine was 'acquired' in quite large quantities by the Viet Cong during the Vietnam war and was used by them to attack American and Vietnamese armour.

The mine consists of a metal body filled with TNT and is detonated by the pressure-actuated M603 fuse. This fuse incorporates a plug which is turned to the armed position, and a subsequent load of 138–184 kg on the pressure plates results in detonation. In addition, a secondary activator well can be fitted with an anti-lift device or remote-detonation device. The blast effect destroys the running gear of most known tanks.

In service with the United States forces and the Vietcong.

M15 anti-tank mine

Manufacturer: **Department of the United States Army**

Dimensions	Height 12·5 cm Diameter 33 cm
Weight	13·6 kg
Body material	Cast steel
Charge	9·9 kg HE
Method of laying	Manual
Actuation	Pressure
Effect	Blast and impact damage
Environment	Pan climatic
Detection	Susceptible to electro-magnetic detectors

The M15 is a pressure-activated, cylindrical, anti-tank mine with a cast-iron body filled with HE. It is not designed to destroy a tank but, on detonation, will cripple the suspension and tracks of all but the heavy tanks.

In service with the United States forces.

M19 anti-tank mine

Manufacturer: **Department of the United States Army**

Dimensions	Height 7·6 cm Base 33 cm square
Weight	12·7 kg
Body material	Plastic
Charge	9·5 kg HE
Method of laying	Manual
Actuation	Pressure
Effect	Blast
Environment	Pan climatic
Detection	Not susceptible to electro-magnetic detectors

The M19 is a box-shaped anti-tank mine for use against heavy tanks and other vehicles. The body and fuse are of plastic, and are undetectable using electro-magnetic devices. The 9·5 kg explosive charge is detonated by a pressure-actuated fuse.

In service with the United States forces.

M21 anti-tank mine

Manufacturer: **Department of the United States Army**

Dimensions	Height 11·3 cm Diameter 23 cm (projectile)
Weight	7·7 kg
Body material	Metal
Charge	4·9 kg HE in saucer-shaped projectile
Method of laying	Manual
Actuation	Pressure
Effect	Penetrates all known belly armour
Environment	Pan climatic
Detection	Susceptible to electro-magnetic detectors

This is a heavy metallic, cylindrically shaped, anti-tank mine which, when actuated, propels a flat, saucer-shaped missile against the belly of the passing vehicle. The 4·9 kg shaped charge, which penetrates most known armour, usually destroys the target.

In service with the United States forces.

M24 anti-tank mine

Manufacturer: **Department of the United States Army**

Weight	8 kg
Charge	Shaped
Method of laying	Manual
Actuation	Tape switch and completion of electrical circuit
Effect	Penetrates all known side armour
Direction	Visual

This mine is similar in effect to the French MAH F1, in that it fires a projectile into the side of a passing tank. It consists of a disposable launcher containing a 9 cm rocket and a pressure-actuated tape switch—similar to the type used for controlling some automatic doors. However, it is so designed that it is only actuated by wide-tracked vehicles. The mine is sighted across a likely approach route and, when the tank passes over the tape, an electric circuit is completed, and the rocket is fired automatically. A hit is almost certain.

In service with the United States forces.

Astrolite, liquid mine

Manufacturer: **Explosives Corporation of America (United States)**

Dimensions	Liquid
Weight	Not known
Charge	HE
Method of laying	Pouring or spraying
Actuation	Remote or with pressure device
Effect	No precise information available
Safety	Inoperative after 4 days in ground
Detection	Not susceptible to any known detector

Astrolite is a recent development, and very little information has been released to date. However, it is understood that it is a liquid HE which can be sprayed from vehicles or aircraft, as well as being poured manually. Astrolite soaks into the first few cms of soil and, as far as is known, is entirely undetectable except, possibly, by dogs. Initiation can be achieved remotely, or by a pressure-type detonator. Unlike conventional minefields which eventually have to be cleared, Astrolite becomes inoperative after 4 days in the ground.

Not yet in service.

Combat Aids

This section deals with numerous miscellaneous pieces of equipment, some of them technically far in advance of the weapons in the earlier part of the book. Many of them are very similar and, for this reason, a relatively small selection has been chosen, more to illustrate their existence than to catalogue them for the researcher. For example, there are very few descriptions of pyrotechnics or bayonets, but this policy may well be changed in future editions if there is a general demand for it.

Considerable ingenuity is shown in the development and manufacture of combat aids, and it is interesting to note how some old ideas are re-thought and reproduced in a new form. Others are straightforward inventions or developments which, for example, have done much to extend the soldier's detection range. The situation in this sphere is perhaps becoming similar for the infantry as it has been for the cavalry in another. It would seem that there is considerable similarity between the escalatory development of the tank and the anti-tank gun with that of the range of small arms and the firer's ability to see further, especially at night.

JOHN OWEN

Bayonets

For many years, the practical use of the bayonet has been under review, but, in the meantime, manufacturers continue to offer this accessory almost without exception.

The bayonet is as old as the gun and, as such, has gone through almost as many changes within its limitations. The original concept of the bayonet was purely practical, namely, to have a secondary weapon available when the gun had been discharged. However, from the early 1900s, bolt actions with magazines which could be rapidly reloaded became available. This factor rather reduced the need for the bayonet. Nevertheless, it was retained.

During World War I, it was felt that the psychological effect on the enemy when faced with the bayonet was so great that at one time General Haig ordered a major offensive to commence at sunrise, rather than at first light, in order that the sunlight should glint off the polished steel of the men's SMLE bayonets. In practice, in the confined spaces of the trenches, the long-bladed bayonets were too clumsy and ineffectual, and a sharpened spade (or similar implement) was considered much more effective.

In the period between the wars, some countries began adopting shorter rifles and correspondingly shorter bayonets. Some rifles were even fitted with folding bayonets, though this again was not a new idea. With the shortening of the bayonet, the weapon began to come into its own once more as it could be used as a fighting knife. However, the British No 4 Mk 1 rifle bayonet was a socket type and with a cruciform cross-sectional blade. Totally useless as a knife, a version was produced with a swivelling pommel and Bowie-type blade to fill the obvious gap that was felt by the infantryman. It is worthy of note that the Germans had by this time removed the traditional quillon from their 98k bayonet, feeling it to be an unnecessary expense.

Different types of blade were fitted for different uses, the most common innovation being the saw-back blade for pioneer use. Different accessories have also been attached to the bayonet such as grenade discharger cups or devices for cutting barbed wire by feeding the wire along the bayonet to the muzzle and thus firing the rifle to cut the wire, or bottle openers.

Nowadays, the bayonet is being designed more as a general purpose tool rather than merely a weapon. It also has its place on ceremonial parades!

Some of the more modern bayonets such as those of the Russian AKM and the French M49/56 are made so that the blade may be hinged on a stud attached to the scabbard and, using a corresponding cutting edge on the outside of the scabbard, the bayonet may then be used as a wire cutter. These bayonets are also capable of floating and feature a thong enabling them to be secured to the leg. Other bayonets produced recently, incorporate screw-driver points and containers. Thus it would appear that the wheel has turned a full circle, and the bayonet has become a useful weapon and combat aid.

A selection of bayonets is illustrated in this section to demonstrate the ingenuity of some of the designs where scope is so limited.

Communist Chinese soldier advancing in full fighting order with a bayonet fixed to his AK 47 rifle.

Short magazine Lee Enfield (SMLE) bayonet and scabbard.

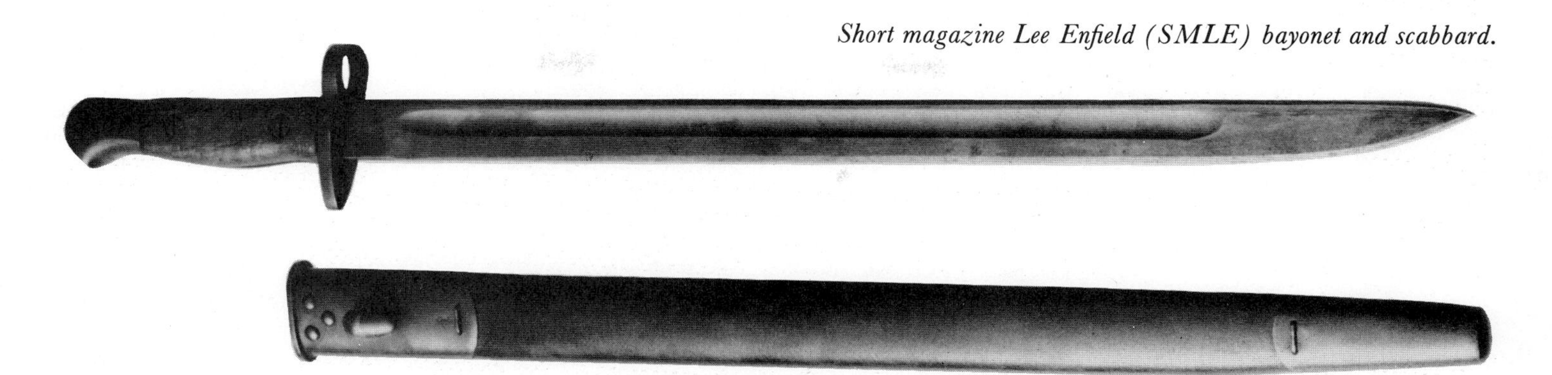

British No 4 Mk 1 bayonet and scabbard.

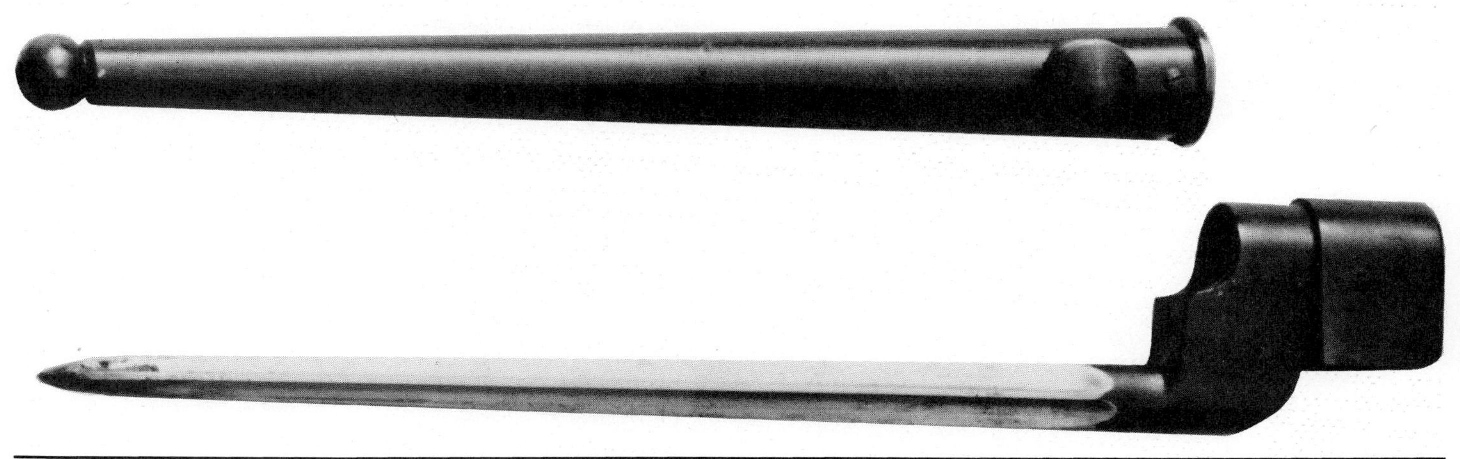

British No 7 bayonet and scabbard (with Bowie type blade).

German 98K bayonet and scabbard.

Russian bayonet for the Kalashnikov AKM rifle.

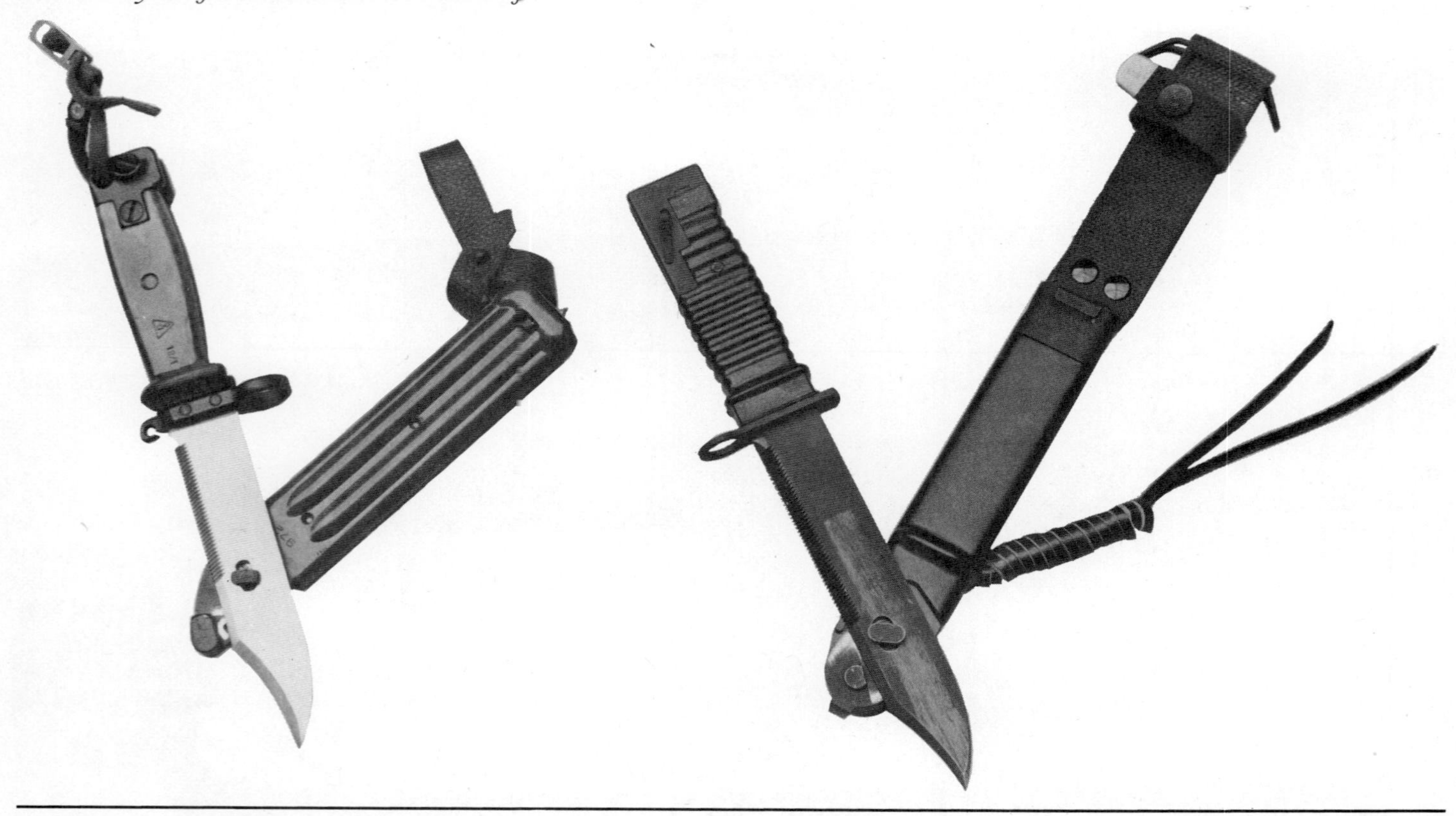

Chinese bayonet Mk II on the Kalashnikov AK 47 rifle.

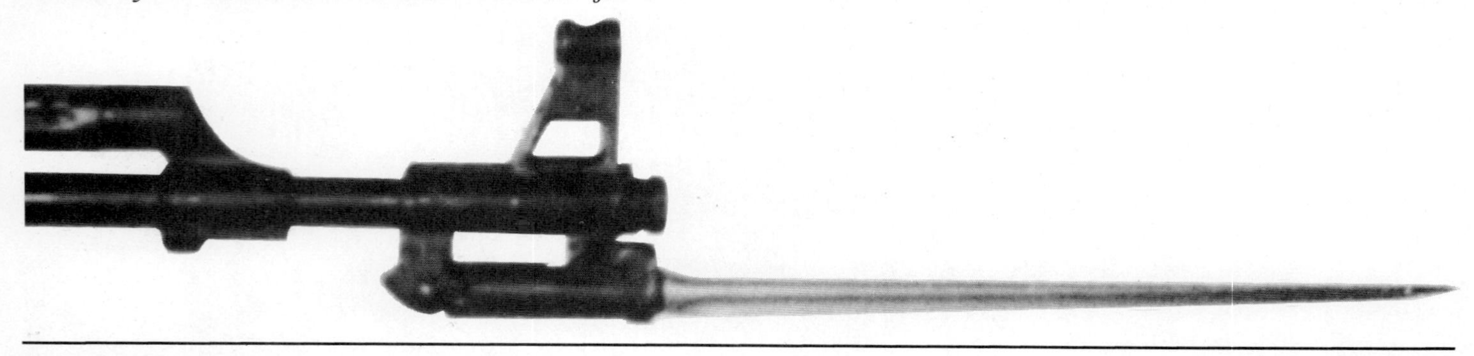

French MAS 36 bayonet.

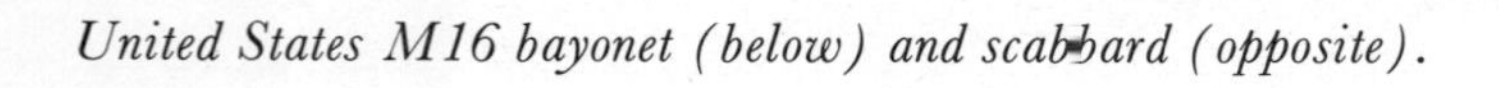

United States M16 bayonet (below) and scabbard (opposite).

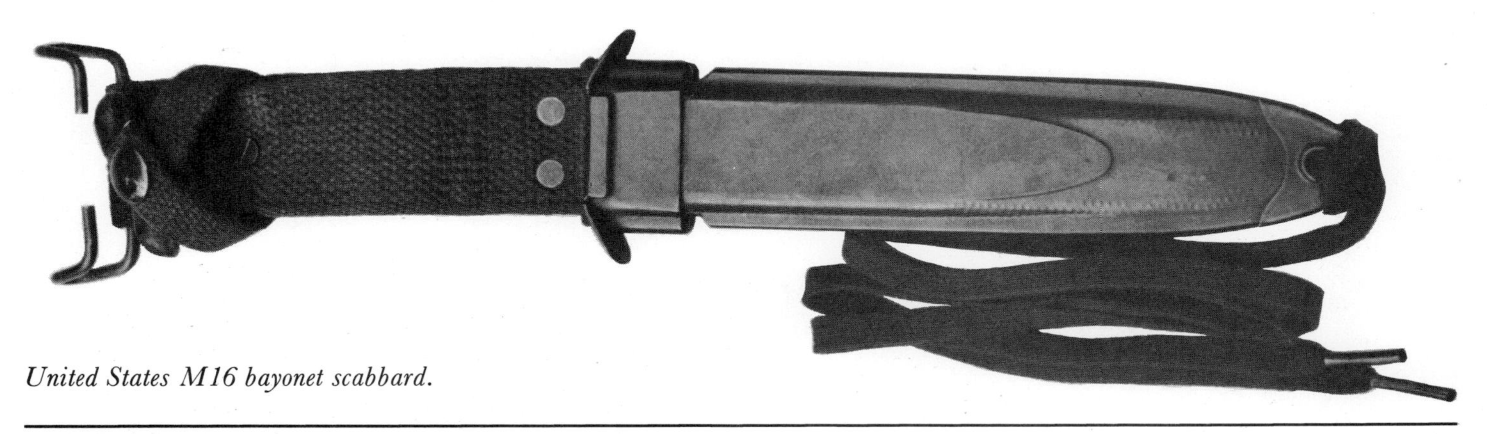

United States M16 bayonet scabbard.

KCB70 bayonet

Manufacturer: **NWM de Kruithoorn (Holland)**

Dimensions	Overall 30·3 cm Blade length 17·5 cm Blade width 3 cm
Weight	0·5 kg (with scabbard)

NWM de Kruithoorn have, in conjunction with Eickhorn and Solingen, designed and developed a new type of bayonet-cum-combat knife and wire cutter. In addition, this weapon can be used as a saw in an emergency, at the extension of the scabbard there is a large screw driver. The handle is partly hollow so that it can be used as a container. Lastly, this ingenious device has been so constructed, by isolating the scabbard and the knife handle from the metal parts, that high tension wires can be cut even though the voltage is 20,000 volts. The pictures show the KCB70 as designed for the Stoner weapons, but it can be adapted for almost any other weapon.

Not yet in service.

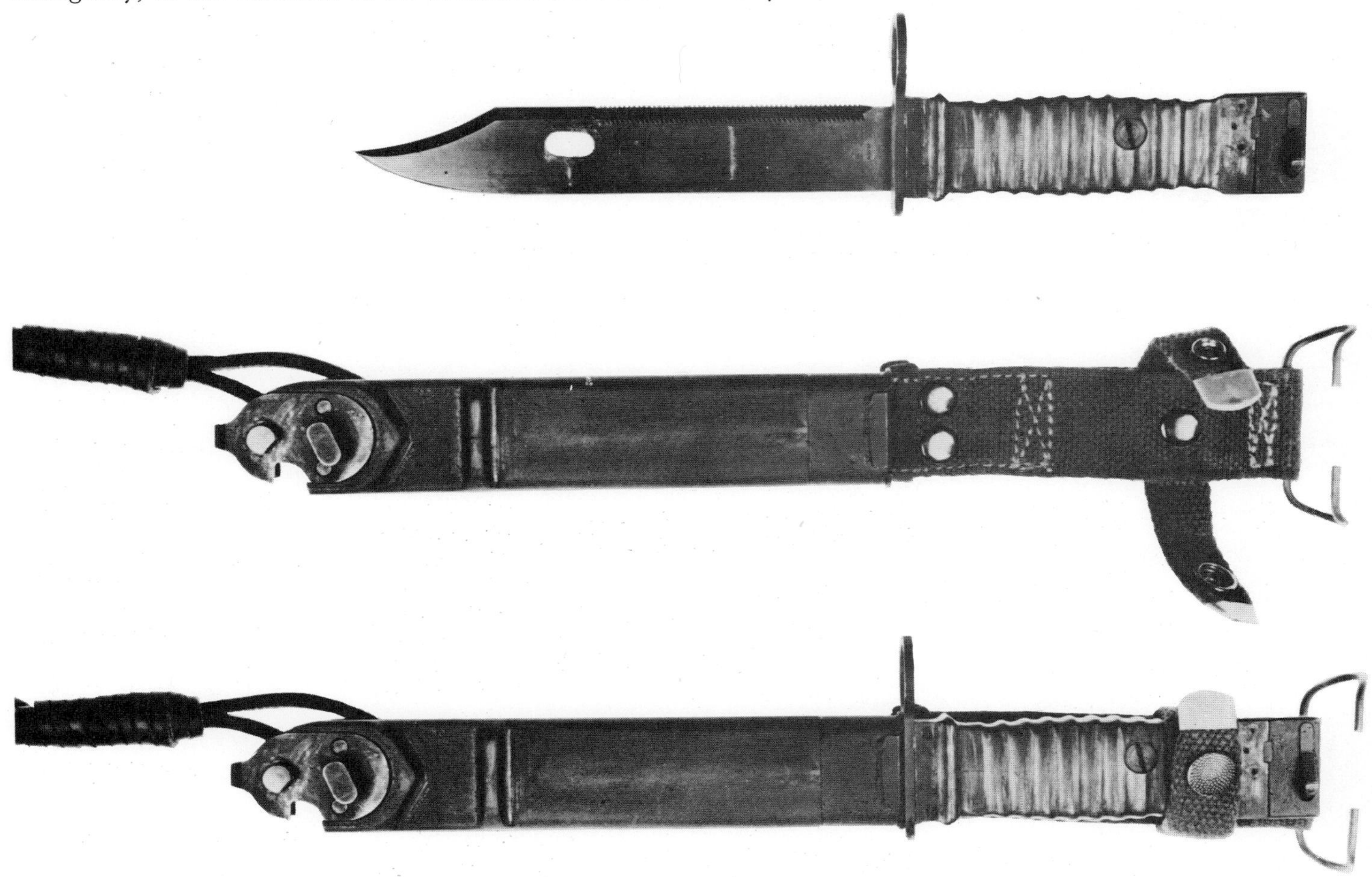

Dutch KCB70 bayonet and scabbard.

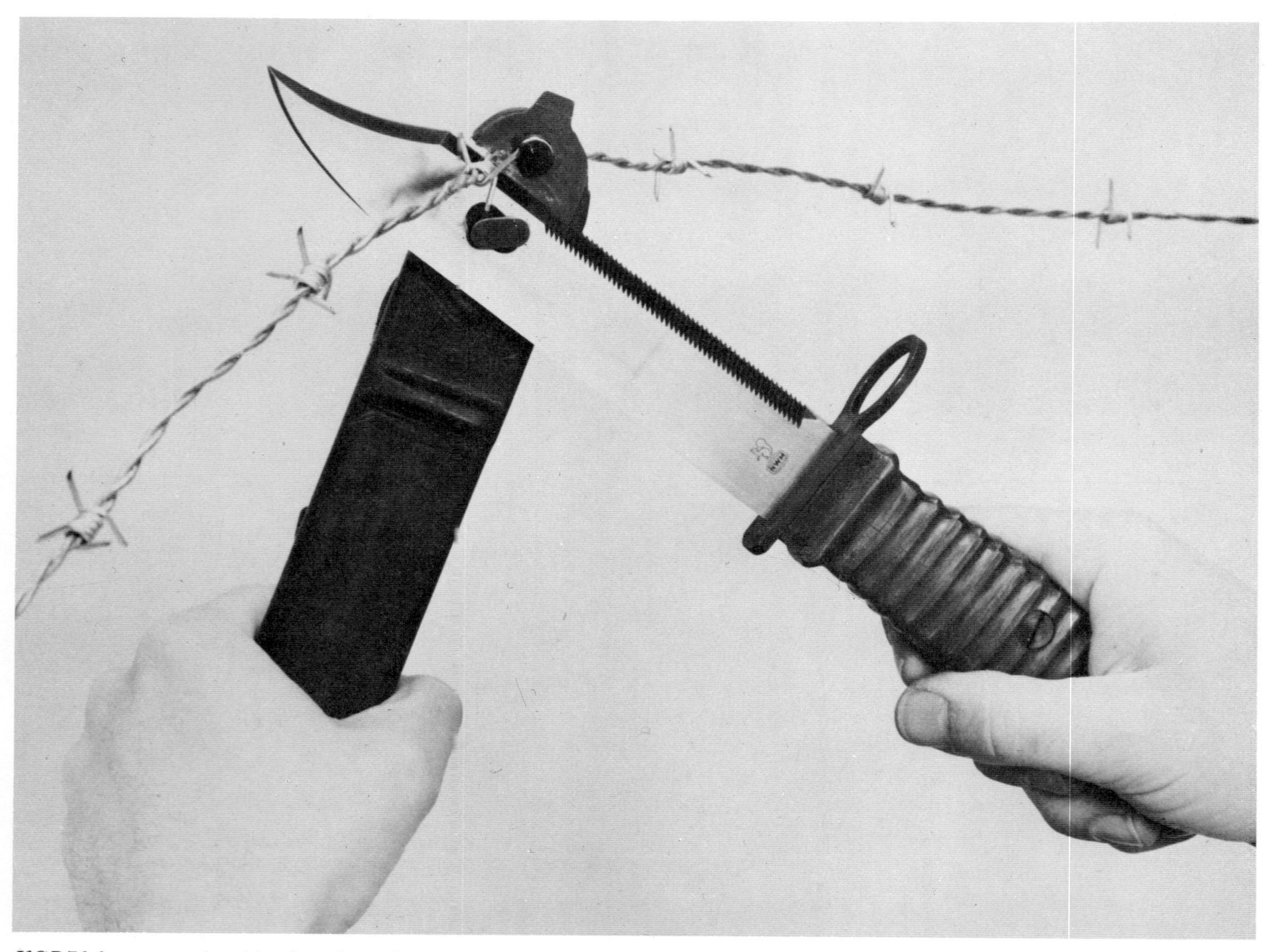

KCB70 bayonet and scabbard cutting wire.

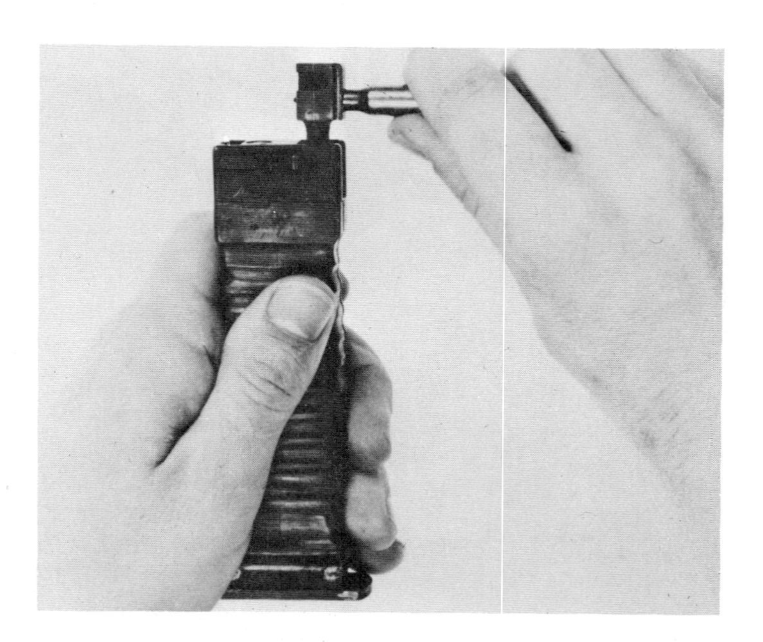

KCB70 bayonet showing the container.

Intruder Alarms

A selection of intruder detectors is shown. There are others either in service or under development which are classified or, if included, would be repetitive. The Americans, for example, are known to have a number of sophisticated systems which were used in Vietnam, and Britain is known to be developing at least two systems other than Tobias and Iris. In general, the modern intruder detection system combines a number of different sensors, seismic, magnetic, sound, infra-red, TV and so forth. Their outputs are fed to a computer where they are sifted and filtered and the results automatically displayed on a relief map.

Some of the American sensors are said to be so sensitive that they can tell the difference between a man and a woman or whether a soldier is carrying a rifle or not!

Finally, not all battlefield radars or sensors have been mentioned—only those small enough to be used by the infantry in the field.

Tobias seismic intruder alarm system

Manufacturer: **Marconi-Elliott Avionic Systems (United Kingdom)**

Weight	Display unit 6·35 kg Sensors 170 gm each
Power source	Battery

Seismic sensors are buried just below the surface of the ground near to likely intruder approach routes and are connected by wires to the display unit which may be many miles away.

The display unit has four separate channels, each of which has a visual indication to show when it is being activated. The operator can audio monitor selected individual channels through headphones and there is also an audio general alarm covering all channels. Whilst monitoring one channel, detections on other channels are shown by their visual indicator so that the operator, even though concentrating on one channel, can see if anything is occurring on the others. The signals of men walking about, running or crawling and moving vehicles as heard by the operator are very similar to such sounds in real life and, with very little training, operators will learn to recognise individual signals. One control unit can handle up to 20 sensors, but they would have to be grouped into four channels. The manufacturers claim that it is virtually impossible for men or vehicles to move within the range of the sensors without being detected.

Tobias has been used with considerable success by British forces during the confrontation in Malaysia, on operations in Aden and elsewhere.

In service with the United Kingdom forces and others.

Tobias display unit.

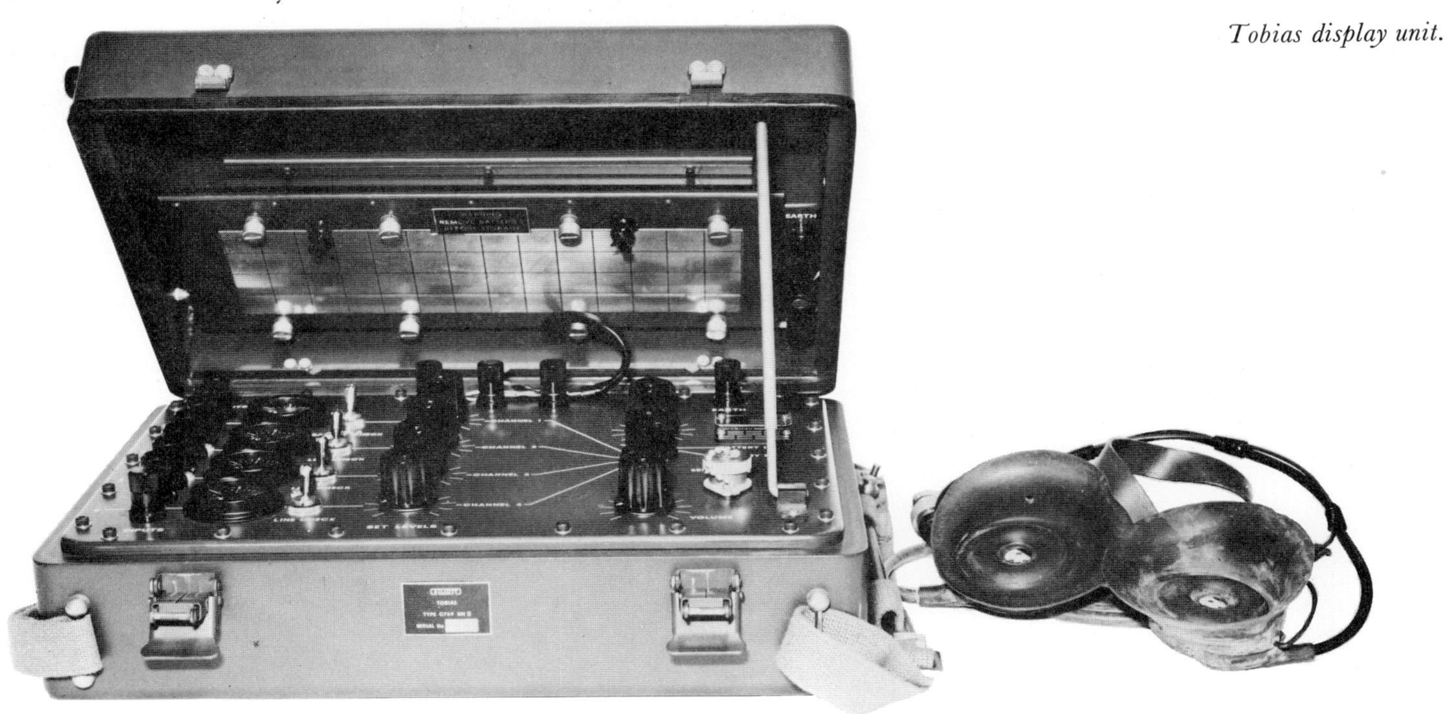

Iris infra-red intruder system

Manufacturer: **Marconi-Elliott Avionic Systems (United Kingdom)**

Weight	Transmitter and sensor 0·25 kg each
	Monitor unit 2·4 kg
	Alignment unit 0·7 kg
Power source	Battery or mains

The system consists of a modulated infra-red beam generated by a transmitter and received by a sensor which is connected to a remotely-positioned control unit.

Complete interruption of the beam causes the alarm to be triggered at the control unit. The circuits include delays which overcome false alarms, such as birds flying through the beam, and include facilities for preventing deliberate tampering with the system. The maximum distance between the transmitter and the receiver is 200 m in average conditions and, to ensure that both units are 'looking' directly at each other, an audio alignment unit is provided to assist in lining them up when the built-in sights prove inadequate, eg at night or when units are partially obscured by foliage. Various beam configurations are possible. The beam, for example, can be bent round corners by means of mirrors, or two beams can be installed one above the other to obviate intruders endeavouring to jump over or crawl under a beam.

In service with the United Kingdom forces.

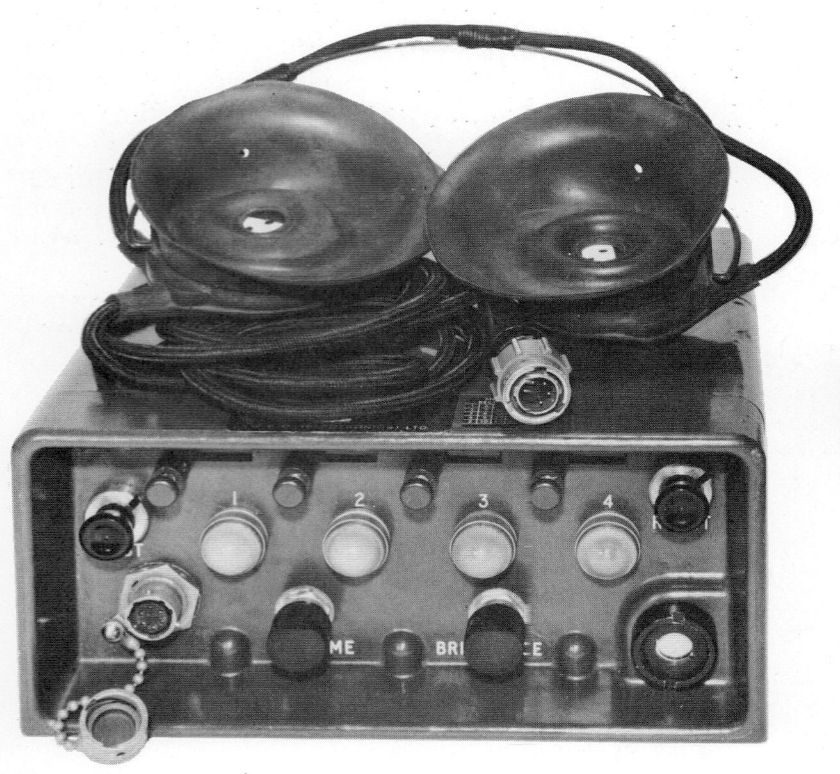

Iris control unit with transmitter and sensor units.

Persid-4A seismic intruder alarm system

Manufacturer: **DEI Industries (Defense Electronics Division) (United States)**

Weight	Control display unit 1·6 kg
Power source	Battery

The equipment is very similar to Tobias. The control display unit has four channels to which up to 24 geophones can be connected in groups of 6. The geophones are buried in the ground and are capable of detecting men on foot out to 100 m and vehicles out to 300 m. It is claimed that high intensity sounds, such as those produced by shells or hand grenades exploding near the geophones, will not impair their ability to detect the movements of men or vehicles.

In service with the United States forces.

Mine Detectors

In simple terms, there are four ways of detecting mines—by electronic equipment, by prodding, by using mine dogs and, in the apocryphal manner by sending one's wife on ahead. This section deals with the first two, which are the most successful and widely used.

VISG M1946 mine detector

Manufacturer: **State factories (Bulgaria)**

Mounting Manpack
Weight 6·2 kg

During World War II, the Bulgarians used both Russian and German mine detectors and, using these as a basis, developed their own, of which the man-portable VISF M1946 is the most likely to be still in use. The VSIF M1946 was developed from the Soviet VIM203, which is now obsolete, but is only just over half as heavy. It consists of a hollow, wooden, square detector-head frame with a metal covering, and a hollow wooden handle attached to the head by an adjustable hinge—at the other end of the handle and attached parallel to it is a large, rectangular battery box containing the power supply of a 1½ volt dry battery and a 60 volt wet cell battery. The headphones are connected by a short cable to the tone-regulator halfway along the handle and from there down the inside of the handle to the aluminium amplifier box, which contains a single pentode amplifier and twin pentode oscillators. In use, the VISG M1946 detector's handle can be extended by an extra three sections and for travel is carried in a canvas pack. Operation is on the beat-frequency oscillation principle, and it is effective only against metallic mines.

In service with the Bulgarian forces.

M10 and M11 mine detectors

Manufacturer: **State factories (Czechoslovakia)**

Mounting Manpack
Weight 12 kg

The Czech M10 and M11 portable mine detectors are two very similar devices operating on the conventional beat-frequency oscillation principle. In both cases the tuning-box is carried in a canvas pack on the back of the operator, whose headphones are connected to both tuning-box and the four-piece aluminium extending handle by wires which pass down the outside of the handle (not inside) to the detector-head. The construction of the head forms the sole difference between the M10 and M11 models: that of the M10 consists of twin overlapping discs, with the handle jointed to the centre of the top disc—the M11 detector-head is a solid figure-8 shape of the same size and with the handle jointed in the same relative position. The tuning-box in the pack also contains the tone-regulator and the three 25 volt dry batteries which, when not in use, are kept in a small pouch on the side of the pack. Only metallic mines can be discovered by these two detectors.

In service with the Czechoslovak forces.

MSG64 mine detectors

Manufacturer: **State factories (German Democratic Republic)**

Mounting Manpack
Weight 4·4 kg

This modern lightweight mine detector is a typical instance of effective German electronic engineering. Whilst the detector itself weighs less than 2·5 kg, it is capable of locating tiny metal objects, even below water up to 18 cm away from the detector-head. As with other conventional mine detectors, the MSG (Minensuchgerat) 64 operates on the beat-frequency oscillation principle. This detector consists of an oval coil detector-head with a four-section aluminium handle which can be extended to a length of 2·4 m. All controls and accessories are directly attached to the handle section permanently fixed to the detector-head—the four 1½ volt dry batteries for the power, the tone-regulator and the timing-box with its twin oscillators. The headphones are connected by wire to the tone-regulator. For carriage when not in use the MSG64 is taken apart and stored in a canvas pack.

In service with the DDR forces.

UMIV-1 mine detectors

Manufacturer: **State factories (USSR)**

Mounting	Manpack
Weight	6·6 kg

The Soviet UMIV-1 detector resembles the East German MSG64, but is considerably heavier, has a much greater range and does not function under water. Like the MSG64, it has an oval-coil detector-head and the tuning-box with its twin oscillators and the tone control are built into the part of the four-section collapsible handle permanently attached to the detector-head. The operator, however, has additionally to carry a large rectangular pack, holding the 3 volt filament and 70 volt plate power supply, to which both his headphones and the free end of the detonator handle are connected by cable. If the handle is fully extended it will reach 1·3 m, and the detector has a range of 45 cm. The UMIV-1 operates on the beat-frequency oscillation principle and is only capable of discovering metallic mines. It is being replaced by the more modern IMP detector.

In service with the Soviet and some Warsaw Pact forces.

UMIV-1 mine detector in action.

IMP mine detector

Manufacturer: **State factories (USSR)**

Mounting	Manpack
Weight	9·7 kg

The replacement for the UMIV-1 portable mine detector is the modern transistorised IMP manpack detector, which not only has the capability of discovering any metal object down to a depth of 1 m, but can operate with equal facility under water. In appearance it is totally different to other Warsaw Pact detectors, the detector-head being housed in a plastic cylinder 42 cm × 4 cm, set at right angles to the collapsible four-part aluminium handle, which is almost 2 m long when fully

IMP mine detector in action.

assembled. The controls and batteries of the IMP are not located on the handle, but in a small rectangular box, comprising the tone-regulator set over the tuning control, working on five transistors powered by four 1½ volt dry batteries—2·5 kg in weight. The headphones and the detector-head are connected directly by cable to the control box. For travel, and when not in use, the whole assembly stows away in a light rectangular metal box.

In service with the Soviet and some Warsaw Pact forces.

DIM mine detectors

Manufacturer: **State factories (USSR)**

Mounting	GAZ/UAZ 69 truck

The DIM mine detector, mounted on the Soviet GAZ/UAZ 69 jeep, was designed originally to clear roads but can, of course, also be used to clear a projected camp site. Once again, however, only metallic mines can be detected by this equipment. The detector-head is formed by the thick tubular front portion of the two-wheeled frame carried on the bonnet of the vehicle. To operate, the frame, hinged to the bumper bar, is lowered to the front on to its own two wheels with the detector-head in front of the wheels a few cms from the ground. If the head discovers any metal object in the ground down to a depth of about 30 cm, an automatic electrical impulse applies the vehicle brakes. But as the detector-head is large it is unable to pinpoint the position of the object—a normal portable detector is therefore an essential accessory. For travel, the whole frame is raised and carried over the vehicle bonnet. A working speed of around 5 kph is possible.

In service with the Soviet and other Warsaw Pact forces.

DIM vehicle-mounted mine detector.

Mine probes

Manufacturer: **State factories (USSR)**

Conventional mine detectors usually have to function on electric power from batteries. It therefore follows that when batteries run flat or are not obtainable, as can easily happen under operational conditions, some other method must be found to search for mines. The Red Army during World War II developed a selection of probes of varying shapes and sizes for this purpose, simply to probe the earth to locate mines. The following examples were then standard and it can be supposed that, if necessary, would be so again:

(1) a simple metal probe like a long fire poker;

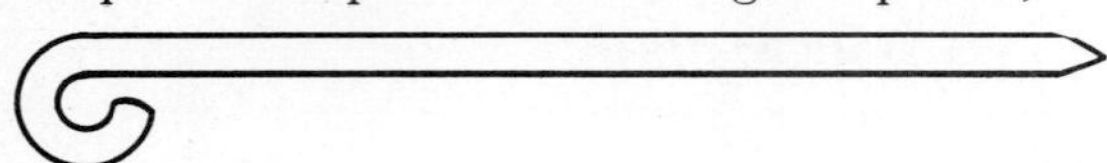

(2) a simple wooden pole with a metal rod projecting from the end;

(3) a multi-section wood or metal pole with a projecting rod;

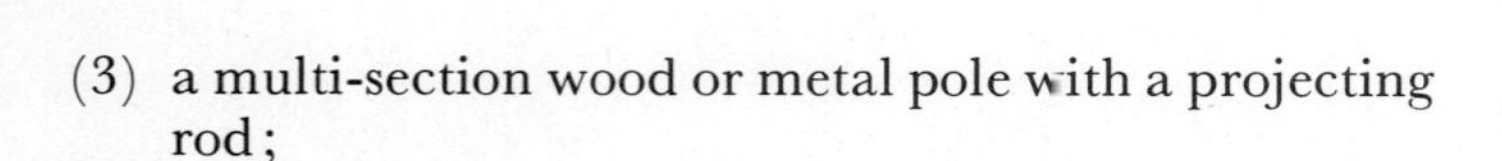

(4) a multi-section probe which folds up rather than takes apart;

(5) a probe with several rods projecting from the end, like a fish spear;

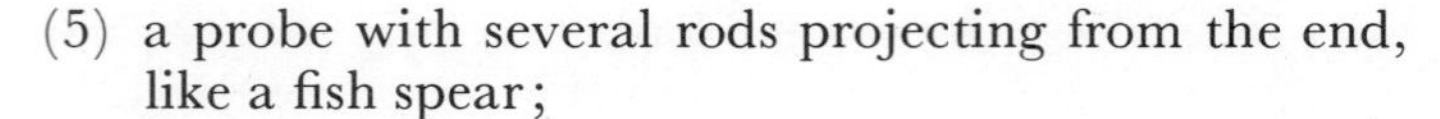

(6) a short collapsible probe for easy handling;

(7) a probe with prongs at both ends;

(8) the Vladimirov probe—equipped with a microphone for detecting delayed action fuses on mines and bombs.

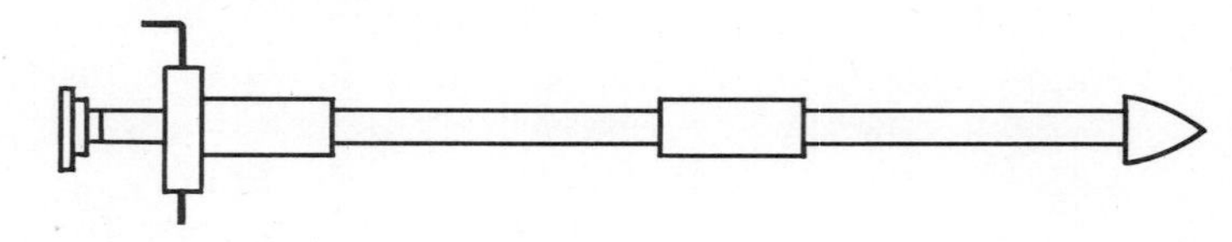

These probes, although somewhat hazardous to use, can be used to discover all types of mines, whether metallic or not.

In service with the Soviet and Warsaw Pact forces.

Mine detector No 4C

Manufacturer: **United Scientific Instruments Limited (United Kingdom)**

Search head	Length 28·5 cm
	Width 18·5 cm
	Height 10·8 cm
	Weight 1·8 kg
Telescopic pole	Length, collapsed 38 cm
	Length, fully extended 128 cm
	Weight 1·15 kg
Amplifier unit	Depth 21·6 cm
	Width 10·8 cm
	Height 10·8 cm
	Weight, complete with battery 1·8 kg
	Battery 9 v dry cell, Type PP6 or equivalent
	Current consumption 3·3–3·6 mA (average
	Operating life of battery 300 hours intermittent use
Complete detector in transit case	Length 53·3 cm
	Width 25·4 cm
	Height 20·3 cm
	Weight 14·4 kg
Performance	Detection range of British Mk 7 or equivalent mine in:
	Normal soil—up to 51 cm
	Pavé—up to 32 cm

The mine detector No 4C now in general service with the British armed forces and the armed services of many other nations in all parts of the world is the logical development of the well-proven models 4 and 4A. The most important innovation is the replacement of the thermionic valve-operated amplifier by a transistorised unit of modern design. As a result, the entire equipment is now much lighter and much more compact and insensitive to mechanical shock and vibration. The weight of the complete unit, including the transit case, is 14 kg.

The mine detector comprises a search head mounted at the end of a telescopic pole, an amplifier unit and headphones, together with interconnecting cables.

The search head contains two mutually reacting inductance coils. Inductance is adjustable by means of a dust core trimmer assembly. When properly adjusted the mutual inductance of the two coils is in balance. If any metal part is then brought within the field of the coils, the balance is upset, resulting in an oscillating difference potential. This is amplified by the amplifier unit and fed to the earphone as an audible signal.

For transport the 4C is stored in a robust wooden transit case, which also contains a spare battery, test boxes, extension cable and other accessories.

In service with the United Kingdom and other forces.

No 4C mine detector in action (note also the probes).

Optical Devices

These are to many the most fascinating of the combat aids. The apparent ease with which image intensification equipment can enable the soldier to see in the dark is remarkable to the layman. One unfortunate consequence, however, is that the soldier is no longer afforded the welcome protection that night used to bring. The parameters have changed—no longer is it the pitting of the soldier's wits against those of his enemy when, for example, he is carrying out a reconnaissance patrol. On patrol he cannot see properly, he cannot make best use of cover as he can by daylight and his enemy can probably watch his every move.

The great advantage of image intensification to the defender, or fire-controller, is that it is a passive system, hence the considerable encouragement given to its development, probably at the expense, rightly, of the infra-red devices which are active and thus detectable and limited in scope.

OB-24-A infra-red binoculars

Manufacturer: **Sopelem (France)**

Weight	2·5 kg
Range	Electro-optical with auxiliary searchlight. Detects infra-red radiation up to 1·2 micron wavelength
Duration of battery	40 hours with EA42 1·3 v cell
Magnification	×4
Field of view	15°
Interpupillary distance	Adjustable between 55 mm–72 mm

The French armed forces and several other countries have adopted these binoculars which are primarily intended for active night observation with an auxiliary infra-red searchlight. They can, however, be used in a passive role to detect infra-red light sources up to the 1·2 micron wavelength. The parallel optical systems with interpupillary adjustment produce an image on the photo-cathode of an image converter tube.

OB-24-A infra-red binoculars.

In service with the French forces and others.

M292 telescopic rangefinder (for ACL/APX80 rocket launcher)

Manufacturer: **Sopelem (France)**

System type	Split image coincidence
Magnification	×4 telescope ×12 rangefinder
Field of view	150 mil for telescope
Periscopic elevation of rangefinder	140 mm
Vertical field of view of rangefinder	16·6 mil
Horizontal field of view of rangefinder	33·3 mil
Accuracy	Within 10 m

M292 telescopic rangefinder.

This monocular rangefinder was specifically designed for the ACL/APX 80 light anti-tank weapon. It is believed that versions for other weapons will also become available. The M292 consists of a sighting telescope and a split image coincidence rangefinder. The rangefinder is preset to two ranges determined by the weapon ballistics. The two fields of view for the rangefinder, and the field of view for the telescopic sight, appear side by side in the eye-piece. The operator can quickly locate the target and compare its location with the two ranges and then adopt the appropriate firing attitude.

In service with the French forces.

A40P periscope rangefinder

Manufacturer: **Jungner Instrument AB (Sweden)**

Length	84 cm
Height in vertical position	103·5 cm
Height with tripod	109·5 cm
Height in horizontal position	34 cm
Weight	4·5 kg
Measuring base	40 cm
Measuring range	100 m–1500 m
Magnification	×8
Accuracy	0·5% (400 m) 2·3% (1500 m)

The A40P is a precision instrument for observation and for measuring ranges up to 1500 m. The makers claim that it is a robust and accurate rangefinder, is easy to handle and able to withstand rough treatment in the field. It is simple to operate, has a good image quality, is easily repaired and is relatively small, neat and easy to handle.

It uses the coincidence principle for measuring, in which the field of view is split into two halves by a separation line. In rangefinding the two parts of the target image are adjusted until a continuous unbroken image of the target has been achieved. The range is then read on a scale close to the field of view in the eyepiece.

In service with the Swedish forces.

A40P periscopic rangefinder operating in the horizontal position.

A40P periscopic rangefinder.

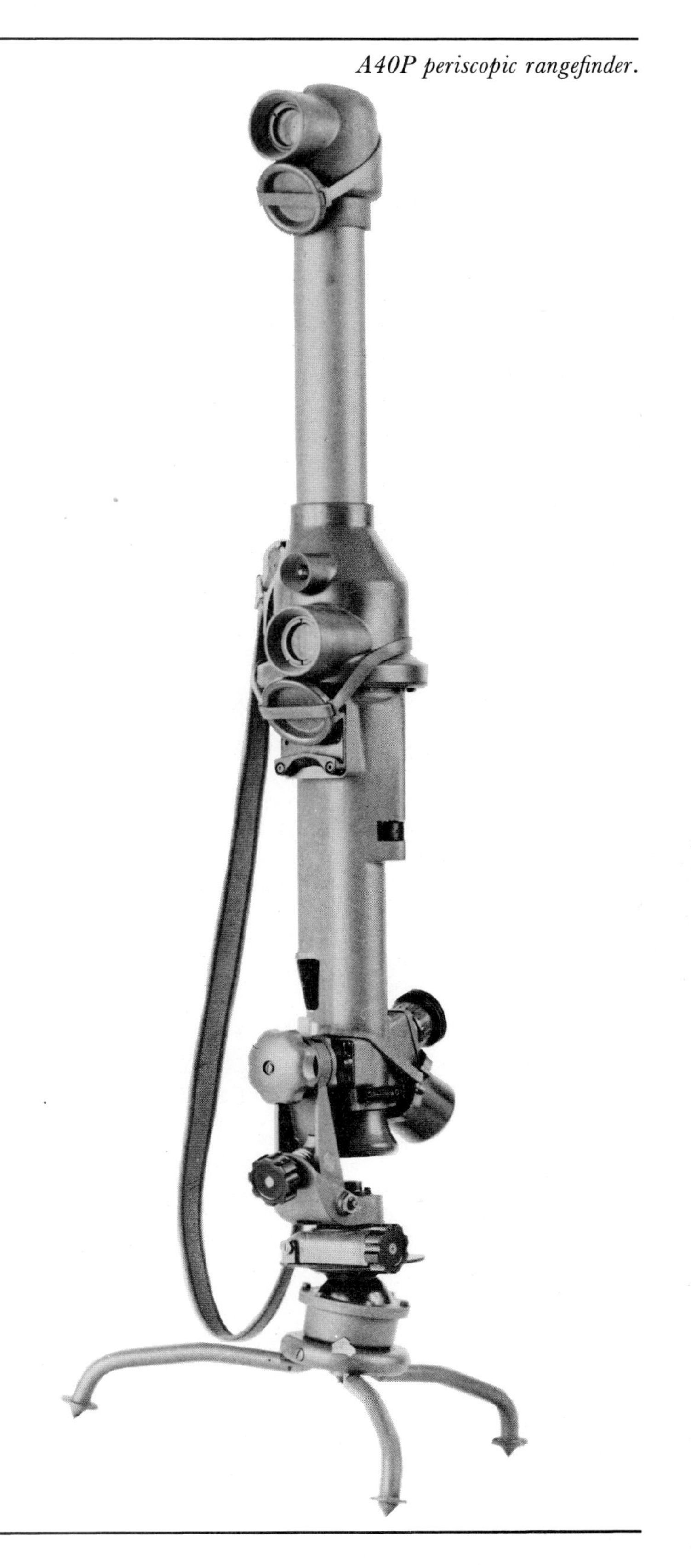

SS32 ('Twiggy') passive night observation device

Manufacturer: **Rank Precision Industries Limited (United Kingdom)**

Dimensions	Length 61 cm Diameter 23·5 cm
Weight	10 kg
Magnification	×5
Focus	20 m–∞
Power source	6·75 v SKB1121 mercury cell
Battery life	100 hours
Field of view	8°
Bracket and mount	Quick release and tripod
Dimensions	18 cm × 21·5 cm (bracket) variable (tripod)
Bracket weight	1 kg

The SS32 is in service with the United Kingdom forces as a surveillance device and is also used for artillery and mortar fire control. The instrument has a sophisticated lens system which gives a high-resolution image, thus providing long range performance in the lowest light conditions. Fire can be successfully controlled on to targets at the normal operating ranges of forward controllers. This instrument is robust and can be carried by one man.

The SS32 is provided with only two controls, an off–on switch and a focus control, which makes it simple to operate. An easily rechargeable mercury battery provides power for the three-stage image-intensifier which has an operational life of at least 2000 hours.

In service with the United Kingdom forces.

SS32 'Twiggy' night observation device.

AN/TVS-4 night vision sight

Manufacturer: **Department of the United States Army**

Length	84 cm
Weight	15·4 kg
Life	72 hours continuous 100 hours intermittent
Magnification	×7·5
Range	1000 m starlight 1200 m moonlight

The AN/TVS–4 tripod mounted night vision sight is designed, like the AN/PVS–2, to perform under conditions of minimum light. It is used mainly for observation and surveillance, but can also be used by forward artillery observers for adjusting fire. It is robust and, like many similar image intensification equipments, extremely useful for night observation work.

In service with the United States and other forces.

Star–Tron night vision systems

Manufacturer: **Smith & Wesson (United States)**

General Ordnance, a Smith & Wesson subsidiary which manufactures Star–Tron equipment, has developed second generation night vision systems. Like much other equipment of this sort, the Star–Tron systems operate on the basic principle of light intensification. All available light is collected by the objective lens which works in much the same way as a camera lens. The makers claim that their lenses have 'transmittance, contrast and resolution characteristics exactly matched to the requirements of the intensifier tube to obtain the highest obtainable level of performance'. This objective lens focuses the available light on to the intensifier tube. Within the tube, the available light is amplified some 50,000 times in the first generation equipment and some 35,000 times in the second generation equipment. The final image, which should be sharp, clear and with maximum contrast, is formed on a screen and is viewed through a binocular eyepiece, or is displayed on a television-type screen.

The manufacturers have produced a whole range of equipments capable of being attached to still and motion picture cameras, television cameras, weapons and for use by individual soldiers for surveillance generally and detailed night observation in particular.

This range of equipment, too numerous to cover in this description, varies in size from some 9 cm to 20 cm in length, from 0·5 kg to 7 kg in weight with a light gain from 35,000 to 85,000. All have an average of between 30 to 40 line pairs per mm.

In service with the United States forces and many police and other forces worldwide.

Star-Tron MK303a night vision system with 135 mm f16 lens.

Star-Tron MK303A with eyeguard on the M16 rifle.

C2 infantry support weapon sight

Manufacturer: **Army Equipment Engineering Establishment (Canada)**

Height	17 cm
Diameter	29·2 cm (case)
Weight	1·2 kg
Magnification	×1·9

Although the C2 sight has been in service for well over 10 years, it still meets the requirements of a sight able to withstand heavy shock and yet able to maintain the required accuracy at long range. All the scales are in mils and accuracy is within ±2.

The elevation drums have two coarse scales. One is for use with mortars and is graduated every 100 mils from 600 mils to 1600 mils. The other, which is for use with machine guns or other low angle trajectory weapons, is graduated every 100 mils from −200 mils to +600 mils.

A fine scale for obtaining fine setting is located at the elevation micrometer knob, and there is a quick release device which disengages the azimuth gears to provide for rapid setting when large changes of angle are necessary. Locking devices on both the elevation and azimuth gears prevent movement during firing. Brackets are provided for holding the light housings which illuminate the scales, bubbles and the reticle. Included in the design is the capability to be easily tested, and adjusted, by a trained soldier so that the sight is zeroed to the weapon.

In service with the Australian, Canadian, Indian, New Zealand and United Kingdom forces.

C2 weapon sight.

L806 telescopic small arms weapon sight

Manufacturer: **Sopelem (France)**

Weight	1 kg
Graticule adjustment	50 mil increments
Magnification	×4
Field of view	75 mil
Back focal length	75 mm
Attachment	Standard dovetail

This rugged waterproof sight is in use with the French and several other armed forces and consists of a simple optical tube providing a ×4 magnification. The graticules are adjustable for elevation and azimuth and range adjustments can be made in 50 m steps. A long back focal length of 75 mm from the exit lens is assured by a perbunan shade, which also protects the firer's eye. The sight is fastened to the weapon by a standard dovetail and is easily detached and adjusted.

In service with the French forces and others.

L806 telescopic weapon sight.

Orion 80 passive night sight

Manufacturer: **Carl Zeiss & Eltro GmbH (Germany)**

Dimensions	Length 28·5 cm Greatest diameter 9·5 cm
Magnification	× 4
Field of view	8°
Focus	20 m–∞
Diopter range	± 5DPT
Reticule adjustment	± 5 mils in 0·5 mil steps
Power source	2·5 v nickel-cadmium battery (rechargeable)
Battery life	25 hours

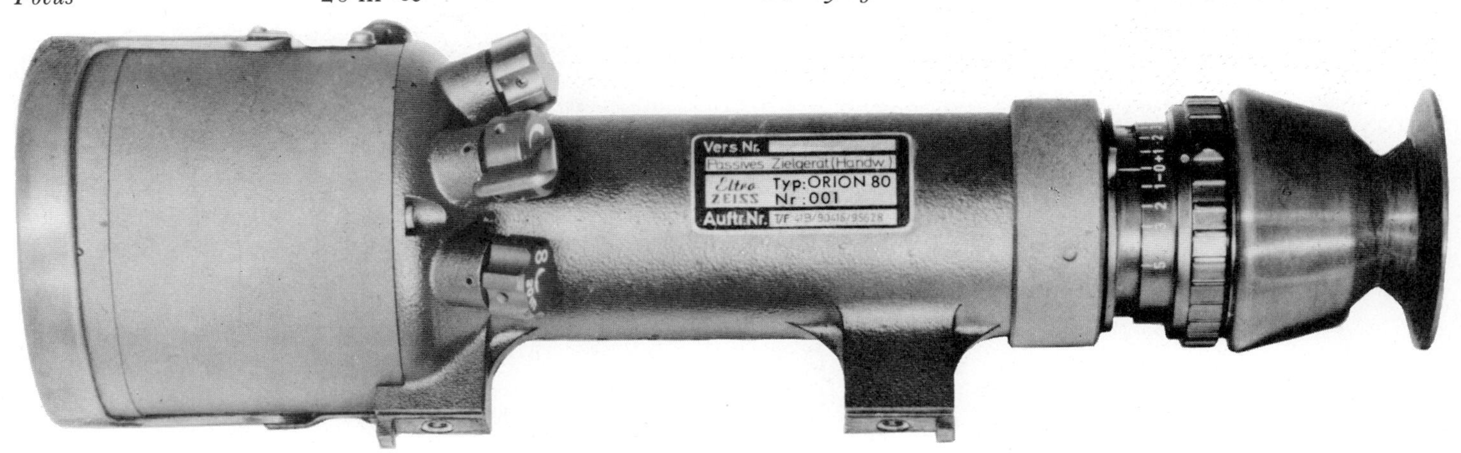

Orion 80 night sight.

Orion 80 is a small arms weapon sight specifically designed for night observation and aiming. It is a passive unit and requires no special light source to operate. A fast mirror lens images the target on a photo-cathode in a three-stage image-intensifier tube. After electron-optical amplification in the tube, an image is visible on a phosphorescent screen. This image is viewed through a ×4 magnifier. An adjustable reticle is projected in the image plane and the brightness of the reticle can be altered by means of a luminescent diode to suit the brightness of the target picture. All image-intensifier sights require an electrical supply to power the amplification process. Orion 80 uses a rechargeable 2·5 v nickel-cadmium battery.

In service with the West German forces.

Orion 110 passive night sight

Manufacturer: **Carl Zeiss & Eltro GmbH (Germany)**

Dimensions	Length 32 cm Diameter 12 cm
Weight	2·4 kg
Magnification	×6
Field of view	6°
Focus	40 m–∞
Diopter range	± 5DPT
Reticle adjustment	± 5 mil in 0·5 mil steps
Power source	2·5 v nickel-cadmium battery (rechargeable)
Battery life	25 hours

Orion 110 night sight.

The Orion 110 operates in the same way as the Orion 80 but is proportionally larger and heavier and has a better performance. However, like the Orion 80, it meets the Finabel requirement and has several components common to the Orion 80.

In service with the West German forces.

NSP2 infra-red night sight

Manufacturer: **State factories (USSR)**

The NSP2 is a conventional infra-red searchlight and optical sight which is used by most Warsaw Pact countries and mounted on AK-47 and AKM-type assault rifles and on light machine guns. It has also been observed being used in place of the normal optical sight on the RPG7V anti-tank grenade launcher and on the old RPG2. It is a rather cumbersome fitting with the 15 cm lens searchlight set above the 25·4 cm long optical sight, which is held 5 cm above the breech-cover of the rifle by the transformer container clamped to the left side of the breech, and an external power-supply cable. Although the NSP2 can be used on the obsolescent Nagant M1891/30 sniper rifle, it is not necessary for the SVD sniper rifle, which already has an infra-red element built into its telescopic sight, to which an infra-red lamp is added when required.

In service with the Soviet and other Warsaw Pact forces.

NSP2 infra-red night sight.

PPN2 infra-red night sight

Manufacturer: **State factories (USSR)**

The Soviet PPN2 night sight, built on similar design principles to the NSP2, is a larger conventional infra-red device with more range. It consists, too, of a cumbersome assembly of a comparatively large infra-red searchlight, set above the long optical sight, which is held above the weapon breech-cover by the transformer-box clamped to the side of the weapon breech, and the external power supply cable. The PPN2 is designed for use on all medium and heavy machine guns.

In service with the Soviet and other Warsaw Pact forces.

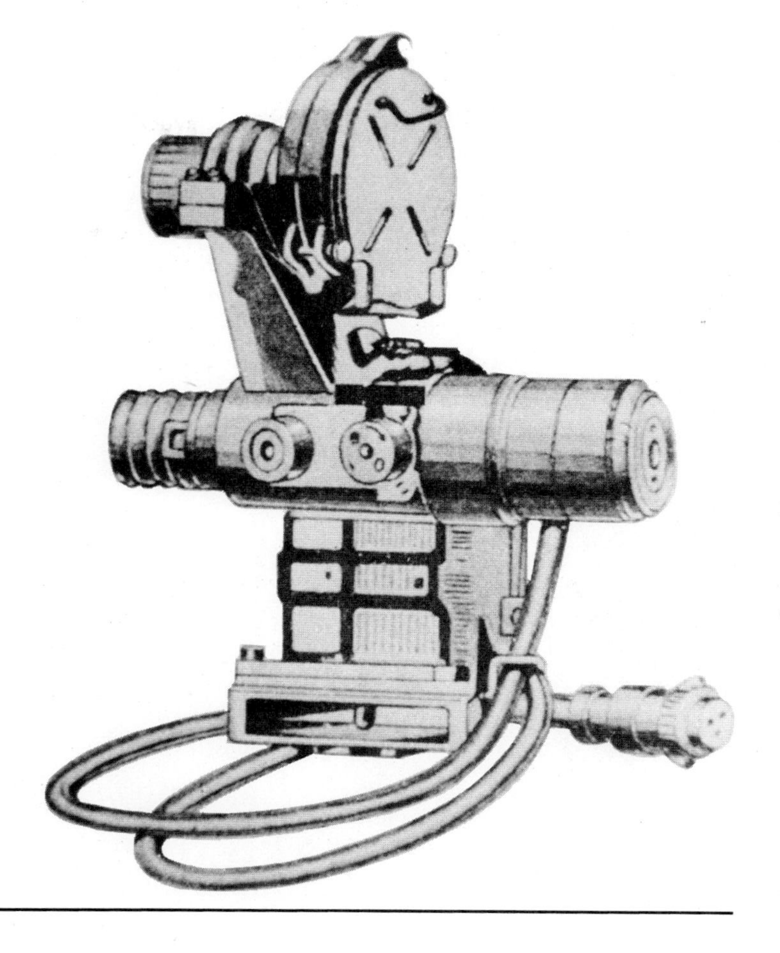

PPN2 infra-red night sight.

Trilux night foresight

Manufacturer: **Royal Small Arms Factory (United Kingdom)**

Dimensions	Dependent on weapon
Light source	Phosphorus and tritium gas
Half-life	8–10 years
Visibility	Visible to firer only
Attachment	Fixed and removable

During the hours of dusk and darkness, soldiers have difficulty in aiming and maintaining a sight picture because the conventional metal foresight merges into the target. Illuminated sights help improve a soldier's night firing potential and the Trilux foresight was developed with this need in mind. It does not suffer from the disadvantages of luminous paints nor does it require an external power source.

This sight consists of a metal blade foresight which incorporates a luminous glass tube in its rear edge. The glass tube is internally coated with phosphorus and contains a quantity of tritium gas which activates the luminescent qualities of the phosphorus. Thus, in poor light conditions, the firer has a foresight which stands out from the target background and though sufficiently luminous to be clearly seen by the firer, it does not blind him nor can it be seen by the enemy. In addition, the light intensity of the Trilux foresight can be varied during manufacture to suit special requirements. It can be used equally well by day.

A number of foresight configurations to suit different weapons have been made and are available in clip-on form or as permanent fixtures replacing the conventional metal sight.

In service with the United Kingdom forces.

Trilux L2A1 small arms weapon night sight

Manufacturer: **Avimo Limited (United Kingdom)**

Dimensions	Length 18·8 cm Width 7·6 cm Height 6·9 cm
Weight	340 gm
Magnification	×4
Objective aperture (clear)	25·5 mm
Field of view	8 degrees (140 mils)
Light transmission	80% plus
Exit pupil diameter	6·6 mm
Eye relief	35 mm
Field distortion	Negligible
Veiling glare	2%
Graticule illumination	Variable red trithium light source
Environment	−75°C to +90°C

The L2A1 sight is designed and developed by the Royal Armament Research and Development Establishment (RARDE) to improve the infantryman's night fighting capability and to assist his target identification at long range in daylight or poor light conditions.

Its compactness and low weight make it suitable for attachment to all rifles, light machine guns and some anti-tank weapons. Removing the sight from the weapon is a simple operation and, when refitted, firing can take place without re-adjustment. Unlike conventional sights, this unit does not have a cross-wire graticule. Instead, an aiming pointer, broad enough to give a positive aim without obscuring the target, is provided. Zero adjustment can be carried out easily with a coin or small screwdriver. The range-adjuster has two positions to the rear for ranges up to 400 m and forward for ranges from 400–600 m. A red trithium light source requiring no external power supply is incorporated to illuminate the aiming pointer and assist positive aim. The volume of light can be adjusted by an external control.

In service with the United Kingdom forces.

Trilux L2A1 weapon sight.

SS20 Mk 1 (IWS L1A1) passive night sight

Manufacturer: **Rank Precision Industries Limited (United Kingdom)**

Dimensions	Length 47·7 cm Width 11 cm Height 18·5 cm
Weight	2·8 kg
Magnification	×3·75
Field of view	10°
Graticule adjustment	± 24 mil elevation and azimuth in ½ mil increments
Power source	6·75 v SKB1121 mercury battery
Battery life	100 hours

The SS20 individual weapon sight is in service with the British Army and can be fitted to many varieties of small arms manufactured throughout the world. It may also be used with platoon and battalion anti-tank weapons and has been successfully used with a 105 mm gun. In its secondary role it is a most effective observation device with a magnification of × 3·75 and a field of view of 10°.

The basic principle involved is image intensification which uses the ambient light present during the hours of darkness. The small quantities of light are gathered and an image formed by highly sophisticated lens systems. The illuminance of the image is then amplified by an electronic intensifier system by up to as much as 100,000 times. This sight is made up of three main units—the primary optical system, which can be focused from 10 m to infinity, the main body containing the power supply oscillator graticule and intensifier tube, and the magnifier.

In service with the United Kingdom forces.

SS20 (IWS L1A1) night sight mounted on a GPMG.

SS20 (IWS L1A1) night sight mounted on a rifle.

Left, the view through the SS20 sight taken on a dark night (10^{-3}) at a range of 35 m in dense woodland.

SS30 passive night sight

Manufacturer: **Rank Precision Industries Limited (United Kingdom)**

SS30 night sight mounted on a Wombat.

Magnification	× 5·7
Field of view	6½°
Graticule	Variable to suit weapon

The sight was specifically developed for battalion anti-tank weapons such as the United Kingdom army Wombat, and is now in extensive use. It has a magnification of × 5·7 and a field view of 6½°. The sight, which has a good surveillance capability, incorporates an illuminated graticule which can be switched on or off as required. Graticules can be manufactured to suit the ballistics of any weapon.

As with the SS20 and SS32, the SS30 operates on the principle of image intensification by gathering the small quantities of ambient light and electronically amplifying the illuminance of an image through an intensifier system.

In service with the United Kingdom forces.

Hyper-miniscope model 9821 passive night sight

Manufacturer: **Varo Incorporated (United States)**

Dimensions	Length 37 cm Diameter 8·6 cm
Magnification	× 4 (× 6 optional)
Field of view	10°
Focus	4 m–∞
Diopter range	+ 2 to + 5
Power source	2·55 v DC battery or external
Battery life	12 hours

The hyper-miniscope was developed by Varo Incorporated in order to utilise already proven components previously used in other devices. It uses an objective lens system with an illuminated reticle and, like most passive observation systems, works on the principle of amplifying ambient light. This device is available with a number of optional extras, such as automatic brightness control in the image tube, additional distortion correction, reticles to match the ballistics of a variety of weapons and improved magnification from × 4 to × 6.

In service with the United States forces.

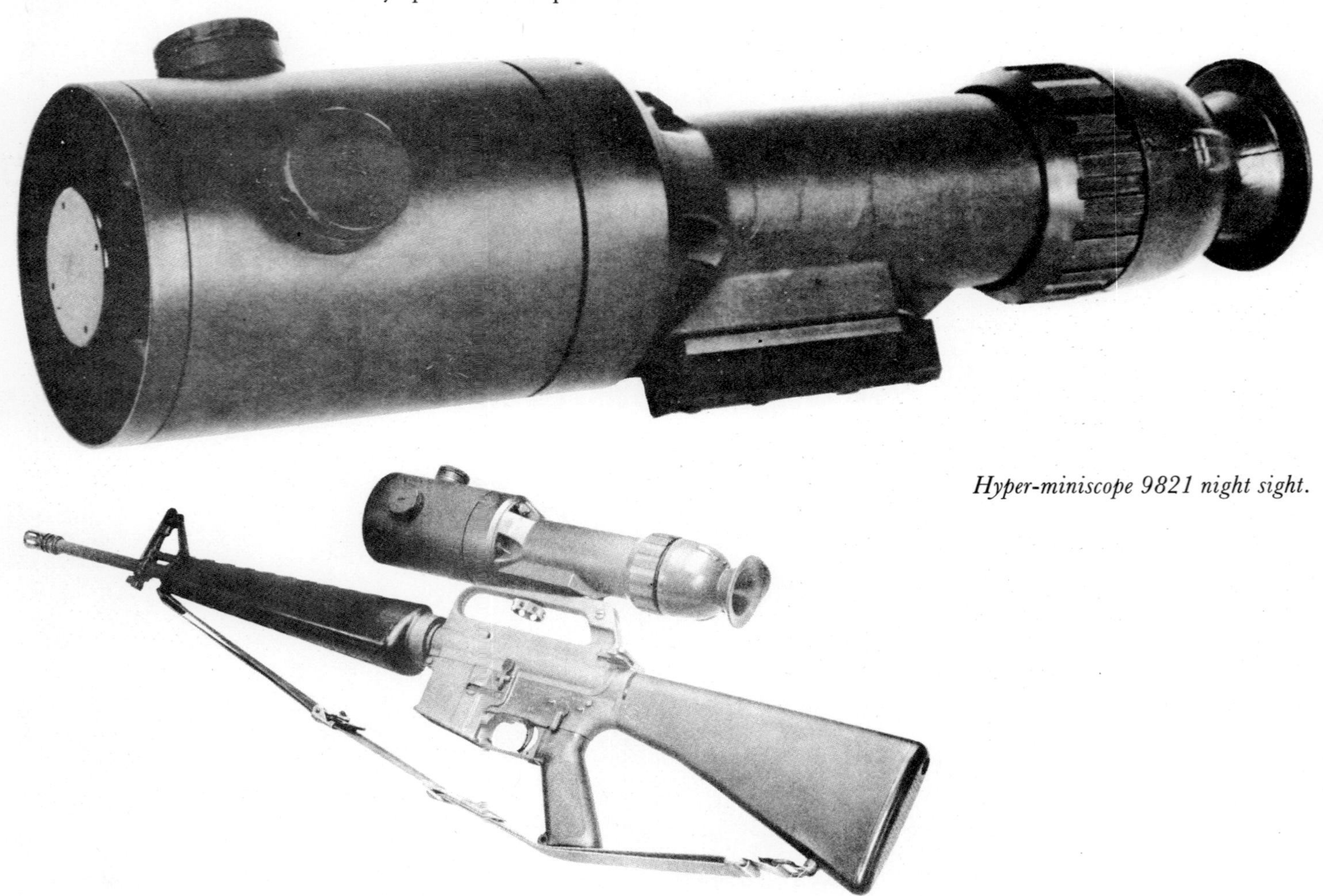

Hyper-miniscope 9821 night sight.

Hyper-miniscope 9821 sight mounted on an M16 rifle.

AN/PVS-2 night vision device

Manufacturer: **Department of the United States Army**

Weight	2·7 kg
Length	44 cm
Life	72 hours continuous 100 hours intermittent
Magnification	×4
Range	400 m moonlight 300 m starlight

AN/PVS-2 night sight.

Better known as the 'Starlightscope' the AN/PVS–2 is a portable, hand-held, electro-optical instrument designed for passive visual observation and for use as a night sight. It is a conventional image intensification device which requires a minimum amount of moonlight, starlight or sky-glow for successful use. It can be fitted to most weapons in current use.

In service with the United States forces.

Pyrotechnics

There is a multiplicity of pyrotechnics varying from hand-held signal flares to coloured smoke bombs, from trip flares to illuminating missiles. Many are designed for civilian as well as for military use and the majority are efficient, reliable and most effective.

Despite the development of radar, seismic intruder devices and night vision systems, the soldier still needs to see for himself in the way he is used to seeing—with his eyes in daylight. Failing that, artificial daylight from a pyrotechnic is better than an eerie greenish image or a blip on a screen. The day this ceases to be true, pyrotechnics may cease to exist, but that day is a long way off.

No 1 illuminating flare

Manufacturer: **Israel Military Industries (Israel)**

Height	10 cm
Diameter	6·25 cm
Weight	650 gm
Illumination	25,000 cp
Duration	Up to 70 sec

No 1 illuminating mine (tripflare).

The body of the mine which contains the illuminating element and the striking mechanism is made of moulded plastic. The mine is attached to a picket at a height of 40 cm above the ground and is actuated when the tripwire is fouled, pulled or cut.

In service with the Israeli forces.

Signal cartridge

Manufacturer: **Schermuly Limited (United Kingdom)**

Calibre	2·6 cm
Length	5·6 cm
Height	76 m
Burning time	5·6 sec

This cartridge has been developed to meet the need for a cost effective signal and illuminating cartridge. Aluminium cased, it will fit the standard one inch Very pistol, as well as the 2·56 mm pistol. It is available with red, green and illuminating stars.

The cartridge consists of an aluminium case, with the rim knurled where necessary for night colour identification. An aluminium cap is used to form a waterproof closure.

In service with the United Kingdom forces.

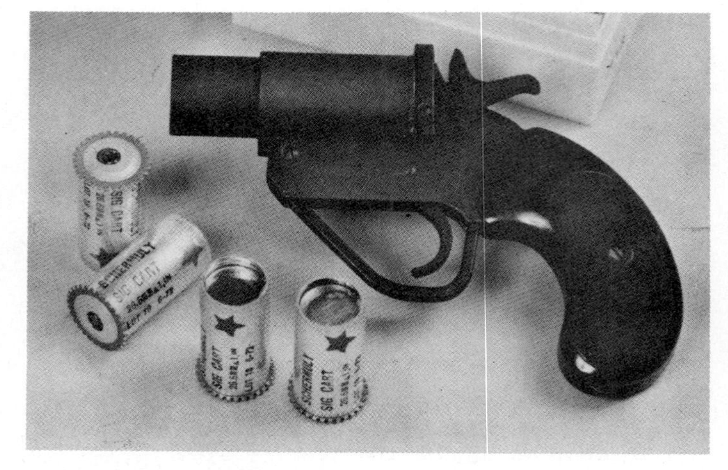

Signal cartridges (and signal pistol).

L3A2 hand-fired illuminating rocket

Manufacturer: **Schermuly Limited (United Kingdom)**

Calibre	3·8 cm
Ground range	300 m
Illumination	800 cp (minimum) for 30 sec

Based on the Schermuly 'Icarus' rocket, this hand-fired percussion ignition illuminator is able to define targets down to man-size at ranges between 100 m and 300 m. A high intensity flare suspended from a parasheet makes accurate small arms fire possible for the duration of the flare.

The adhesive tape securing the metal top cap is removed, leaving the cap itself in position. A similar cap at the base is removed and the firing lever is disclosed. Tape holding this firing lever is peeled away and the lever pulled out and held at the side of the rocket. Pressure on the lever activates the striker mechanism and the rocket is fired instantaneously. Maximum altitude is gained in about 5 sec and the payload ejected. Variations in firing elevation are practicable, ranging from vertical ejection at 400 m altitude to 30 degrees giving a ground range of over 300 m.

The discharger is a resin-bonded weatherproof cylinder, with the lever-operated percussion ignition system fitted in the base. The rocket is of light aluminium, housing the solid propellant and payload. The drum tail and slow spin imparted by the motor design ensures maximum accuracy and consistency in flight path.

In service with the United Kingdom forces.

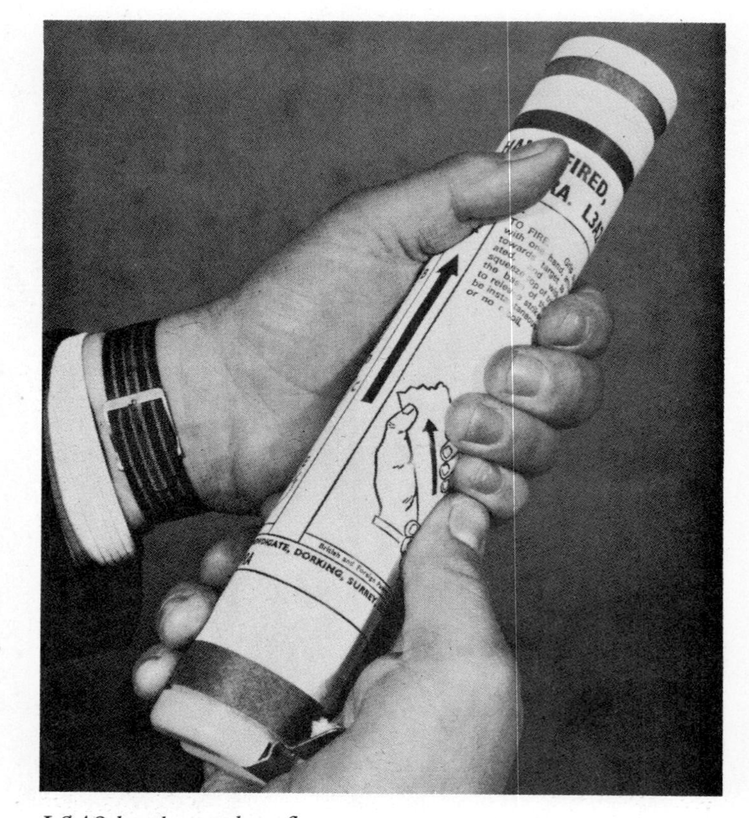

L3A2 hand parachute flare.

Hand flare signal

Manufacturer: **State factories (USSR)**

Calibre	40 mm

The 40 mm hand-launched flare signal is the bigger of the two devices of similar function (the other being a 30 mm flare) which have been taken into service recently in most Warsaw Pact countries, replacing the conventional signal pistol. The device consists of a two-part tube, one part being the disposable hand-held launcher, and the other the flare, made up of the illuminating charge, the propellant charge and a parachute to ensure that best advantage is gained from the 10 sec duration of the illumination. A height of 200 m can be attained by the flare and a large number of different types of flare-filling can be obtained. Most other Warsaw Pact countries are beginning to produce these flares for themselves in the same design and sizes.

In service with the Soviet forces.

Signal pistol

Manufacturer: **State factories (USSR)**

Calibre	26·5 mm
Length	22 cm
Weight	0·8 kg

This signal pistol is one of several similar equipments used in the Warsaw Pact countries, all being single shot, smoothbore weapons of the same calibre. The Soviet pistol, made of blued steel with a plastic grip, has no sights or trigger-guard and the trigger recesses into the front of the pistol-grip. To load, the breech is opened by pressing a stud located just below the trigger while downward pressure is applied to the barrel—the flare is inserted into the rear of the breech, which is then snapped shut. No safety-catch is provided. Many different types of flare can be fired from this pistol, but it is believed that in the Warsaw Pact forces signal pistols are gradually losing favour and are being replaced by the disposable and less cumbersome hand-launched flares. The pistol is carried in a holster and a lanyard is normally attached to the butt-ring.

In service with the Soviet and some Warsaw Pact forces.

Radar

There are two basic types of battlefield radars—those used by one man, either hand held, mounted on his chest or mounted on a tripod on the ground; and those which can be carried by two or more men and are set up on the ground or in a vehicle.

The small one-man equipment often has a limited power output and is designed more as a warning device rather than an accurate locator. However, even these, particularly when mounted on a tripod fitted with some form of azimuth ring, can produce some amazingly accurate results, but their range is limited, partly by lack of power and partly by their low antennae.

The larger radars, with greater powers, naturally produce longer detection range and are more often used for perimeter defence. Their maximum range on vehicles is of the order of 10 km to 18 km and on men about 5 km to 8 km.

All battlefield surveillance radars operate on the doppler principle, that is to say they can only detect moving objects. Within this limitation, operators can often tell by the type of doppler tone heard in their earphones the number of objects detected, their speed and nature (eg vehicles or men). Battlefield radars are, of course, dependent upon the type of territory which they have to cover. The ideal site for a radar is in an elevated position, overlooking flat country unobstructed by woods, hills or houses.

In general, in order to reduce the sizes of the radars, very short wavelengths are used. This has the disadvantage that the radars will be capable of detecting moving objects of sizes similar to their wavelength. Thus moving branches or leaves may give an indication which could be mistaken for men. Similarly the radars are often adversely affected by rain. Any radar's transmission can of course be intercepted by the enemy and the transmitting radar can often be accurately pin-pointed by DF (direction finding). Whether this is of vital consequence or not depends upon the tactical situation. With radars guarding a well-known strong-point, for example, it is of less consequence if their presence and position are found out by the enemy than with radars accompanying a clandestine operation. It follows therefore that there may well be occasions on which radar cannot be used in the field.

It will be noted that there are large numbers of radars of similar types in NATO armies. Most of them are American, often developed as a result of the Vietnam war. Their performances are very similar and it is not clear why it was necessary to develop quite so many. Among European NATO forces there are at present only two operational hand-held radars—the French Oliphant II and the Italian Sentinel. The British Shrimp, which is of the same category, has not yet been fully evaluated.

There is a serious need for some form of standardisation within NATO both of the hand-held radars and of the more powerful ground or vehicle-mounted ones before the NATO nations either develop their own or buy differing American ones. At present, it seems possible that every European NATO army or marine corps will end up with a whole range of different radars.

Oliphant II hand-held battlefield surveillance radar

Manufacturer: **Thomson-CSF (France)**

Weight	9 kg
Range	Men 1800 m
	Vehicles 2500 m
Accuracy	±1·5 m
Operational mode	Coherent pulse doppler
Power source	Battery
Frequency	Ku band

A one-man radar developed under a contract from the French Government for issue to the infantry and designed to meet the NATO recommendations for very short range land-based radars.

It consists of three basic units. The radar-head and controls, the power unit and the headset. With the carrying harness and connecting cables it is easily carried and operated by one man. In addition, certain optional accessories are available to extend the radar's operational capabilities. These include a tripod, additional

Oliphant II radar in action.

Oliphant II mounted on a tripod.

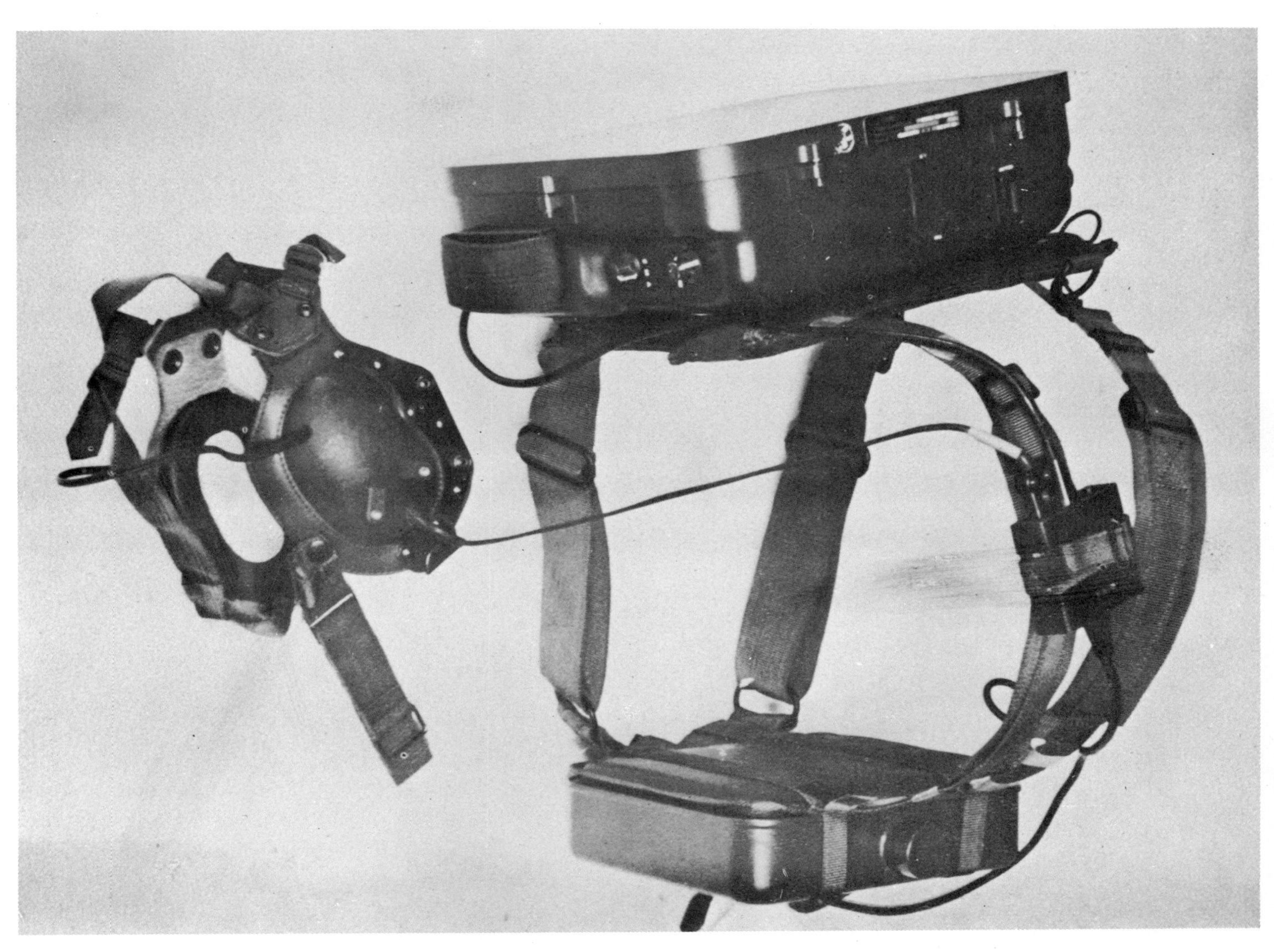

Oliphant II components.

headset, a compass and supplementary storage batteries. The radar proper, together with its controls, is contained in a rectangular box, the front face of which is flat and incorporates the aerial. The power pack is carried on the operator's back and contains ten sealed nickel-cadmium elements. The radar is mounted on the operator's chest and trained by turning the body. Detection is indicated by a doppler tone in the earphones and the operator can identify the type of target by the nature of the pitch and rhythm of the tone. To obtain range the operator turns the range control knob until the audio signal reaches a maximum and then reads the range off a small indicator.

In service with the French and United Kingdom forces.

Rasura portable battlefield surveillance radar

Manufacturer: **Electronique Marcel Dassault (France)**

Weight	60 kg
Range	Men 7 km
	Vehicles 10 km
Accuracy	±25 m
Operational mode	non-coherent pulse doppler
Power source	Battery
Frequency	X band

Available in either a vehicle-mounted version or as a man-portable equipment. In either version the operating capabilities are identical, but the vehicle-mounted version is equipped with a converter and is powered from the vehicle's battery.

The portable version breaks down into three, 20 kg man-packs, one of which contains spare batteries. The equipment mounts on a tripod which is designed so that the scanner can be placed either in a lowered position, where it is almost at ground level, or in a raised position where it is about head-high. Detection is indicated by audio signals in the operator's earphones and range and bearings are read off from the readouts provided.

Azimuth scanning can be done manually or automatically in 4 degree steps. Range scanning is also carried out manually or automatically. In the auto-mode three different range sectors can be scanned—either 0–2000 m, 1500 m–3000 m or 3000 m–5000 m. When a

Rasura radar.

target is picked up the operator switches to manual and pinpoints the target by using the fine tuners for range and azimuth. Although primarily designed for ranges of up to 5000 m, the radar is quite capable of picking up vehicles out to 10,000 m and the range scale can be increased to this figure if desired. Normally the equipment is set to scan automatically in range and manually in azimuth. The equipment can be operated by one man and the manufacturers claim that it can be set up in three minutes.

In service with the French, West German, Dutch and Spanish forces.

Rasura mounted on a vehicle.

Rasit portable battlefield surveillance radar

Manufacturer: **Laboratoire Central de Télécommunications (France)**

Weight	150 kg
Range	Men 7 km Vehicles 14 km–20 km
Accuracy	Range ±20 m azimuth ±6 mils
Operational mode	Coherent pulse doppler
Power source	24 v battery
Frequency	X band

Rasit can be divided into 9 loads for transportation, which is normally by vehicle. Automatic scanning of selected sectors is provided. Detection is indicated by an audio tone in the operator's earphones. He then tunes for maximum signal and reads off the range and azimuth on the readouts provided. It is said to be able to detect one man at 7 km, two men at 10 km, light vehicles at 14 km and a tank at 20 km.

Not yet in service, but undergoing trials with the French forces.

Rasit 72A (Rapière) portable battlefield surveillance radar

Manufacturer: **Laboratoire Central de Télécommunications**

Weight	70 kg
Range	Men 14 km Vehicles 20 km
Accuracy	Range ±20 m azimuth ±6 mils
Operational mode	Coherent pulse doppler
Power source	Battery
Frequency	X band

A development of the shorter range Rasit radar, the equipment can be carried in four loads, the heaviest of which weighs 25 kg. In operation the antenna and radar-head are mounted on a tripod and the display and control unit can be placed up to 50 m away. Automatic antenna scanning is provided. Echoes are displayed on a B scope and the single operator can hear the doppler tone either on a loudspeaker or in his earphones. An automatic system can be arranged to trigger an alarm as soon as a target enters the surveyed zone. Provision is also made for data transmission of target information. There is also a Rasit 72B which is a lightweight version of the 72A with the antenna controlled by hand, and a 72C which is similar, but has a shorter range.

Not yet in service, but undergoing trials with the French forces.

Rasit 72A (Rapière) radar in action.

Sentinel man-portable battlefield surveillance radar

Manufacturer: **Selenia Industrie Elettroniche Associate SpA (Italy)**

Weight	5 kg approximately
Range	Men 500 m Vehicles 3800 m
Operational mode	CW-FM with 0–180° phase modulation
Power source	Battery
Frequency	X band

Normally mounted on a tripod. There are two operating modes—surveillance and ranging. In the surveillance mode, all targets within the range coverage of the equipment can be detected and moving targets give a doppler tone in the operator's earphones from which he should be able to identify the type of target, but not its range. In the ranging mode, only those targets within a selected range gate can be detected. To obtain the range, the operator turns a range control knob for maximum signal strength and reads off the range on a dial.

In service with the Italian and some other forces.

UAP 40301 man-portable battlefield surveillance radar

Manufacturer: **L M Ericsson (Sweden)**

Weight	2·5 kg
Range	Men 300 m
	Vehicles 2000 m
Power source	Battery or mains 10–30 v DC
Frequency	X band 10·5 gHz

UPA 40301 radar.

A small lightweight radar for use as an intruder alarm against moving men or vehicles. It is designed for perimeter surveillance and can be powered either by an integral rechargeable battery or an external power source. The box-head contains a fixed antenna with a pencil beam globe which gives information about the direction of the target. Detections are indicated by a pilot lamp, and identification of different types of targets is made from the audio signals received in the operator's earphones. Remote control is provided by feeding into a remote control box which can take inputs from four different radars. The remote control boxes are situated at a central control point and they are equipped with pilot lamps and audio warnings, as are the main displays at the radar.

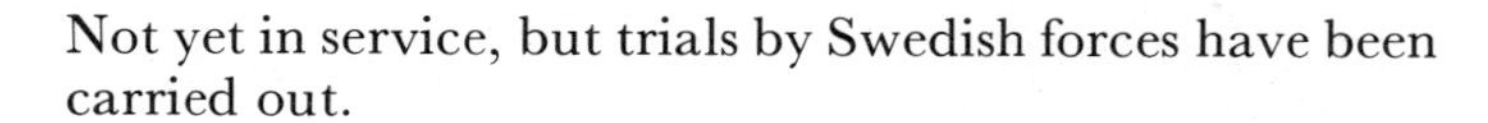

Not yet in service, but trials by Swedish forces have been carried out.

Shrimp hand-held battlefield surveillance radar

Manufacturer: **Marconi-Elliott Avionic Systems Limited (United Kingdom)**

Weight	3 kg
Range	Men 500 m
	Vehicles 2000 m
Operational mode	Non-coherent pulse doppler
Power source	Battery
Frequency	Probably X band

Carried by one man and normally hand-held, but can be tripod mounted. Designed in conjunction with Britain's Royal Radar Establishment, it has independent search and ranging modes. A remote visual display is under development.

Not yet in service, but under evaluation.

ZB298 portable battlefield surveillance radar

Manufacturer: **Marconi-Elliott Avionic Systems Limited (United Kingdom)**

Weight	32·3 kg (25·9 kg if silver zinc batteries are used)
Range	Men 5000 m
	Vehicles 10,000 m
Accuracy	Range ±20 m bearing ±10 mils
Operational mode	Non-coherent pulse doppler
Power source	Battery
Frequency	X band

Normally carried by two men. The radar head can be mounted on a tripod or on a vehicle. The display and control unit may be positioned up to 30 m from the radar head and can be operated by one man. Detections are indicated on a visual display and, by making a switch, as a doppler tone in the operator's earphones. The video display shows target echoes in any selected 1000 m range zone which is adjustable in 500 m steps by means of the outer of three concentrically mounted controls. The middle control selects the position of a 50 m audio range-gate as indicated by horizontal lines on the display. The inner control, in conjunction with the audio display and azimuth control, permits accurate location in range and azimuth. Range, azimuth and elevation readouts are provided. Scanning is controlled by a handwheel on the control unit. An audio alarm switch permits audio-monitoring of all moving targets appearing within the 50 m range gate, or alternatively the whole of the selected 1000 m range zone.

In service with the Danish and United Kingdom forces.

ZB298 radar.

AN/PPS 5 portable battlefield surveillance radar

Manufacturer: **Cutler Hamer Incorporated (Airborne Instruments Laboratory) (United States)**

Weight	Radar 25·4 kg Remote unit 16 kg
Range	Men 5000 m Vehicles 10,000 m
Accuracy	±20 m
Operational mode	Non-coherent pulse doppler
Power source	6 v battery or 24 v DC source
Frequency	Ku band 16·0–16·5 gHz

The system can be separated into three manpacks and can be assembled in less than 10 minutes. The equipment consists of a parabolic antenna, the radar transmitter/receiver and a remote control unit. The antenna and the radar are mounted on a folding tripod, and the remote control unit can be placed up to 6 m away. The basic radar without the remote control unit will give an aural indication of target detection, but the remote control unit contains both a B scope and an A scope and can give visual indication of both moving and stationary targets.

Automatic scan of 531 mils, 1062 mils or 1947 mils sectors can be set. Moving and fixed targets appear on the radar scopes and, on being seen, can be located more precisely by stopping the scan and centering the antenna on the target whilst adjusting the movable range gate for maximum signal. Azimuth and range can be read off from digital counters on the control indicator unit. An audio output in the operator's earphones also gives an indication of moving targets.

In service with the United States forces.

AN/PPS 5 radar remote unit.

AN/PPS 5 radar unit.

AN/PPS 5 radar (complete) in action.

AN/PPS 6 man-portable battlefield surveillance radar

Manufacturer: **General Instrument Corporation (United States)**

Weight	20 kg
Range	Men 1500 m Vehicles 3000 m
Accuracy	Range ±25 m, azimuth ±18 mils
Operational mode	Non-coherent pulse doppler
Power source	Battery
Frequency	X band 9·0–9·5 gHz

A lightweight radar which can be carried by one man. Major components are the transmitter/receiver and the angular control assembly. Both mount on top of a folding tripod.

Search can be carried out either automatically, with a choice of 600 mils, 900 mils and 1200 mils sectors in azimuth, or manually. In the automatic mode the radar is set to search an area of a depth in range of 315 m. There are two search modes: in mode one, the radar scans the sector to a range depth of 315 m beyond that set on the range dial for one sweep, and then on the next sweep it scans the sector at a range depth of a further 315 m. Thus one complete scan searches an area of 630 m. In mode two, the radar scans left and right through the selected sector, both scans being at the same 315 m depth.

In the manual mode, a range depth of 45 m is set. In all modes, the presence of a moving target is indicated by an audible tone in the operator's earphones. In the automatic mode the operator then stops the scan and adjusts for maximum tone in the earphones. The location of the target is established by direct readout of the manual range control and azimuth and elevation indicators.

In service with the United States forces.

AN/PPS 6 radar.

AN/PPS 9 hand-held battlefield surveillance/target-acquisition radar

Manufacturer: **Radio Corporation of America (United States)**

Weight	5·89 kg
Range	Men 1500 m Vehicles 3000 m
Accuracy	Good
Operational mode	Coherent CW doppler with correlation
Power source	Battery
Frequency	X band

Capable of being carried and operated by one man, the equipment consists of a transmitter/receiver and an angular control assembly, both of which can be mounted on a folding tripod or hand-held. There are only four controls to operate and there are both aural and visual displays to locate and identify moving targets.

The makers claim that their unique CW doppler system gives better performance than radars weighing five times as much. It also gives fine resolution for separation of multiple targets, high range accuracy, high clutter rejection and detection through foliage. A further advantage is that the background noise is very low. There is a choice of all range, coarse range and acquisition mode operation with high resolution. The equipment is all solid state and a 3000 hour MTBF is claimed.

Not yet in service, but undergoing trials in both the United States and West German forces.

AN/PPS 10 man-portable battlefield surveillance radar

Manufacturer: **General Dynamics International Corporation (United States)**

Weight	4·5 kg
Range	Men 1500 m Vehicles 3000 m
Operational mode	Coherent CW doppler
Power source	Battery
Frequency	X band

Search is carried out using either a manual or an automatic antenna scan of a selected sector. Detections are indicated by an audio tone in the operator's earphones. He then tunes for maximum signal and reads out the range and azimuth. The operator can choose between all range surveillance and discrete target acquisition channels.

Not yet in service, but testing has been carried out by the United States and West German forces.

AN/PPS 11 (formerly known as 2019 M2) hand-held battlefield surveillance radar

Manufacturer: **Radio Corporation of America (United States)**

Weight	4·5 kg
Range	Men 500 m Vehicles 1000 m
Accuracy	±8 m
Operational mode	Modulated CW doppler with correlation
Power source	24 v rechargeable battery
Frequency	X band 8·75 gHz

The equipment is contained in a small box weighing only 1 kg which can be hand-held or mounted on a tripod. There are only three controls. One selects the mode of operation, one the range segment required and the third controls the volume of the doppler signal heard in the earphones. Detection is indicated by the doppler tone in the earphones and by a visual azimuth display. There are two operating modes—acquisition and location. In the former, the radar detects moving men from 0 to 500 m distant and vehicles up to 1000 m. The location mode allows the operator to use the radar to locate and track men or vehicles with a higher resolution (25 m) than in the acquisition mode, but only out to 500 m.

Not yet in service, but undergoing trials with the United States forces.

AN/PPS 15 portable battlefield surveillance radar

Manufacturer: **General Dynamics International Corporation (United States)**

Weight	6·3 kg without batteries
Operational mode	Coherent CW doppler
Power source	28 v supply. Battery
Frequency	X band

Very little is known about this radar. It was developed as a follow-on to AN/PPS 9 and AN/PPS 10 and is reputed to have an improved performance and reliability. It can be carried in a manpack or mounted in a vehicle.

Not yet in service, but undergoing trials with the United States forces.

AN/PPS 17 man-portable battlefield surveillance radar

Manufacturer: **General Instrument Corporation (United States)**

Weight	Under 20 kg
Range	Men 1500 m Vehicles 3000 m
Accuracy	Range ±25 m, azimuth ±18 mils
Operational mode	Non-coherent pulse doppler with IFF
Power source	Battery
Frequency	X band 9·0–9·5 gHz

Developed specifically for the United States Marine Corps, it is very similar to the AN/PPS 6 with the same performance, but the Marine Corps specification called for a lighter version. See AN/PPS 6 for further details.

Not yet in service, but undergoing trials with the United States Marine Corps and in competition with AN/PPS 18.

AN/PPS 17 radar under test.

R2000 man-portable battlefield surveillance radar

Manufacturer: **General Instrument Corporation (United States)**

Weight	9·5 kg
Range	Men 1500 m Vehicles 3000 m
Accuracy	±25 m
Operational mode	Non-coherent pulse doppler
Power source	Battery
Frequency	X band 9·0–9·5 gHz, tunable

The R2000 is a follow-on to AN/PPS 17, but it has complete automatic operation and can be operated by remote control at a distance of up to 30 m. It can be hand-held or mounted on a tripod. The control unit can be mounted on top of the set for hand-held operation, at the back of the set for tripod operation, or on the ground in a remote control position. Detections are indicated by a small light and by a doppler tone in the operator's earphones. Various search sectors can be selected and range gates set. Range is read off a numeric range indicator. The equipment is claimed to be extremely reliable with a MTBF greater than 10,000 hours.

In service with the United States forces.

AN/PPS 18 man-portable battlefield surveillance radar

Manufacturer: **Radio Corporation of America (United States)**

Weight	15·8 kg
Range	Men 1500 m Vehicles 3000 m
Accuracy	Range ±25 m, azimuth ±18 mils
Operational mode	Pulse doppler
Power source	Battery
Frequency	X band 8·75 gHz

Developed specifically for the United States Marine Corps. Like AN/PPS 17, it is very similar to AN/PPS 6 with the same performance, but is lighter. See AN/PPS 6 for further details.

Not yet in service, but undergoing trials with the United States Marine Corps and in connection with AN/PPS 17.

AN/TPS 21 portable battlefield surveillance radar

Manufacturer: **Admiral Corporation (United States)**

Range	Vehicles 18 km
Accuracy	±23 m or 1% of range whichever is the greater
Operational mode	Pulse doppler
Frequency	X band

Very little has been released about this radar except that scanning in range can be either manual or automatic. Detections are indicated by a doppler tone in the operator's earphones.

In service with the United States forces.

AN/TPS 33 portable battlefield surveillance radar

Manufacturer: **Admiral Corporation (United States)**

Range	Vehicles 18 km
Accuracy	Range ±23 m (or 1% of range whichever is the greater), azimuth ±25 mils
Operational mode	Pulse doppler
Frequency	X band

Little is known of this radar except that it is similar to AN/TPS 21 but has an additional A scope display.

In service with the United States and West German forces.

5019 hand-held battlefield surveillance radar

Manufacturer: **Radio Corporation of America (United States)**

Weight	15·8 kg
Range	Men 5000 m Vehicles 10,000 m
Accuracy	Range ±16 m, azimuth ±20 mils
Operational mode	Modulated coherent CW doppler with correlation
Power source	12 v battery or mains
Frequency	X band

Can be hand-held or mounted on a tripod. When so mounted, automatic sector scanning is provided. The display and control unit can be situated remotely up to a distance of 30 m. There are two operating modes—the search mode which enables search to be carried out to 5000 m, or from 5000 m to 10 000 m, and the tracking mode which permits target location, tracking and identification out to 10 000 m.

When automatic scan is used, scan sectors up to 180° can be selected. Detections are indicated by a doppler tone in the earphones and on an A scan display which provides target range to a resolution of 50 m. Range and azimuth are shown on direct numerical readouts.

In service with the United States forces.

4019 M2 man-portable battlefield surveillance radar

Manufacturer: **Radio Corporation of America (United States)**

Weight	6·4 kg
Range	Men 1500 m Vehicles 2500 m
Accuracy	±8 m
Operational mode	Modulated coherent CW doppler with correlation
Power source	Battery
Frequency	X band 8·75 gHz

The equipment is contained in a box weighing 3·6 kg which can be hand-held, but is more generally mounted on a tripod or on a vehicle. When so mounted, automatic scanning is possible of selected sectors of up to 270°. There are four operating modes. Firstly, the detection mode in which the radar will detect men moving from 0 to 1500 m and vehicles out to 2500 m. Next the acquisition mode in which the operator can determine the range of a single target while continuing to search for other targets. The coarse range mode provides target range with an accuracy of 250 m, and lastly the fine range mode which provides target range with an accuracy of 25 m. Detections are indicated by the doppler signal in the operator's earphones but, in addition, an indicator light and threshold meter provide a visual indication of a detected target and a relative measure of target signal strength corresponding to the aural signal. Range is read off dials, and azimuth from the angular control assembly on the tripod.

Not yet in service.

R2010 man-portable battlefield surveillance radar

Manufacturer: **General Instrument Corporation (United States)**

Weight	13·3 kg
Range	Men 5000 m Vehicles 10 000 m
Accuracy	±25 m
Operational mode	Non-coherent pulse doppler
Power source	Battery
Frequency	X band 9·0–9·5 gHz, tunable

A more powerful version of the R2000 with the same method of operation, but giving a peak power of 1 kw as opposed to 5 w. Intended more for perimeter defence than for use in the field. The equipment, too, is almost identical with the R2000 but an optional B scope visual display unit can be provided. The radar can be hand-held or mounted on a tripod. The control unit can be mounted remotely up to 30 m. Reliability claimed is 2000 MTBF.

Not yet in service, but under evaluation by the United States forces.

R2010 radar.

GLOSSARY AND ABBREVIATIONS

(for guidance only)

ABC	America, Britain and Canada
AP	anti-personnel
AV	anti-vehicle
Ball ammunition	live small arms ammunition
Ballistite round	bulletless cartridge used for firing rifle grenades
Benelux	Belgium, Netherlands and Luxembourg
BT	bullet trap (see grenades section)
C	centigrade
Cal	calibre
cm	centimetre
cp	candle-power
CW-FM	continuous wave—frequency modulation
DC	direct current
DDR	Deutsche Demokratische Republik (East Germany)
Finabel	France, Italy, Netherlands, Belgium and Luxembourg
gm	gramme
GPMG	general purpose machine gun
HE	high explosive
HEAP	high explosive anti-personnel
HEAT	high explosive anti-tank
HMG	heavy machine gun
HEPAT	high explosive penetrating anti-tank
HEP—T	high explosive penetrating—tracer
IFF	interrogative friend or foe
in	inch
IR	infra red
kg	kilogramme
Largo	a bullet shape
lb	pound
LMG	light machine gun
m	metre
MG	machine gun
mil	mil—a measurement of angle
min	minute
Mk	mark
mm	millimetre
m/sec	metres per second
MTBF	mean time between failure
NATO	North Atlantic Treaty Organisation
Parabellum	a bullet shape
PEPA/LP	projectile emperné à propulsion additionelle/longue portée (finned with additional propulsion)
Primacord	instantaneous fuse
PRPA	projectile rayé à propulsion additionelle (rifled with additional propulsion)
rpm	rounds per minute
sec	second
SMC	sub machine carbine
SMG	sub machine gun
SMLE	short magazine Lee Enfield (rifle)
TNT	Tri-nitro-toluene (explosive)
UK	United Kingdom
US/USA	United States/United States of America
USAAF	United States Army Air Force
USSR	Union of Soviet Socialist Republics
v	volt
WP	Warsaw Pact
×2	magnification of two

Table of armies and their infantry weapons

COUNTRY	PISTOLS & REVOLVERS	SUB MACHINE GUNS & CARBINES	RIFLES & CARBINES	MACHINE GUNS	MORTARS	MISSILES & ROCKETS
Abu Dhabi						Vigilant
Afghanistan						SPG 82
Africa (South)				MAG GPMG		
Albania					M1937 M1938 M1943	
Argentina	Colt M1911A1 M1927 (Ballester Molina)	M56	SAFN 49	MAG GPMG ·30 Browning MMG	MO-120-60 (light)	BO810 Cobra 2000
Australia		F1A1	M16	M60 GPMG		
Austria		Steyr MP69 MP40	G3	MG3 LMG		KAM 3D SR Carl-Gustav M2
Belgium	Browning HP35	Vigneron Uzi	FN CAL	MAG GPMG		RL-83 Swingfire (& Beeswing) Blowpipe
Bolivia			SIG510-4			
Brazil		INA 953 Madsen M46, M50 & M53	SAFN 49			
Bulgaria*						B10 (or RG82)
Canada	Browning HP 35	C4 (Sterling)		C1 MMG		M20 & M20A1 M72 & M72A1 M72A1G1. Sterling L2A3. SR Carl-Gustav M2
Chile			SIG510-4 M1 carbine	MG3 LMG		
China		Type 36 Type 43 Type 50 M3A1	SKS carbine Type 53	Type 53 & 57 MMG Type 56 & 56-1 LMG RP42, DP & DPM, RPD LMG Type 54 HMG		Type 51 Type 56 Type 63 B10 (or RG82) RPG2

COUNTRY	PISTOLS & REVOLVERS	SUB MACHINE GUNS & CARBINES	RIFLES & CARBINES	MACHINE GUNS	MORTARS	MISSILES & ROCKETS
Costa Rica		38/49 (model 4)				
Czechoslovakia*	Vz61 Skorpion	M24 & M26	Vz58 M54 sniper	Vz52 & Vz52/57 LMG Vz59 GPMG Vz43 HMG		T21 (Tarasnice) M59 & M59A P 27 (Pancerovka)
Colombia		Madsen M46, M50 & M53	SAFN 49			
Cuba		M23 & M25				
Denmark	Browning HP35 SIG M49	Madsen M46, M50, M53 M49 (Hovea)	G3 CETME M1 Garand	MAG GPMG MG3 LMG ·30 Browning MMG		SR Carl-Gustav M2
Dominican Republic		Cristobal Model 2 38/49 (Model 4)	G3	·30 Browning MMG		
Egypt (UAR)	Beretta M51	38/49 (Model 4) Carl-Gustav M45B	Type D Browning SAFN 49 AG42 Hakim Rashid			RPG7V, RPG7 RPG7D. Sagger AT-3 Sam-7
Finland	Lahti M35				81mm Tampella 120mm Standard Tampella.	Vigilant
France	M50 Walther PP & PPK	MAT 49	MAS 36 & M1936CR39 M49 & M49/56 fRfl	M1924/29 LMG MAS (or AAT) 52 GPMG. ·30 Browning MMG M621 HMG M693 HMG	60mm Commando MO-60-63 MO-81-61C MO-81-61 MO-120-60 (light) MO-120-AM5O MO-120-RT-61	89mm Strim F1. Milan M20 & M20A1
Germany (DDR)*	Pistole M			IMG-K LMG		B10 (or RG82)
Germany (West)		Hk4A2 & Hk 5A3 (or MP5) Uzi	G3	MG LMG MK20 Rh202 HMG	MO-60-63	PZF44 BO810 Cobra 2000 Milan Mamba Tow (XM-71A) Redeye (XM-41EZ)

COUNTRY	PISTOLS & REVOLVERS	SUB MACHINE GUNS & CARBINES	RIFLES & CARBINES	MACHINE GUNS	MORTARS	MISSILES & ROCKETS
Greece				·30 Browning MMG		
Guatemala		Madsen M46, M50 & M53				
Holland	Browning HP35	Uzi		·30 Browning MMG		Tow (XM-71A)
Hungary*	Walther PP & PPK 48 M PA-63	M48				
India				MAG GPMG		
Indonesia	Browning HP35 Colt M1911A1	Madsen M46, M50 & M53 Carl Gustav M45B	SAFN 49 Mauser Kar 98K. G3 M1 Garand M1 carbine	Madsen Saetter LMG		
Iran	Colt M1911A1	M22		MG3 LMG SB30 LMG		RPG7V, RPG7 RPG7D M40A1 Tow (XM-71A)
Israel	Beretta M51	Uzi	Galil	MAG GPMG ·30 Browning MMG	52mm 60mm Tampella 81mm Tampella 120mm light Tampella 120mm standard Tampella	M40A1
Ireland (Eire)						SR Carl-Gustav M2
Italy	Beretta M51	Model 12	BM59	MG3 LMG BM 59 LMG		Mosquito Bantam M20 & M20A1
Japan	Colt M1911A1		Model 63 M1 carbine	M62 GPMG ·30 Browning MMG		
Korea (North)		Type 49 K50		RP46, DP & DRM, RPD LMG		
Korea (South)			M16			

Table of armies and their infantry weapons *continued*

COUNTRY	PISTOLS & REVOLVERS	SUB MACHINE GUNS & CARBINES	RIFLES & CARBINES	MACHINE GUNS	MORTARS	MISSILES & ROCKETS
Kuwait						Vigilant Tow (XM-71A)
Luxembourg			SAFN 49			
Mexico	Obregon Colt M1911A1	M1 Carbine		RM2 LMG		
New Zealand		Sterling L2A3				
Norway	M19114 Colt M1911A1		G3 CETME	MG3 LMG ·30 Browning MMG		SR Carl-Gustav M2
Pakistan			G3 CETME	MG3 LMG		
Paraguay		Madsen M46, M50 & M53				
Poland*	Pistolet TT Model 64 Radom WZ35 M63	PPS43 & 43/52		Wz 43 HMG		B10 (or RG82)
Portugal		FBP M/48	G3 CETME	MG3 LMG HK21 LMG		M20 & M20A1
Rumania				SB30		
Spain	Super Star	Z62 Star	CETME	MG3 LMG ·30 Browning MMG	ECIA 60-C ECIA 60-L ECIA 81-L ECIA 105-L ECIA 120-SL ECIA 120-L	
Sweden	Walther P38 (P1) M40	Carl Gustav M45B	G3 CETME AG42	MAG GPMG		Miniman SR Carl-Gustav M2 Carl-Gustav M2-550
Syria		M23 M25				SPG82 RPG7V, RPG7, RPG7D. Sagger AT-3 SAM-7
Switzerland	SIG M49		Stg 57	M51 LMG SIG710 GPMG		Bantam Vigilant

COUNTRY	PISTOLS & REVOLVERS	SUB MACHINE GUNS & CARBINES	RIFLES & CARBINES	MACHINE GUNS	MORTARS	MISSILES & ROCKETS
Taiwan	Browning HP35 Colt M1911A1		M16 M1 carbine		M2	
Thailand		Madsen M46, M50 & M53 38/49 (model 4)				
Turkey	Walther PP & PPK		SAFN 49 Mauser Kar 98K	·30 Browning MMG		
Tunisia		38/49 (model 4)				
United Kingdom	Browning HP35	Sterling L2A3	Lee Enfield no 4 Mk1 M16	MAG GPMG Bren LMG L4A1 LMG L7 Series GPMG ·30 Browning MMG	2 inch 81mm L1A1	SR Carl-Gustav M2 Wombat Vigilant Swingfire (& Beeswing) Blowpipe M20 & M20A1 M72 & M72A1 & M72A1G1
USSR*				RPK LMG DSLK 38/46 HMG KPV HMG	M1937 M107/M1938 M1938 M1943	SPG9 SPG2
United States	Colt M1911A1		Browning M1 Garand M1 carbine M14 & M14E2 M16 M1903A4 sniper Remington model 700 sniper	M60 GPMG Browning M2 LMG	T18E6 M2 M1 M29	M72 & M72 A1G1 M67 M40A1
Venezuela		Madsen M46, M50 & M53	SAFN 49			
Vietnam (North)					M1937 M107/M1938 M2	Type 56 Type 63 T 21 (Tara-snice) P27 (Pancer-ovka) B10 (or RG82)

COUNTRY	PISTOLS & REVOLVERS	SUB MACHINE GUNS & CARBINES	RIFLES & CARBINES	MACHINE GUNS	MORTARS	MISSILES & ROCKETS
Vietnam (North) *(continued)*						B11 (or RG 107) RPG2 B40 RPG7V, RPG7, RPG7D SAM-7
Vietnam (South)	Colt M1911A1		M16	M60 GPMG	M2 M1	Redeye (XM-41EZ)
Vietcong		MAT K50			M1937 M2	Type 56 H-12 Type 63 M488 T21 (Tarasnice) P27 (Pancerovka) 140mm B10 (or RG82) B11 (or RG107) RPG2 DK2-B SAM-7
Warsaw Pact (generally)	Makarov	PPS43 & 43/52	SKS carbine SVD Dragunov sniper Moisin-Nagant	RP42, DP & DPM, RPD LMG PK GPMG Goryonov SG 34 & SGM MMG DSLK 38/46 HMG KPV HMG	M1937 M107/M1938 M1938	SPG9 RPG7V, RPG7, RPG7D Sagger AT3 SAM-7 B11 (or RG107)
Yemen		38/49 (model 4)				
Yugoslavia	M57 M67		M59/66	SARAC LMG M65A & M65B LMG 30J LMG	MO-81-61C MO-81-61 M8 M57 M31 M68 BB1 UBM52	Sagger AT-3 RB57 M60 M65
Zaire			SAFN 49			

*See also Warsaw Pact

MANUFACTURERS' ADDRESSES

ADMIRAL CORPORATION — United States
3800 West Cortland Street
Chicago
Illinois 60647
USA

AEROSPATIALE — France
37 Boulevard de Montmorency
Paris 16e
France

MINISTRY OF DEFENCE — Argentina
Baseo Colon 255
Buenos Aires
Argentina

ARMERIA FABRICA DE ARMAS — Dominican Republic
c/o Ministerio de Defensa
Santa Domingo
Dominican Republic

ARMALITE INC — United States
18 East 16th Street
Costa Mesa
California
USA

ARMY EQUIPMENT ENGINEERING ESTABLISHMENT — Canada
National Defence HQ
Ottawa
Ontario
Canada

SMALL ARMS FACTORY — Australia
c/o Department of Defence
Government Building
Canberra
Australia

AVIMO LIMITED — United Kingdom
140 Tottenham Court Road
London W1P OJD
England

PIETRO BERETTA — Italy
25063 Gardone VT
Italy

BONIFACIO ECHEVERRIA SA — Spain
Apartad 10
Eibar
Guipuzoa
Spain

AB BOFORS — Sweden
Ordnance Division
Box 500
S-690 20
Bofors
Sweden

ORDNANCE FACTORY BRAZIL — Brazil
Ministerio Ejercito
Esplanada dos Ministeries
Bloco 4
Brasilia
Brazil

BRIDGE TOOL AND MANUFACTURING COMPANY — United States
Philadelphia
USA

BRITISH AIRCRAFT CORPORATION LIMITED — United Kingdom
Guided Weapons Division
Six Hills Way
Stevenage
Hertfordshire SG1 2DA
England

BRITISH SMALL ARMS COMPANY — United Kingdom
Studley Road
Redditch
Worcestershire
England

STATE FACTORIES — Bulgaria
c/o Ministry of Defence
Sofia
Bulgaria

CANADIAN ARSENALS LIMITED — Canada
PO Box 717
Postal Station B
Ottawa
Ontario
Canada

CARL GUSTAV — Sweden
FFV Eskilstuna
Sweden

Agent: FFV — United Kingdom
22 Roslin Way
Bromley BR1 4QT
Kent
England

CARL ZEISS — West Germany
7082 Oberkochen
PO Box 35/36
West Germany

CESKOSLOVENSKA ZBROJOVKA (or CESKA) — Czechoslovakia
c/o Ministry of Defence
Prague
Czechoslovakia

CENTRO DE ESTUDIOS TECNICOS DE MATERIALES ESPECIALES — Spain
Ministerio del Ejercito
Alcada 51
Madrid
Spain

STATE FACTORIES — China
People's Republic of China

COLT INDUSTRIES — United States
Fire Arms Division
150 Huyshope Avenue
Hartford
Connecticut 06102
USA

CONTRAVES ITALIANA SpA — Italy
Via Tiburtina 965
00156 Rome
Italy

CRVENA ZASTAVA SAVEZLI FEKREDERIKAT — Yugoslavia
Zamarotnu Odbra
11000 Belgrade
Yugoslavia

CUTLER HAMMER INC — United States
Airborne Instruments Laboratory
4201 N 27 Street
Milwaukee
Wisconsin
USA

STATE FACTORIES — Czechoslovakia
c/o Ministry of Defence
Prague
Czechoslovakia

CARL WALTHER WAFFENFABRIK AG — West Germany
Sportwaffenfabrik
D 79 Ulm-am-Donau
Box 882
West Germany

*DANSK INDUSTRI SYNDIKAT AS MADSEN — Denmark
AS Madsen
København
Denmark

DEI INDUSTRIES — United States
Defence Electronics Division
5455 Randolph Road
Rockville
Md 20854
USA

DIRECTION TECHNIQUE DES ARMEMENTS TERRESTRES — France
DTAT/GIAT
Caserne-Sully
92211 St Cloud
France

(*formerly Dansk Rekyriffel Syndikat AS Madsen)

ELECTRONIQUE MARCEL DASSAULT — France
55 Quai Carnot
92214 St Cloud
France

ELTRO GmbH — West Germany
Gesellschaft für Strahlungstechnick
6900 Heidelberg 1
Kurpfalzring
Postfach 520
West Germany

LM ERICSSON — Sweden
Fack
S-431 20
Molndal 1
Sweden

ESPERANZA Y CIA SA — Spain
Marquina (Vizcayza)
Spain

ETABLISSEMENTS RUGGIERI — France
Département Armement
122 rue La Boétie
75008-Paris 9e
France

EXPLOSIVES CORPORATION OF AMERICA — United States
(Address unknown)

FABRICA DE ARMAS — DF Mexico
Secretaria de la Defenza Nacionale
Lomasode Sotelo
DF Mexico

FABRICA DE ARMAS DE OVIEDO — Spain
Oviedo
Spain

FABRICA DE BRACO DE PRATO — Portugal
Rua Fernando Palha
Lisbon 6
Portugal

*FABRIQUE NATIONALE HERSTAL SA — Belgium
B-4400 Herstal
Belgium

FORENADE FABRIKSVERKEN (FFV) — Sweden
Huvudkontoret
S631 87 Eskilstuna
Sweden

FORSVARETS FABRIKSVERK — Sweden
(Svenska Staten)
c/o Sorsdars Departmentet
PO 10320
Stockholm 16
Sweden

(*formerly Fabrique Nationale d'Armes de Guerre)

GENERAL DYNAMICS INTERNATIONAL CORPORATION — United States
1 Rockefeller Plaza
New York NY 11802
USA

GENERAL INSTRUMENT CORPORATION — United States
600 West John Street
Hicksville
New York NY 11802
USA

GENERAL MOTORS CORPORATION — United States
Inland Manufacturing Division
Dayton
Ohio
USA

STATE FACTORIES — East Germany
German Democratic Republic

GROUP INDUSTRIEL DES ARMEMENTS TERRESTRES — France
DTAT/GIAT
Caserne-Sully
92211 St Cloud
France

CG HAENAL WAFFEN UND FAHRRADFABRIK AG — West Germany
7897 Tiengen
Postfach 1147
West Germany

HAERENS VABENARSENALAT — Denmark
c/o Ministry of Defence
Slotsholmsgade 10
1216 Copenhagen
Denmark

HECKLER & KOCH GmbH — West Germany
7238 Oberndorf-Neckar
Postfach 130
West Germany

HARRINGTON & RICHARDSON INC — United States
320 Park Avenue
Worcester
Massachusetts 01610
USA

HOTCHKISS-BRANDT — France
Branche Armement et Mécanique Générale
52 Avenue des Champs-Elysées
75008 Paris
France

HUGHES AIRCRAFT CORPORATION — United States
Culver City
California 90230
USA

STATE FACTORIES — Hungary
c/o Ministry of Defence
Budapest
Hungary

HUSQVARNA VAPENFABRIKS — Sweden
Husqvarna
Sweden

INGLIS & COMPANY — Canada
Toronto
Canada

ITHACA GUN COMPANY — United States
Ithaca
New York
USA

ORDNANCE FACTORY IRAN — Iran
c/o Ministry of Defence
Teheran
Iran

ISRAEL MILITARY INDUSTRIES — Israel
c/o Ministry of Defence
Hakirya
Tel Aviv
Israel

KAWAKAKI HEAVY INDUSTRIES LIMITED — Japan
World Trade Centre Building
4-1 Hamamatsu-dho 2-Chrome
Minato-ku
Tokyo
Japan

London Agent: Kawasaki Heavy Industries Limited
3 St Helen's Place
London EC3
England

STATE FACTORIES — North Korea
North Korea

LABORATOIRE CENTRAL DE TELECOMMUNICATIONS — France
18-20 Rue Grange-Dame-Rose
78 Velisy — Villacoubley
BP 40
France

LOSFELD INDUSTRIES — France
13 & 15 Rue Thiebault
94220 Charenton
Paris
France

LUCHAIRE SA — France
Department STRIM
180 Boulevard Haussmann
Paris 8e
France

LYSAGHTS — Australia
Newcastle Works
Newcastle
New South Wales
Australia

McDONNELL DOUGLAS ASTRONAUTICS COMPANY — United States
PO Box 600
Titusville
Florida 32780
USA

MANUFACTURE D'ARMES DE CHATELLERAULT — France
Chatellerault
France

MANUFACTURE D'ARMES DE TULLE — France
Tulle
France

MARCONI-ELLIOTT AVIONIC SYSTEMS LIMITED — United Kingdom
Elstree Way
Borehamwood
Hertfordshire WD6 1RX
England

MARLIN-ROCKWELL CORPORATION — United States
New Haven
Connecticut
USA

MATERIALS D'ARMES DE SAINT-ETIENNE — France
Saint-Etienne
Loire
France

MECAR SA — Belgium
6522 Petit-Roelux-Les-Nivelles
(Par Feluy)
Brussels
Belgium

Agent: Allied Instruments Limited — United Kingdom
Jermyn Street
London SW1
England

MAUSER WERKE AG — West Germany
Oberndorf-an-Neckar
West Germany

MESSERSCHMITT-BOLKOW-BLOHM GmbH — West Germany
8 München 80
Postfach 80 11 09
West Germany

MILITARY ARMAMENT CORPORATION — United States
440 Glover Street
PO Box 6307
Marietta
Georgia 30062
USA

MINISTRY OF DEFENCE — United Kingdom
Whitehall
London SW1
England

NWM DE KRUITHOORN BV — Holland
PO Box 1050
's-Hertogenbosch
Holland

FORSVARETS DEP — Norway
Oslow Dep
Oslo 1
Norway

STATE FACTORIES WYGOWNICTWA MON UL GRZYBOWSKA — Poland
Warsaw
Poland

POUDRERIES REUNIES DE BELGIQUE SA — Belgium
12 Avenue de Broqueville
1150 Brussels
Belgium

PRECISION LIEGEOISE SA — Belgium
Rue de 3 Juin
109 Herstal-Liège
Belgium

PRODUCTOS MENDOZA SA — Mexico
Bartolache 1914
Mexico City
Mexico

RADIO CORPORATION OF AMERICA — United States
Moorestown
New Jersey 68057
USA

RANK PRECISION INDUSTRIES LIMITED — United Kingdom
Contracts Division
Langston Road
Debden
Loughton
Essex LG10 3TW
England

REMINGTON ARMS COMPANY INC — United States
Bridgeport
Connecticut 06602
USA

RHEINMETALL GmbH — West Germany
4 Düsseldorf 1
Postfach 6609
West Germany

ROYAL ORDNANCE FACTORIES — United Kingdom
c/o Ministry of Defence
Whitehall
London SW1
England

ROYAL SMALL ARMS FACTORY — United Kingdom
Enfield Lock
Middlesex
England

STATE FACTORIES — Rumania
c/o Ministry of Defence
Bucharest
Rumania

SAVAGE ARMS CORPORATION — United States
Westfield
Massachusetts 01085
USA

SCHWEIZERISCHE INDUSTRIE-GESELLSCHAFT (SIG) — Switzerland
CH-8212 Neuhausen am Rheinfalls
Switzerland

SCHERMULY LIMITED — United Kingdom
Newdigate
Dorking
Surrey RH5 5AN
England

SELENIA — Italy
Industrie Elettroniche Associate SpA
Via Medina 40-CCIA
Rome
Italy

SMITH & WESSON — United States
Springfield
Massachusetts 01101
USA

SHORT BROTHERS & HARLAND LIMITED — United Kingdom
PO Box 241
Airport Road
Belfast BT3 9DZ
Northern Ireland

SOCIETE ALSACIENNE D'ETUDES ET D'EXPLOITATION — France
7 Rue du Général Foy
75008 Paris
France

SOCIETE D'ETUDES DE REALISATIONS ET D'APPLICATIONS TECHNIQUES — France
46 Rue de la Bienfaisance
75 — Paris 8e
France

SOPELEM — France
102 Rue Chaptal
92306 Levallois-Perret
France

SPRINGFIELD ARMORY — United States
Springfield
Massachusetts
USA

STATE FACTORIES—Listed alphabetically by countries

STERLING ENGINEERING COMPANY — United Kingdom
Sterling Works
Rainham Road South
Dagenham
Essex
England

STEYR-DAIMLER-PUCH AG — Austria
Werke Steyr
PO Box 4
A-4400 Steyr
Austria

STOKES-BRANDT — France
DTAT/GIAT
Caserne-Sully
92211 St Cloud
France

THOMSON CSF — France
173 Boulevard Haussmann
75360 Paris
France

UNION SWITCH & SIGNAL — United States
Swiss Vale
Pennsylvania
USA

ORDNANCE FACTORY — United Arab Republic
c/o Ministry of Defence
Cairo
Egypt

UNITED SCIENTIFIC INSTRUMENTS LIMITED — United Kingdom
140 Tottenham Court Road
London W1P OJD
England

DEPARTMENT OF THE UNITED STATES ARMY — United States
(1) HQ United States Army Missile Command
Restone Arsenal
Alabama 35809
USA
(2) Department of Defense
Washington DC
USA

STATE FACTORIES — USSR
c/o Ministry of Defence
Moscow
USSR

VALTION KIVAARITHEDAS — Finland
Puolustuslimisterio
Etelainen Makasiinikatu 8
Helsinki 13
Finland

VARO INCORPORATED — United States
Box 828
2201 Walnut Street
Garland
Texas 75040
USA

VICKERS-ARMSTRONG LIMITED — United Kingdom
PO Box 177 Vickers House
Millbank Tower
Millbank
London SW1P 4RA
England

STATE FACTORIES — North Vietnam
c/o Defence Ministry
Hanoi
North Vietnam

WEST GERMAN FEDERAL MINISTRY OF DEFENCE — West Germany
53 Bonn
Postfach 161
West Germany

WINCHESTER REPEATING ARMS COMPANY — United States
(Division of the OLIN CORPORATION)
277 Winchester Avenue
New Haven
Connecticut 06511
USA

STATE FACTORIES — Yugoslavia
Savezli Fekrederikat
Za Marotnuodbranu
11000 Belgrade
Yugoslavia

INDEX

Missiles and Rockets *Page*

Grenades *Page*

Grenade Launchers *Page*

Flamethrowers *Page*

Mines *Page*